# MICROSCOPIC ANATOMY
# OF VERTEBRATES

BY

JAMES I. KENDALL, Ph.D., D.Sc.

*Assistant Professor in Biology in the City College, New York City*

*THIRD EDITION, THOROUGHLY REVISED*
*WITH 225 ILLUSTRATIONS*

## LEA & FEBIGER
### PHILADELPHIA
### 1947

Kendall, James Irving, 1906–

Microscopic anatomy of vertebrates. 3d ed., thoroughly
rev., with 225 illus. Philadelphia, Lea & Febiger, 1947.

354 p. illus. 25 cm.

First ed. (1935) by G. G. Scott and J. I. Kendall.
Bibliography: p. 320–342.

1. Vertebrates—Anatomy.    i. Scott, George Gilmore, 1873–
ii. Title.

## CHAPTER XII

### THE EXCRETORY SYSTEM

## CHAPTER XIII

### THE FEMALE REPRODUCTIVE SYSTEM

## CHAPTER XIV

### THE MALE REPRODUCTIVE SYSTEM

## CHAPTER XV

### THE ENDOCRINE GLANDS

## CHAPTER XVI

### TECHNIQUE

# MICROSCOPIC ANATOMY OF VERTEBRATES

## CHAPTER I

## INTRODUCTION

In courses of animal biology, or zoölogy, students usually begin by studying the Protozoa where a single cell constitutes an individual possessing a complete organization and carrying on all functions essential to life. This conception of cellular independence and self-sufficiency is modified upon consideration of simple multicellular animals, such as are found among the Cœlenterates. In such animals a large number of cells are interdependent, their functions finding expression in the activity of the individual they constitute. Cellular specialization becomes evident; certain cells become particularly active in secretion or in absorption; others serve for protection; still others function in contraction or conduction of stimuli. Among the higher groups of animals cellular differentiation and interdependence becomes more marked, so that within the individual animal body there are organization of cells having the same structural and functional features. Such organizations of cells, structurally similar, and their products, if any, are called tissues. The different types of tissues recognized on the basis of the structural and functional characteristics of the cells and cellular products composing them are epithelium, connective tissue and blood, muscle, and nerve.

Histology concerns itself with the study of the structural characteristics of these tissues and their interrelationships with one another. The various types do not exist independently, but are associated in the formation and function of various organs. A better appreciation of how organs function is possible after a study of their tissue composition or microscopic anatomy. Histology and microscopic anatomy are but continuations of anatomy which concerns itself with the internal and external structures of the animal body as determined by dissection. The close association of structure and function obliges a student of anatomy to consider various aspects of function with relation to the structural features, although this study is primarily the problem of physiology.

The study of histology and microscopic anatomy rests upon the structural and functional differentiations of the cells. Although

( 13 )

the knowledge founded on studies of the protoplasmic structure and function of cells belongs to the science of cytology, it is essential that the student of histology should know some of the general structural features of the cell in order to understand the conditions met with in the tissues and organs of his preparations. Embryology is that branch of biology which follows the progressive steps whereby a mature individual develops from the single cell stage normally representing the fusion of a sperm and an egg cell.

The study of living cells is possible but is still far from being sufficiently practical to be used as a method for teaching undergraduate classes, therefore, in order to cover the basic histological material in the time normally allotted for laboratory study it is necessary to rely primarily upon dead tissues and organs stained to accentuate their characteristic features. It will be a very valuable experience, wherever practical, to supplement study of such preparations with observations of living tissues and organs *in situ* and also of small pieces carefully excised and placed in saline so that a comparison may be made between structural appearance in the living and prepared material.

It is true that the methods used in fixed preparations subject the cells to a number of chemical and physical changes, but the features shown by such methods have been repeatedly checked so that in knowing the reaction of cells to these procedures there are relatively constant factors with which to work. Many of the structures easily seen in prepared material are not visible in the living cell or are visible only with great difficulty. The cellular structures and also the intercellular materials as they appear in fixed preparations may be called artifacts but will give useful information regarding characteristic structures and reactions of tissues following treatment with the various standard methods of preparation.

*Vital staining* is the term applied to methods whereby living tissues are subjected to certain dyes to which they react in a characteristic manner. Some of the dyes can be introduced into a living animal and specific cells or tissues will react to such *intravitam* staining, as for example the phagocytosis of trypan blue or carmine by histiocytes. In another approach, called *supravital* staining, living tissue is removed from the animal and then subjected to the dyes, as for example the staining of mitochondria with Janus green B. Cultivation of small pieces of tissue on nutrient media, tissue culture, makes possible the study of cells and their products with vital dyes under controlled conditions which admittedly vary from normal *in situ* conditions but give valuable information. Whole organs may be kept alive in media and also studied outside the

body, *in vitro*, as contrasted with *in vivo* study under the normal environment of the body.

Development of histochemical and histophysiological methods serve to clarify morphological studies by demonstrating definite components of cells and their products by their reactions to various chemicals under controlled physiological conditions. A better analysis of functional phenomena from this approach, will serve to more closely relate histology with physiology and chemistry.

The use of the electron microscope is adding to knowledge of ultra microscopic details of cell and tissue composition, and by the use of microincineration the inorganic components have been demonstrated in sectioned material.

## THE CELL

Although there is great variation in the size, shape, and particular functions of different cells, there are certain general structural features that can usually be demonstrated in all. An animal cell may be defined as a small mass of protoplasm externally limited by a cell membrane and containing a spherical body, the nucleus, enclosed in its own membrane. The body of the cell, or cytosome, includes all the protoplasm outside the nucleus, both nucleus and cytosome being composed of protoplasm whose composition differs in each case.

**Protoplasm.**—Protoplasm is chemically a complex mixture of proteins and their derivatives, carbohydrates, lipoids, and inorganic salts associated with a large amount of water. Physically, protoplasm has the properties of a complex colloidal system, capable of those changes in viscosity which are due to reversible gels occurring in the living cell. Living cells are visible as pale, colorless, homogeneous masses in which, with proper illumination, various refractive structures may be observed. The cell membrane and the nuclear membrane may appear brighter because of the higher refractivity of their components. The chromosomes of the nucleus, and some of the granular or fibrillar elements of the cytosome, may stand out due to refraction of light. For the most part, our knowledge must depend upon examination of fixed and stained material in which the various elements of the protoplasm are precipitated as insoluble substances which are then stained with various dyes. The precipitation process also preserves the membranes. Other structures of the cytosome, such as the mitochondria, Golgi apparatus, and centrioles, can be precipitated or preserved for staining and study by using special methods.

**Cytosome.**—The appearance of the cytoplasm in fixed materials varies with the method used in preparation, and also with the type and physiological state of the cell. It was this variability with fixatives which caused much of the early disagreement and debate as to the nature of protoplasm. Some investigators held that protoplasm was essentially granular; others believed it to be alveolar and to resemble an emulsion; still others held that it had a reticulum of slender fibrils associated with fine granules. Actually all these conditions may be observed in the same type of cell if it is prepared during different phases of activity and also by different techniques. In general, the cytoplasm reacts to acid dyes and stains from light pink to red in routine preparations where eosin is used. Within an undifferentiated and relatively homogeneous cytoplasm certain definite structures are differentiated.

*Mitochondria* (chondriosomes) are elements demonstrated within the cytoplasm after certain techniques are employed. They are quite universal in occurrence, though variable in shape. Usually they are granular in inactive, young or embryonic cells, but are filamentous or rod-shaped in the older and active tissue cells. They are composed of phospholipids and proteins in varying proportions and are soluble in fat solvents, so are not preserved in routine preparations but require special techniques. Janus green B reacts with them in the living cell, and their activities may be followed after staining with this dye. Various observers have associated them with the formation of fat, of fibrils, and of secretion granules. They move about in the cytoplasm, grow and divide, and transform from the granular to the rod or filamentous forms (or *vice versa*) in the living cell.

*Golgi Apparatus.*—This much studied and controversial structure is not apparent in most routine preparations. It has been demonstrated by using osmium tetroxide in fixation and in such preparations it is commonly composed of osmophilic lipoids which are preserved and blackened by the osmium to show a lamelliform or platelike structure usually located like a collar about the nucleus. In single sections this material gives the appearance of a reticular structure but by supravital methylene blue staining it has been recorded as a fluid filled vesicular structure which shrinks in dehydration or fixation to leave the reticular formation. The Golgi apparatus has recently been associated with the elaboration of fat. Its structure varies in appearance with different physiological states of the cells observed and small globules or granules indicative of secretory activity in glandular cells usually appear near the region occupied by the Golgi apparatus.

*Centrosome.*—Close to the nucleus there is found another structure of almost universal occurrence in animal cells, the central apparatus, or centrosome. It is inconspicuous in the resting cell, but becomes prominent during mitotic (indirect) division of the cell. During this process, a single small granular body, the centriole, is surrounded by a clear area of cytoplasm, the centrosphere. After treatment with protein precipitating agents, a spindle of numerous fine protoplasmic rays may be observed extending into the cytoplasm in all directions from the centrosphere. The so-called astrosphere thus formed is intimately associated with cell division.

*Fibrils and Granules.*—In addition to the structures already mentioned, there are other common ones distributed in the cytoplasm of special cells to be observed in the study of prepared sections of various tissues. In nerve cells and striated muscle fibers, abundant and distinct fibrils may occupy much of the cytosome in prepared sections but may not be visible in the same tissues in the living state. The cells in the early divisions of the frog embryo contain yolk granules, and glycogen can be demonstrated as a stored substance in the cytoplasm of liver cells. Droplets of fat form and accumulate in certain connective tissue cells. Granules of secretory nature are recognizable in various gland cells, as in the pancreas; pigment granules (melanin) occur in the cytoplasm of epithelial cells in the avian and mammalian epidermis and in certain connective tissue cells, the chromatophores, located in the dermis of amphibians; and granules are a characteristic feature of several blood cells.

*Cell Membrane.*—A limiting membrane is not clearly evident in all cells. Some investigators believe it to be merely a condensation of the peripheral cytoplasm which probably contains lipins. By microdissection it has been possible to indicate that this membrane possesses some degree of elasticity. It is semipermeable and appears to regulate the passage of oxygen and nutritive materials into the cell cytoplasm as well as the passage of carbon dioxide and nitrogenous wastes out of the cell. The surface of some epithelial cells may have a thick, tough external cuticle or other structural modifications of the free surface. Certain groupings of cells are not completely separated by individual cell membranes and form a syncytium as in the case of cardiac and skeletal muscle.

**Nucleus.**—The nucleus is a globular or ovoid body composed of special proteins, the nucleoproteins, the nucleic acid portion of which determines the basophilic staining reaction common to nuclei. A nuclear membrane separates the nuclear material from the cytoplasm. Fixation and use of basic stains bring out a granular network that increases in density as organization of the nucleus for

2

division advances, until the chromosomes stand out clearly as solidly staining bodies. Cytogenetics has demonstrated that it is the chromosomes which carry the hereditary factors, the genes.

Whereas the cytoplasm usually takes acid stains, therefore staining red with eosin, the chromatin of the nucleus reacts mainly to basic stains so that when hematoxylin is employed the stained chromatin gives the nucleus a color varying from blue to black. In the resting nucleus the chromosomes are not apparent. Their disappearance as solid bodies is due to physiological changes involving chemical changes in the nucleoproteins so that in preparations of the interphase or interkinetic ("resting") cell the chromatin material appears as scattered granules or a loose network.

Within the interphase nucleus there is usually present at least one small spherical body, the nucleolus, which is highly refractive in living cells and acidophilic in most fixed preparations. It usually disappears with the beginning of cell division and reappears in the nucleus of each newly formed cell. The function of this structure is not definitely known.

The nucleus is regarded as being the regulator of cellular activities and changes in its appearance and reactions are associated with the changing states of the cell as a whole. The major cellular function for which associated structural nuclear changes can be demonstrated is cell division or reproduction.

**Cell Reproduction.**—The formation of new cells is most active in the embryo, yet the process takes place in many tissues of the adult vertebrate body notwithstanding the fact that there are surprisingly few cells in the active process of division to be seen in the usual microscopic preparations. Probably most of the cells of which adult tissues are composed have a longer life than one would at first suppose. Each cell should be considered as a complicated biochemico-physical system whose organization is maintained for a long time, even though the materials of the system change.

Two types of cell division have been recognized, mitosis and amitosis. Mitosis, or indirect cell division, is the normal method of cell division and a brief presentation of this process may serve to recall the major features.

Mitosis.—The mitotic process is usually arbitrarily divided into four stages: namely, prophase, metaphase, anaphase, and telophase. These imperceptibly grade into one another, since they are but easily distinguishable steps in a continuous sequence of phenomena. (Fig. 1.)

*Prophase.*—This phase of nuclear activity is preceded and accompanied by activity of the two centrioles in the center of the centro-

some. When activity begins, the centrioles move apart until they occupy a position 90 degrees from their resting position, thus being opposite each other, with the nucleus between them. Astral rays then appear radiating into the cytoplasm from each centriole. In preparations, these rays resemble fine fibrils and those radiating between the two centrioles form the achromatic spindle. Simultaneously the nuclear membrane and nucleolus disappear. The chromatin, which may appear granular in preparations of the interphase, becomes apparent as a tangled threadlike network which forms a specific number of chromosomes through condensation of

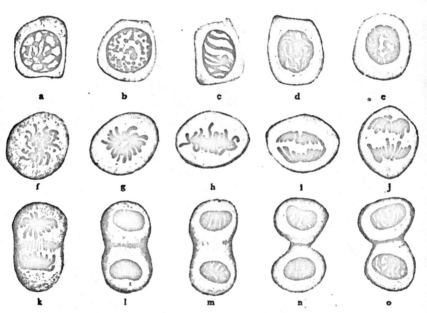

FIG. 1.—Mitosis. Epidermal cells of a mouse. Bouin fixation; iron hematoxylin stain. *a–b*, resting; *c–d–e*, prophase; *f–g–h*, metaphase; *i–j–k*, anaphase; *l–m–n*, telophase; *o*, resting. (Bremer–Weatherford's Textbook of Histology, courtesy of The Blakiston Co.)

its constituents. The chromosomes forming at this stage are usually constant in number for all somatic cells of each species and maintain their identity even during the interphase state, although not demonstrable as units during this time. The chromosomes move so that they lie on the spindle in an imaginary plane midway between the two centrioles at right angles to the axis and each chromosome has spindle fibers associated with it. Longitudinal splits in the chromosomes now become apparent as grooves, though they may actually have split much earlier in the prophase stage.

*Metaphase.*—During this second phase longitudinal splitting is completed and each chromosome is found to be equally divided into two longitudinal halves. The two halves of each chromosome separate and move toward their respective centrioles, a feature marking the beginning of the anaphase.

*Anaphase.*—The chromosomes progress toward the centrioles in this third stage. In late anaphase a groove appears in the cell membrane corresponding with the location of the equatorial plane, which is marked by a granular line. This groove deepens as the chromosomes pass to opposite poles. The assembling of the chromosomes at opposite poles marks the beginning of the telophase.

*Telophase.*—The equatorial constriction, or groove, continues in this final phase so that eventually two daughter cells are formed each with its own cell membrane. Two daughter nuclei are organized in the same way as was the original interphase nucleus, though they are smaller in size. A nuclear membrane forms about each daughter nucleus and the chromatin becomes distributed as it was in the resting nucleus of the parent cell. A nucleolus usually appears in each nucleus at the end of the telophase, and the centriole divides into a diplosome, or two centrioles, near each daughter nucleus. If the daughter cells chance to be part of an embryo, the next cell division will occur very quickly. Some time may elapse before these cells divide again if they are part of an adult organism. Binucleated, multinucleated or syncitial conditions may result with failure of cell membrane formation to accompany the nuclear division.

AMITOSIS.—Now and then cells appear to divide directly by constriction without the elaborate preparations that occur in mitosis. This process has been named amitosis. In such cases the nucleus first separates into two parts by constriction, after which the cytoplasm likewise divides. It has been observed in pathological tissues and in the case of some old cells in tissue cultures. In most of the so-called cases of amitosis, the technique may have been at fault or the cells only appear to divide amitotically, due to some abnormal condition interfering with the mitotic process.

Cell Metabolism.—The living cell is a dynamic system in which chemical and physical changes are constantly taking place. All such transformations of matter and energy occurring in living protoplasm are included in the term metabolism. Nutritive substances taken into the cell are subjected to the action of enzymes which facilitate the breaking down of the complex compounds into their simpler units. These units are then utilized in building up the elements of protoplasm which serve for cell differentiation and growth. The energy liberated by oxidation reactions is utilized

for the chemical and physical changes involved in movement, in secretion and excretion, and for the continuation of those metabolic changes constantly involved in the maintenance of life.

All cells, regardless of the degree of their functional specialization, must still carry on a basic general metabolism necessary to maintain their own life. Thus a muscle cell, in addition to the basic metabolism maintaining its life, has special metabolic processes endowing it with the property of contraction.

Cytomorphosis designates the sequence of structural changes undergone by a cell in its passage from the embryonic state, through its differentiated phase to senescence and death. Death or necrosis of cells is followed by cellular disintegration, at which time the enzymes active in the living cell in the synthesis of proteins from amino-acids begin breaking down the proteins into amino-acids which are then diffused from the cell. During this process of autolysis or self digestion the chromatin of the nucleus may first contract into a dense irregular chromatic mass, described as *pycnotic*, then fragment before completion of the dissolution process. Dead cells of the integument and of duct or cavity linings are lost from these surfaces and present no problem in disposition of their disintegration products. In most regions of the body dead cells undergo dissolution away from such surfaces and phagocytic cells ingest and dispose of the remnants of dissolution. In some cases resorption following cell destruction is incomplete and may be accompanied by calcium deposits and cyst formation about the destroyed area.

**Histogenesis and Organogeny.**—In the embryonic development of all forms the fertilized egg cleaves and by repeated divisions of subsequent cells three layers of cells form the ectoderm, endoderm, and mesoderm. As the embryo continues its development from the early state in which it is composed of these three germ layers, the cells of these layers multiply and differentiate to give rise to the variety of tissues found in the adult. *Histogenesis* is the process of development through which tissues pass from the early germ layer stage to their fully differentiated state as epithelia, connective tissue, blood, muscle, or nerve. *Organogeny* is the process whereby the developing tissues associate and differentiate to give rise to the various organs of the adult. The development of similar tissues and organs differs in some respects in the different classes of vertebrates and the problems of their development rightly belong to the field of comparative embryology. However, a reference will be made to the histogenesis and early organogeny as each tissue and system of organs is considered.

The following list briefly summarizes tissues and organs under the germ layer or layers from which they are usually and normally derived.

### From Ectoderm

Epidermis of skin; hairs; nails; sweat and sebaceous glands; claws; feathers; lens of eye; part of cornea; retina; conjunctiva; lacrimal gland; most of pituitary body; epithelium lining mouth and nasal cavities; sensory cells of many sense organs; pineal gland; medulla of adrenal gland; enamel of teeth and scales; all nerve cells and most neuroglia cells.

### From Mesoderm

Cartilage, bone, perichondrium, periosteum, tendons, ligaments; other connective tissues; microglia cells; almost all muscle tissue; blood cells; marrow; blood-vessels and lymph vessels; gonads and kidneys; gonaducts and urinary ducts; cortex of adrenals; pleuræ; pericardium; peritoneum; lymph organs; scales in fishes except enamel; and bony plates in reptiles.

### From Endoderm

Epithelium of digestive tract from pharynx to rectum; glands of this tract, including pancreas and liver; epithelium of larynx, trachea, and lungs; glandular epithelium of thyroid and parathyroid glands; epithelium lining the Eustachian tube and middle ear

# CHAPTER II

## THE EPITHELIAL TISSUES

THE various types of epithelial tissues are composed of one or more layers of cells lying so close to one another that there is practically no intercellular material. The three germ layers of the embryo are epithelial in character and in their later development all three give rise to epithelial membranes which cover the free surfaces of the body and line not only the ducts connecting with these surfaces, but also cavities within the body not connected with the outer surface. One of the chief general functions of these tissues is protection, such as preventing the loss of body fluids or the invasion of foreign material. Most types of epithelia have some secretory activity, but those lining numerous glands are primarily secretory. Epithelia are intimately concerned in processes involved in respiration, in the assimilation of nutritive materials, in the elimination of wastes, in the reception of stimuli and in reproduction.

Classification.—It must be admitted that any classification of the various types of epithelia will be artificial, and the justification of any scheme will lie in the ease and completeness it offers for dealing with the types in question. A classification of epithelia is not possible on the basis of function alone, for the exact function of many types is not yet clear, and others may have more than a single function. Embryological origin likewise fails, since often the same type is derived from ectoderm, endoderm, and mesoderm. The most satisfactory scheme uses the form and arrangement of the cells. Even on this basis, allowances must be made for intergrading forms and changes in form which commonly accompany changes in physiological activity. Two large groups are separated depending upon the presence of one or more than one layer of cells in the tissue. Tissues belonging to the first group have a single layer of cells and are called simple epithelia. In the second group are the stratified epithelia, where more than a single layer of cells compose the tissue. Various types within these two groups are then separated with reference to the form and arrangement of the cells composing each.

All types of epithelia agree in that they rest upon connective tissue which carries a vascular and nerve supply and, with few exceptions, this supporting connective tissue forms a *basement membrane* immediately adjoining the epithelial tissue. The basement membrane is a non-cellular structure that appears as a very narrow band.

It is unfortunate that in the study of histological preparations the field presented by the microscope is primarily two-dimensional. The third dimensional aspect of the objects under study may be obtained by focusing up and down through the section, and in the case of very thin sections it is necessary to study a series of consecutive sections and develop the ability to form a composite picture incorporating this aspect. In studying sections of epithelial membranes it is essential to realize the effects produced on cell form by the nature of the section made. As an example of limitation imposed by studying the two dimensions presented by histological preparations under the microscope, consider the possible sections through a cell having the form of a hexagonal column with a central bean-shaped nucleus. (Fig. 2.) If a series of cuts pass through such a cell

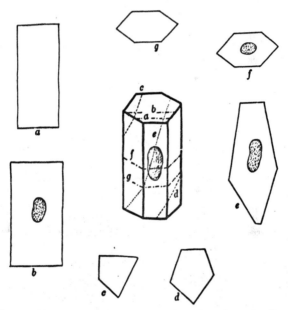

Fig. 2.—Diagrams of the appearance of a variety of sections of a diagrammatic columnar epithelial cell.

parallel with the long axis, thin sections will be obtained which appear as rectangles, and not all sections will have the nucleus represented (*a, b*). Furthermore, if the first cut through the region of the nucleus takes only a small portion of its convex surface, such a section will appear to have a spherical nucleus, while sections through the body of the nucleus will have an ovoid form. No one section so obtained gives clear evidence of the third dimensional aspect or the picture of the cell as a whole. If another series of thin

sections is obtained using cuts at an angle of 45 degrees with the long axis, then there will be a variation from trapezoids without nuclear portions to rectangles containing roughly spherical nuclear portions (*c, d, e*). As the angle of cutting approaches a right angle with the long axis, the hexagonal structure of the cell appears in the sections, although distorted. Sections from cuts made at right angles to the longitudinal axis will show hexagons, some of which will have no nuclear portion, while others will have a spherical nucleus centrally situated (*f, g*). Therefore, in order to visualize the complete structure of such a cell it would be necessary to have at least several sections at right angles to and parallel with the long axis. Observations should always be made while focusing up and down through the field with the fine adjustment to check on any variations that may be present at different levels of the sectioned material. An ability to visualize the third dimensional aspect should be cultivated in studying sections of tissues and organs, and the relationship of the cells with each other should also be considered. In the example just considered the cell was a regular, independent unit, but as a part of tissues all cells are modified by pressures of adjoining cells and internal pressures, so that the common form is an irregular fourteen-sided figure which in sections presents a variety of polygonal figures.

### SIMPLE EPITHELIA

A subdivision of the simple epithelia into squamous, cuboidal, columnar, and pseudostratified is based upon the structural characters of the cells composing the single layer characteristic of these

SQUAMOUS     CUBOIDAL     COLUMNAR

FIG 3.—Diagram of types of simple epithelial cells.

membranes. Such terms are convenient for indicating types but between these types there exist intermediate forms.

In general, those cells which appear nearly isodiametric in sections passing through their central region at right angles to their base are spoken of as cuboidal. Cells appearing as rectangles in sections passing at right angles to their base are spoken of as columnar cells, but are long prismatic structures when the third dimensional aspect is considered. The squamous cells are irregular discoidal elements which appear fusiform in sections resulting from cutting at right angles to their proximal or attached surface. The three types indicated show great variation as a result of irregularities imposed by adjacent cells and the location of the tissue. (Fig. 3.)

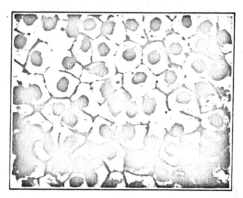

Fig. 4.—A photograph of a surface view of squamous cells forming the topmost layer of a frog's epidermis. 4 mm. obj. and 5× oc.

**Simple Squamous Epithelium.**—The term squamous literally means scaly, and epithelia of this type are composed of flattened, plate-like cells whose cytoplasm is so scanty that the nucleus, which is centrally placed, causes a slight bulge. (Fig. 3.) In some cases

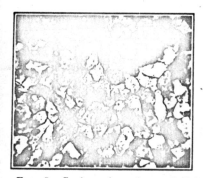

Fig. 5.—Surface view of mesothelial cells outlined by silver nitrate preparation. Photomicrograph. 4 mm. obj. and 5 × oc.

Fig. 6.—Diagram of endothelium.

the lateral faces or edges adjoining other cells are regular, but more often the boundaries are irregular and interlock with irregularities in adjacent cells. In sections which may pass at right or oblique angles to their bases, such cells appear fusiform when the central nuclear region is represented, or they appear as a very narrow band with indistinct cellular outlines when sections miss the nuclear

region. A simple squamous epithelium is found, for example, forming Bowman's capsule and the thin loop portions of the uriniferous tubules of the kidney, and forming portions of the respiratory surfaces of the lungs and gills. Squamous cells are found sloughing from the surface of stratified squamous membranes to be observed later. (Fig. 4.)

A membrane of simple squamous cells forms the *endothelium* lining the blood-vessels and a membrane of cells ranging from simple squamous to columnar lines the body cavities and is called *mesothelium.* (Figs. 5, 6 and 31.) Both arise from mesoderm by way of mesenchyme and under normal conditions appear as epithelial membranes but will be considered with connective tissues since they have potentialities not characteristic of true epithelia, as shown in tissue cultures and under conditions of inflammation where endothelium and mesothelium have been observed to give rise to connective tissue cells.

**Simple Cuboidal Epithelium.**—In this type the epithelial membrane is composed of cells whose three dimensions are approximately equal and appear in sections as rough squares. (Fig. 3.) Cuboidal epithelium is found in portions of the excretory ducts of many glands and in the uriniferous tubules of the kidney. (Fig. 7.) When arranged about small ducts the cells are usually somewhat truncated with the free end smaller than the base. Cuboidal cells lining various ducts may have a striated or a brush border distally, or cilia may extend from this free surface.

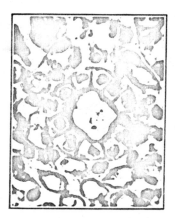

FIG. 7.—Photograph of simple cuboidal epithelium of a collecting tubule of the rat kidney. Surrounding it are a number of capillaries and loop tubules with walls composed of simple squamous cells. 4 mm. obj. and 5× oc.

**Simple Columnar Epithelium.**—The cells of this type show variations from those whose length is only slightly greater than their

other two dimensions to cells which are greatly elongated. (Fig. 3.)
The nuclei may occur in the central region of such cells, but more
commonly are found in the lower half. The low columnar cells
closely resemble the cuboidal and it is often difficult to decide
whether to call a given membrane cuboidal or low columnar unless
a number of cells can be observed. In sections where the cut has
been parallel to the long axis, columnar cells appear as rectangles,
but sections at right angles to this axis show irregularly polygonal
figures. (Fig. 8.) When serving to form ducts columnar cells

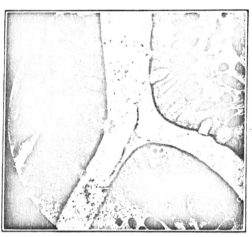

Fɪɢ. 8.—Photograph of simple columnar epithelial cells with striated border
forming the intestinal lining of Necturus. Several goblet cells are shown with their
distal portions filled with mucous secretion, and one in the center is shown with the
secretion mass extruded from the.cell. 4 mm. obj. and 5× oc.

may taper from proximal (basal) to distal (free surface) regions,
thus having the form of elongated wedges, or roughly pyramidal
figures in section. Areas also occur where oblique sections through
a simple columnar membrane may present an appearance of several
cell layers or stratification.

Epithelium of a columnar form is found lining the digestive tract
and the many small glands in the wall of the stomach and intestine
of vertebrates generally. The duct systems within the larger
digestive glands, such as the liver, pancreas, and salivary glands are
lined by columnar epithelium. Columnar cells with a striated
distal border line the small intestine and ciliated columnar cells are
found lining the oviducts.

*Goblet Cells.*—Single cells of a simple columnar epithelium may elaborate
and accumulate mucinogen droplets until the distal end is much distended
with the secretion and resembles a goblet. (Figs. 8 and 9.) Such cells

are called goblet cells and occur abundantly in the lining of the intestine where their secretion is liberated as mucin which together with water forms the layer of mucus covering the gut lining. Liberation of the secretion may be a gradual or an abrupt and complete process followed by a

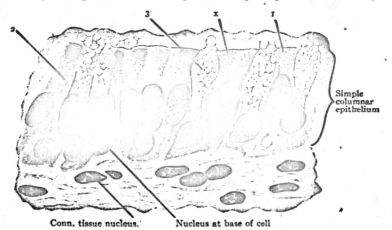

Fig. 9.—Wall of intestine of Necturus; formation of mucin. 1, 2, 3, cells in progressive stages from mucigen granules to mucin; "x," upper part of cell cut in this section. (Bremer-Weatherford's Texbook of Histology, courtesy of the Blakiston Company.)

repetition of secretion and accumulation. Where liberation of secretion is a gradual and continuous process, as in the stomach lining, these cells may retain their goblet formation, but where liberation of secretion is abrupt the cells collapse until renewal of secretion again distends them. The mucoproteins composing the mucus formed by epithelium have been differentiated from those elaborated in the connective tissues.

**Pseudostratified Columnar Epithelium.**—This term is commonly used for epithelia resembling a stratified type. (Fig. 10.) It has the appearance of several strata of cells with columnar cells forming

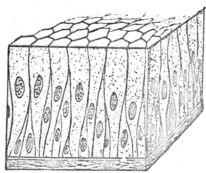

Fig. 10.—Stereodiagrammatic representation of pseudostratified columnar epithelium showing the relationship of the cells to the basement membrane and to each other. The long columnar cells of this type are frequently ciliated

the surface layer. It has been demonstrated that all the cells rest upon a common basement membrane, the apparently superficial cells have long tapering proximal portions with polyhedral and fusiform smaller cells of various sizes filling in among them. Many routine preparations do not show the lateral boundaries of the cells clearly enough to trace all attachments to the basement membrane and such membranes may be easily confused with the less common stratified columnar type where cell outlines are usually much more readily determined.

Pseudostratified epithelium forms the lining of the trachea and bronchi of mammals and many regions of the gut of lower vertebrates. Large ducts are commonly lined by this type. The columnar cells very commonly have cilia on their distal surface and many others are of the goblet type in the respiratory tract.

## STRATIFIED EPITHELIA

When considering stratified types several subdivisions are possible on the basis of the shape and arrangement of the cells, with the emphasis on the type of cell forming the superficial layer. The basal layer of cells is generally prismatic and appears as cuboidal or low columnar in sections. The cells between the base and the surface appear as irregular polygonal figures, showing considerable variation in size, regularity, and number of layers. In one type the cells flatten out as they near the surface, until those of the superficial layer are squamous in form; in another type, the cells retain a prismatic structure even at the surface, save that their free boundaries are usually convex; a third type has surface cells which are elongated prisms and appear as wedge-shaped cells with their tapering bases passing among the underlying polygonal cells. Four subdivisions of stratified epithelia are discussed in the following paragraphs.

**Stratified Squamous Epithelium.** — This is a common stratified type serving as a protective membrane and the number of cell layers composing the membrane varies in different parts of the same animal. The basal layer of cells appears cuboidal or low columnar in sections. Progressing upward there are several layers of polyhedral cells showing a gradual change toward the surface where flattened squamous cells occur. (Figs. 11, 12.) The superficial squamous cells are constantly being worn away and replaced by underlying cells. The cells of the basal layers divide frequently and after each division one daughter cell remains in the same position as the mother cell while the other is pushed upward into the next

layer. The newly formed cells are constantly undergoing chemical alterations as they move closer to the surface of the membrane, until finally they die and become part of the surface layers which

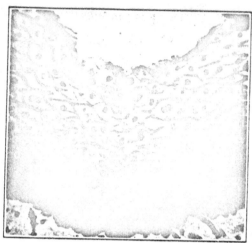

Fig. 11.—Photograph of stratified squamous epithelium from esophagus of monkey, 4 mm. obj. and 5× oc.

continually wear away. Microscopic examination of saliva reveals a number of such desquamated cells from the lining of the mouth. This type forms the epidermis of most vertebrates but there is considerable variation in the thickness of the membrane and its cellular composition in different regions of the same animal or in

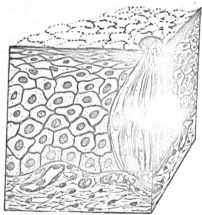

Fig. 12.—Stereodiagrammatic representation of neuro-epithelial cells as they are organized in a stratified squamous epithelium to form taste buds in the tongue or neuromasts of the lateral line system. The black fusiform cells are the sensory cells associated with nerve fibers while the light elongated cells are supporting elements. A pore opens to the surface.

animals of different classes depending to some extent upon environmental conditions. In fishes and amphibians some of the cells of such a membrane forming the epidermis become spherically distended by accumulation of secretions which are later liberated on the skin surface.

*Neuro-epithelial Cells.*—Within the epithelial membranes of such regions as the mouth, ear, eye, and lateral line there are groups of epithelial cells which receive stimuli that are conveyed to associated nerve fibers as olfactory, auditory, and visual sensations. These sensory epithelial cells, called neuro-epithelial cells, are derived from the ectoderm and have a fusiform shape. One end of such cells extends to the surface of the membrane within which it occurs and a proximal tapering portion makes contact with a nerve fiber ending. (Fig. 12.)

**Stratified Cuboidal Epithelium.**—In this type, the basal cells are cuboidal or low columnar, the intermediate region of several cell layers has irregularly polygonal cells, and the surface cells are roughly cuboidal with a rounded outer margin. This type is commonly found forming the epidermis of urodeles, and lining the cloaca and cloacal bladder of amphibia generally. In the epidermis there are scattered cells, called club cells, which become distended

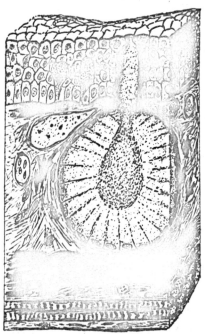

Fig. 13.—Stereodiagrammatic representation of the integument of Necturus, showing the scattered glandular cells, an alveolar mucous gland, the stratum vasculare with chromatophores, and the stratum compactum adjoining the sheaths of the skeletal muscles.

with their secretion products until they appear almost spherical. (Fig. 13.) Most commonly a broken layer of dead flattened cells lies along the surface.

Stratified Columnar Epithelium.—The basal layers and intermediate cell layers are similar to those of the preceding stratified types, but the superficial cells are elongated prisms that appear columnar in sections. It may be found lining the vas deferens and some of the larger excretory ducts of compound glands of mammals where, in

FIG. 14                                    FIG. 15

FIG. 14.—Photomicrograph of a section through the frog's esophagus showing columnar ciliated and goblet cells forming the distal layer of stratified columnar epithelium. 4 mm. obj. and 5× oc.
FIG 15.—Stereodiagram of same section used for Figure 14.

some cases, as in the vas deferens, the columnar cells are ciliated. Among the lower vertebrates this type is more commonly distributed and appears in parts of the alimentary tract and in the excretory ducts where many of the columnar cells are ciliated and others transform into goblet cells. This type forms the lining of the oral cavity and esophagus of the frog.

Transitional Epithelium.—At the surface of this type are very large cells, convex on the distal boundary and with proximal concavities into which the distal parts of underlying cells fit. (Fig. 16, *A*.) The basal layer of cells appears cuboidal or low columnar in sections. Binucleated cells are common in the top and middle layers of cells. Transitional epithelium lines the pelvis of the kidney, the ureters, the bladder, and part of the urethra in mammals, to which class it appears to be limited. The cells of such a membrane are capable of considerable displacement under tension so that in a distended membrane of this type, as found in a full bladder, there

3

appear to be only two or three layers of cells. (Fig. 16, *B*.) The surface cells stretch most and the underlying cells are drawn out into thin layers; when the tension is released the cells slide back into position so that the thickness and marked stratification of the relaxed membrane is apparent.

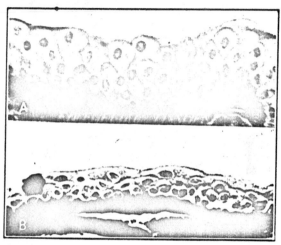

Fig. 16.—Photograph of transitional epithelium occurring in mammalian bladder. *A* represents the relaxed condition and *B* shows the effects of distention on cellular arrangement. 4 mm. obj. and 5× oc.

## SURFACE MODIFICATIONS OF EPITHELIAL CELLS

The free boundaries of epithelial cells may be modified in various ways. The superficial layer of protoplasm in some cases is condensed into a firmer portion continuous with subjacent less dense protoplasm. Such a surface condensation appears as a bright line in sections and may extend about the entire cell or be limited to the exposed surface. The denser layer of cytoplasm or membrane may be crossed by striations perpendicular to its surface which are considered as fine hairlike processes of protoplasm held together by intervening less differentiated protoplasm; an arrangement known as a *striated border* and usually associated with absorption. The surface of other cells has a *brush border* in which densely packed, non-motile, hairlike, protoplasmic structures project slightly beyond the surface. Such modification may serve to hold the covering mucus, such as covers the lamprey, or may serve in retention of material for absorption as in parts of the uriniferous tubule. A more conspicuous differentiation is found in various types of epithelial cells where fine, hairlike, protoplasmic

processes are much longer than those of the brush border. These processes, the *cilia*, of which there may be as many as a hundred from a single cell, usually possess the power of movement. Less commonly cells have single, whiplike, protoplasmic processes, called flagella, which are usually motile.

Little can be observed in histologic preparations as regards the actual composition of cilia, but according to one interpretation cilia possess a protoplasmic shell enclosing a hollow core, which being rhythmically filled and emptied with more fluid protoplasm imparts to these structures their characteristic movement. Another concept considers cilia to have a contractile band along each of two opposite surfaces and the movement is effected by the alternate contraction of these bands. Whichever interpretation may be proven correct, the movement appears as a sharp initial bending and a slow recovery. The motion of one row of cilia apparently initiates similar activity in adjacent rows, so that a series of waves pass along the field of cilia. Since the beat is in one direction, particles caught on the tips of the cilia are usually propelled in the direction of the beating. Ciliated epithelia lining the respiratory passages tend to move dust particles and any mucous material in the lumen towards the pharynx. Ciliary action is independent of nerve action, as may be demonstrated by removing the ciliated membrane from the roof of the frog's mouth and studying it in a saline solution hours after the frog itself is dead. Cilia possessing the power of movement are called *kinocilia*, to distinguish them from static cilia or *stereocilia*.

Another structural feature associated with the surface of some epithelia is a *cuticle*. The distal protoplasm of the cell is not modified in any marked manner and is not continuous with this modified border which is formed by the cell during development. The cuticle may become impregnated with various salts and be firm and hard. Such modifications play an important rôle in the formation of the exoskeleton of invertebrates but are rare among vertebrates. The epidermis of Amphioxus is covered by a cuticle. The attached or proximal surface of simple epithelia and the proximal surface of the deepest layer of the stratified types may possess a thickened membrane or produce a cuticle as in the case of enamel covering the placoid scales and teeth. In addition, most epithelial cells rest upon and are attached to a distinct *basement membrane*, which is a homogeneous layer of non-cellular substance derived from the subjacent connective tissue with which it is intimately associated.

The adjoining boundaries of some epithelial cells may be so delicate that they do not show clearly in routine preparations but in others a distinct membrane may be observed. A silver nitrate technique demonstrates boundaries clearly by a black silver deposit which outlines the individual cells. Some believe that an intercellular substance is essential to cement adjoining surfaces of cells and thus form epithelial membranes, but it is also possible that cells are held together through adhesion of their adjoining membranes. A cementing material may be demonstrated at the boundaries of the free surface of each cell where it adjoins its neighbors. At these points thin cylindrical black bars, *the terminal bars*, appear in preparations stained with iron hematoxylin and are considered as sealing the intercellular space between adjoining cells. These bars occur as minute black bands or dots depending upon how the section passes through them. Such cementing bars would hold the surface intact when membranes stretch and account for the return to original positions with release of tension.

*Protoplasmic bridges* may be observed under certain conditions between adjoining cells and are a relatively constant feature in stratified squamous epithelium. They are interpreted as protoplasmic strands between intercellular vacuoles, but have also been interpreted as artifacts due to fixation and subsequent preparation of the intercellular fluid. Such intercellular fluid may arise in part from diffusion of tissue fluid of the underlying connective tissue. Inasmuch as capillary supply is limited to this connective tissue, exchange of nutrients and products of metabolism in epithelial membranes may take place by diffusion through the intercellular fluids as well as through the cells.

One of the characteristics of epithelial tissues is the fact that they rest upon connective tissue. Even in those cases where the epithelial membrane is much folded, connective tissue fills in the spaces between the folds. This subjacent region of connective tissue carries a network of blood and lymph vessels which come into close contact with the base of every epithelial membrane, but do not usually extend in among its cells except as carried in by connective tissue papillæ. There is a plexus of nerve fibers in the connective tissue below the basement membrane and some of these fibers pass along the base of the cells while others may extend between the cells.

## GROWTH AND REGENERATION OF EPITHELIA

As one might expect from the exposure of various epithelia to mechanical and physiological wear, there is a varying quantitative loss of cells that must be replaced. The continual wearing away of the superficial layers is characteristic of stratified squamous

epithelia. This is especially pronounced in the case of the epidermis of the skin, which protects underlying tissues and still retains a sensitiveness to external stimuli. If the upper superficial scaly layers of dead cells accumulate to considerable thicknesses, there is an increased protection with an accompanying loss of general sensitivity. This occurs in the callosities localized at points of constant friction and pressure. The maintenance of a protective layer despite the wearing away of the superficial layers is made possible through the continual replacement of cells from the basal layers where they are being produced through normal mitotic activity. A lesion in this type of epithelium is quickly repaired through the activity of these basal cell layers. Epithelia of other types in other locations are also subject to gradual or abrupt destruction and loss of cells. Dead cells of the columnar type, in the alimentary tract, are replaced by mitotic activity of adjoining or less differentiated cells intercalated among them. Mitosis may be observed very rarely in sections of some organs and tissues but in others, such as in the epithelial cells of the epidermis and in the epithelia lining the uterus, mitotic figures can be found easily.

In healing of surfaces from which the epithelium has been lost through injury the newly formed cells of the bordering region apparently migrate by a sliding movement to form a simple thin covering layer prior to the regeneration of the type characteristic of the injured region. Experiments have also shown changes in type from squamous to cuboidal and columnar, and from simple to stratified types. For example, the pseudostratified ciliated epithelium of the trachea of the cat formed a stratified squamous membrane after repeated treatments with a formalin solution, but returned to the original simple type when the irritating stimulus was removed.

## SECRETORY EPITHELIAL CELLS AND GLANDULAR ORGANIZATIONS

Probably all epithelial cells to some extent elaborate active substances through biochemical processes of their protoplasm; these processes being collectively spoken of as secretion. Although protection and absorption are the major tasks of some epithelial cells, there are others primarily concerned with this process of secretion. In those cells active in secretion there occurs an accumulation of very small granules in the cytoplasm. The origin of these granules is debated, but they appear first in the basal region, then usually pass toward the surface of the cells where they are discharged to become part of the active secretion. There is considerable variation in the method by which secretion is carried to completion in different types of glandular cells. The use of the term glandular to indicate such secretory cells places the emphasis upon function, but the form of most of these cells will fit into the classification of types already studied.

Groups and organizations of actively secreting epithelial cells are called glands, and two broad divisions are separated on the basis of whether the secretion formed is liberated into a lumen from the free boundary of the cells or whether it passes in the opposite direction to enter the vascular system. Those organizations of cells secreting by the first method, that is by liberating their secretion into ducts which carry it to the surface of the epithelial membrane from which the gland developed, are called exocrine glands. The endocrine glands are those glandular tissues lacking excretory duct systems and whose secretions pass into the vascular system.

**Exocrine Glands.**—The secretory process is completed in several ways in different types of exocrine glands. In *merocrine* glands, granules form in the cytoplasm of the cells and accumulate toward the free boundary to be discharged as the active secretion; the process is then repeated. Most glandular secretions, such as those of the digestive glands, are derived in this manner. In a *holocrine* gland, as exemplified by a sebaceous gland in the skin of a mammal, the major portion of the active cell develops into a secretion mass which, when dislodged to form the secretion, is accompanied by the death and disintegration of the cell. A new cell then forms from the underlying layers of the stratified epithelium forming such glands and the process is repeated. Another type of secretion is termed *apocrine*. In this type, as exemplified by cells of the mammary gland, a secretion mass forms in the distal portion of the cell, becomes enlarged, and is finally cut off from the basal (proximal) nucleated portion. Such cells do not disintegrate following the liberation of the secretion but develop a new portion and repeat the process. A convenient classification of the exocrine glands may be built upon their organization regardless of the method of secretion.

*Unicellular Glands.*—Scattered single secretory cells occur in the epidermis of fishes and amphibians and goblet cells are numerous among the columnar cells of the gut lining. In the case of goblet cells, already mentioned under columnar epithelia, mucigen, which is elaborated in the cytoplasm, collects toward the distal end, until the volume of the secretion is increased so that the distal end becomes much distended. (Figs. 8, 9 and 17, *A*.) This distention progresses until there remains so thin a sheath of cytoplasm about

the secretion that a rupture occurs and there is a discharge of the mucus. Such goblet cells may undergo a number of repetitions of this apocrine type of secretion before disintegrating. Similar cells of less accentuated goblet type may produce mucigen and liberate mucin gradually and more constantly as do the cells bordering the

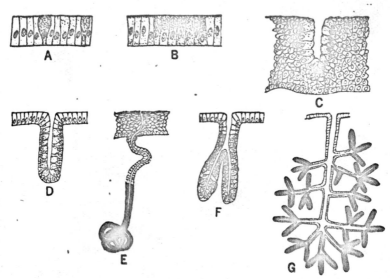

FIG. 17.—Diagram of glandular organizations. *A*, Unicellular glands represented by goblet cells; *B*, secreting area among simple columnar cells; *C*, glandular pocket as found in the cloaca of a reptile; *D*, simple tubular gland with numerous goblet cells as found in the large intestine of mammals; *E*, coiled tubular gland representing the sweat gland found in mammalian skin; *F*, branched tubular gland found in the stomach; *G*, compound tubular gland with secretory portions in black.

lumen of the stomach. Single cells with an accumulated content occur among fishes and amphibia in the epidermis and liberation of their secretion mass occurs as the cells reach the distal or free epithelial surface and disintegrate, a holocrine process.

*Secreting Areas.*—As a further step beyond the unicellular condition, there are areas in some epithelial membranes where small aggregations of cells function as special secreting groups; while the surrounding cells, although similar in form, function chiefly in protection and absorption. Such areas occur among the columnar cells lining the uterus, in the epithelial membrane lining the trachea, and in the thin membrane of cuboidal or low columnar cells forming the choroid plexes in the brain. (Fig. 17, *B*.)

*Glandular Pockets.*—Occurring at intervals in the epithelial membranes lining the various ducts there are shallow pockets lined by secretory cells. Such small pockets, usually lined with mucous secreting cells, may occur in the trachea, cloaca and urethra. The cells near the mouth of the pocket are commonly cuboidal or short columnar, with larger cells lining the pocket. (Fig. 17, *C*.)

*Simple Tubular Glands.*—These glands result from tubular invaginations of epithelial membranes during development. The cavity surrounded by the secretory cells is the *lumen*, and in tubular glands it is a blindly ending tubule that may vary greatly in length. The secretions of the cells pass into the lumen and out to the surface of the epithelial membrane from which the gland originated. (Fig. 17, *D*.) The oviducts of the frog and other egg-laying forms are usually lined with tubular glands whose secretions are added to the descending eggs. The epithelial wall of the large intestine of mammals possesses a multitude of simple tubular glands closely adjoining each other, their walls composed of columnar cells, of which the majority are of the goblet type. A modification of the straight tubular gland can be observed in the sweat gland where a long non-secretory portion acts as an excretory duct and spirals from the epidermis through the underlying connective tissue to the deeper, coiled portion composed of actively secreting cells. (Fig. 17, *E*.) The epithelial membrane covering the fundus of the stomach in mammals is composed of branched tubular glands with a single short excretory duct portion and two or more longer, slightly twisted, tubular portions composed of secretory cells.

*Simple Alveolar Glands.*—These glandular invaginations arise in the same manner as simple tubular glands but develop a spherical termination instead of the tubular type. The enlarged spherical secretory terminal portion of simple alveolar glands is called an *alveolus*. This type of gland is well represented in the integument of amphibians but does not occur among mammals. (Fig. 18, *A*.) Numerous simple alveolar glands occur in the integument of the frog and Necturus where their secretory alveoli lie below the stratified epithelium of the epidermis and connect with the surface by passageways through the strata of epithelial cells. (Figs. 13 and 113.) This simple type of gland may also be modified by having two or more alveoli attached to the end of a single excretory duct, as in the case of the sebaceous glands where alveoli are connected with the lateral walls of a common excretory duct. (Fig. 18, *B*.)

*Compound Tubular Glands.*—The formation of compound glands may be visualized by assuming that, instead of stopping with the simple tubular invagination of embryonic development, the early invagination has gone on developing branches from its deeper portions. These secondary branches give rise to tertiary ones, and so on until a large compound gland is formed with multiple secretory

end-pieces connecting with the original main excretory duct by numerous smaller excretory ducts. (Figs. 17, *G* and 19.) The outermost end-portions of the smallest branches usually possess the secretory cells and the other portions form the excretory duct system. The testis, kidney and liver develop first as compound tubular glands but

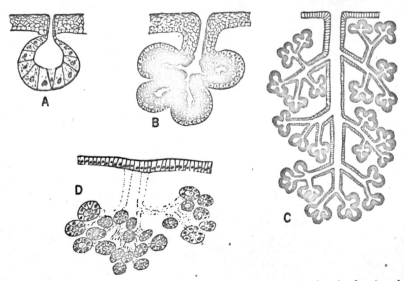

FIG. 18.—Diagram of glandular organizations. *A*, Simple alveolar gland as found in amphibian integument; *B*, branched alveolar gland representing conditions in the sebaceous gland of mammalian integument; *C*, compound alveolar gland with secretory alveoli in black; *D*, endocrine gland (thyroid) with dotted lines indicating ducts lost after formation of the secretory end pieces.

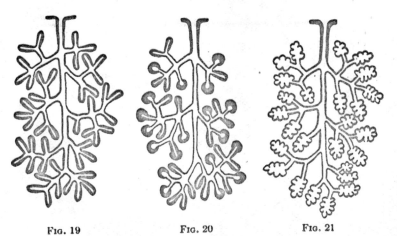

FIG. 19                FIG. 20                FIG. 21

FIG. 19.—Compound tubular gland.
FIG. 20.—Compound tubular-alveolar gland (submaxillary).
FIG. 21.—Compound alveolar gland (lung).

later development modifies their structure, as will be observed in studying these organs.  The rectal gland of the dogfish is compound tubular in structure.

Compound glands are invested with loosely arranged connective tissue extending between the excretory ducts and secretory end-pieces.  The larger masses thus separated by connective tissue are known as lobes and the smaller subdivisions are called lobules. The main excretory ducts accompanied by blood and lymph vessels, and nerves are carried in the connective tissue between the lobules. Immediately surrounding the basement membrane of the gland cells of the secreting end-pieces is a capillary network and also a plexus of nerve fibers.

*Compound Alveolar Glands.*—The manner in which these glands develop is similar to that in the case of tubular glands, but the secreting end-pieces are expanded into alveoli.  (Figs. 18, *C* and 21.) The lung develops as this type and may be considered as secreting carbon dioxide and absorbing oxygen.  The mammary gland is another example illustrating the structure of a compound alveolar gland.  Many of the compound glands are tubulo-alveolar as are the salivary glands and pancreas where there is an outward alveolar appearance to the secretory end-pieces but a tubular lumen.  (Fig. 20.)  Such an end-piece is commonly called an acinus rather than an alveolus.

**Serous and Mucous Glands.**—On the basis of the type of secretion, glands which produce a thin watery secretion are called serous glands and those producing a thicker, viscous, mucus are described as mucous glands.  The cells secreting these two types of material have certain distinctive features, although the secretion of each type may show some chemical differences in composition not only in different glands but in the same gland.

The *serous cells* are roughly truncated pyramids surrounding a narrow lumen.  A small spherical, deeply staining nucleus is located basally in preparations.  The cytoplasmic region between it and the lumen surface contains numerous coarse acidophilic granules and the cytoplasm has a cloudy appearance in routine preparations.  Minute intercellular canals, the *secretory canaliculi*, may be demonstrated extending to the lumen from between adjoining membranes of the serous cells.  The pancreas offers good material for the study of serous cells.

The *mucous cells* are irregular cuboidal or columnar in form and surround a broader lumen than in the case of the serous type.  The cytoplasm, which has numerous small globules of mucigen in the living cell, is precipitated in routine preparations so that it appears clear save for strands of the secretory material which takes basic stains. The nucleus is oval and usually flattened along the base of the cell.  Both mucous and serous cells may enter into the composition of the same secretory end-piece, as in the submaxillary gland, and a mixed mucoserous secretion is then produced.

**Endocrine Glands.**—These are glandular organizations composed of cords of secretory cells or vesicles without excretory ducts. A rich network of capillaries supplies such glands and into this blood supply the endocrine secretion enters from the proximal region of the secreting cells to be circulated by the vascular system. The thyroid, which is an example of this type of gland, begins develop-

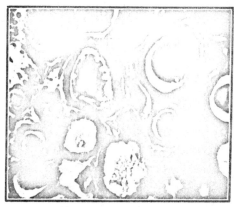

Fig. 22.—A section of the dog's thyroid to show colloid filled vesicles lined by cuboidal epithelium. Photomicrograph. 4 mm. obj. and 5× oc.

ment as do other glands by invaginating from an epithelial membrane, but the end-pieces become separated by the loss of the connecting duct system. As a result, the mature gland is composed of separate small spherical vesicles of varying size with their walls composed of a single layer of cuboidal epithelium. (Figs. 18, *D* and 22.) The other endocrine glands are best studied in the chapter dealing with them.

**Pigmentation in Epithelial Cells.**—Epithelial cells, in some locations, normally contain melanin pigment granules, and this constant characteristic has led to speaking of such epithelia as being of the pigmented type. However, this does not indicate the morphology of the cells, which may be classified as cuboidal or other types. To follow the scheme of morphology in classification, such cells should be classified on the basis of their form and arrangement and then the presence of the pigment should be noted for the given type and location. An example of this tissue occurs in the outer layer of the retina, where hexagonal cells adjacent to the inner surface of the choroid coat are heavily pigmented. Pigment granules also occur in the lower layers of cells of the stratified epithelium forming the epidermis and in the liver cells of various vertebrates. (Fig. 117.)

The origin of the melanin in pigmented epidermis is uncertain. There is some evidence to indicate that certain cells found in the underlying connective tissue, melanoblasts and melanophores, elaborate the pigment and liberate it in the germinatinum layer where much of it is picked up by the epithelial cells. Some also occurs intercellularly.

## EPITHELIAL TISSUES

Simple squamous

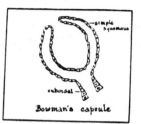
Bowman's capsule

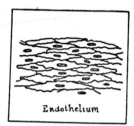
Endothelium

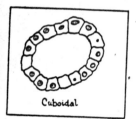
Cuboidal

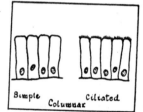
Simple Columnar    Ciliated

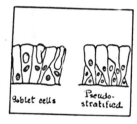
Goblet cells    Pseudo-stratified

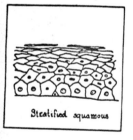
Stratified squamous

Stratified Cuboidal

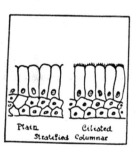
Plain    Ciliated
Stratified Columnar

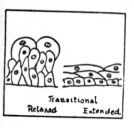
Transitional
Relaxed    Extended

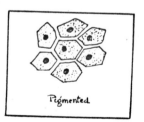
Pigmented

Neuro-epithelium
taste-bud

FIG. 23.—Schematic summary of epithelial types.

# CHAPTER III

## THE CONNECTIVE TISSUES

In the classification of the connective tissues emphasis is placed upon the nature and arrangement of the intercellular material in contrast to epithelial tissues, where intercellular material is absent or insignificant in amount. The cells of connective tissues are partially or completely separated from each other by the various types of intercellular material. The development of the intercellular products of connective tissues is closely correlated with the rôle they play. In general, connective tissues act as packing and supporting elements for the body, from the finer networks supporting the capillaries to the heavy framework formed by the bony skeleton. In addition to playing a part in the formation of intercellular products some of the cellular components of the tissues are active in storage and phagocytosis. The various types of differentiated connective tissues trace their origin back to the mesoderm of embryonic development.

Classification.—As might be expected from the nature of connective tissues, classification is based not only upon the cellular constitution but also upon the nature and arrangement of the intercellular deposits. Two types, mesenchyme and mucous tissue, are primarily embryonic. The following types are distinguished in the adult vertebrate: loosely organized fibroelastic (areolar) tissue, reticular tissue, adipose tissue, densely organized fibrous and elastic tissue, cartilage, and bone. Intergrading types of cells and intercellular material within these major types will be considered when describing the features of each.

### MESENCHYME

As soon as the three germ layers are well established in embryonic development, cells begin moving away from the mesoderm to form the mesenchyme which occupies spaces between mesoderm and ectoderm, and between mesoderm and endoderm. (Fig. 24.) These undifferentiated wandering cells have an irregular stellate form with the branching cytoplasmic processes associating the cells intimately with each other, if not actually forming a syncytium. The nucleus is relatively large and mitotic figures are often evident.

An apparently homogeneous, liquid intercellular substance fills the spaces between the adjoining cells. (Fig. 25.) From proliferation and differentiation of these embryonic mesenchymal cells, the variously differentiated cells are derived that form the cellular

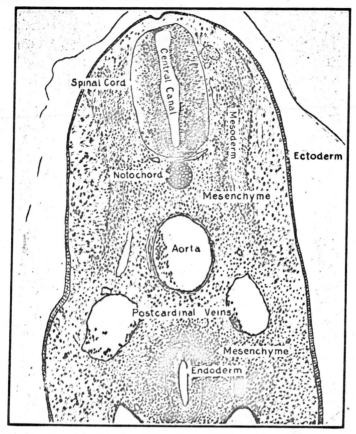

Fig. 24.—A section of a chick embryo.   16 mm. obj. and 5× oc.

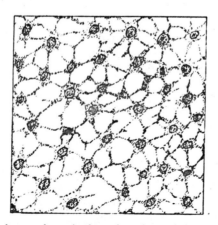

Fig. 25.—Diagram of mesenchyme in the early embryo; the spaces between the cells
is occupied by tissue fluid in the living state.

elements of the connective tissue types of the adult. Mesenchyme also gives rise to the cells that in turn differentiate into endothelium, mesothelium, blôod, and some muscle cells.

**Endothelium.**—Undifferentiated mesenchyme cells wander out from the early mesoderm and give rise to this thin continuous cellular membrane which lines the heart and all branches of the blood and lymph vessels. The endothelial cells composing it are stretched along the vessel lumen as irregularly fusiform simple squamous cells. The irregular cell boundaries are clearly shown lining the small blood-vessels present in spreads of mesentery treated with silver nitrate. Such boundaries are not readily observed in sections and the cytoplasm appears as a very thin indistinct membrane with the nucleus bulging into the vessel lumen; the latter condition is not true in the living state. The cytoplasm is lightly stained with acid dyes. The oval or elongated nucleus is filled with small basophilic chromatin granules and usually does not have a nucleolus present. Although the endothelial membrane can be classified as a simple squamous epithelium structurally, it differs functionally from all true epithelial types by retaining a feature inherent in the mesenchyme from which it originated; namely, an ability to differentiate into fibroblasts under inflammatory conditions. True epithelia, although capable of changes in form and function, give rise only to epithelial cells.

**Mesothelium.**—Like the endothelium, this tissue is derived from mesenchyme but forms the surface cellular layer of the serous membranes (mesenteries, pleura, and peritoneum) lining the body cavity. It is commonly composed of simple squamous cells among the mammals but in other vertebrate classes many areas are composed of cuboidal or columnar cells whose free surface may be modified by a brush border or cilia. (Fig. 31.) The cell boundaries of mesothelium may be observed in silver nitrate preparations of mesenteric spreads as in the case of endothelium. The mesothelial cells may have irregular, interlacing boundaries but are not elongated like the endothelial cells. (Figs. 5 and 6.) Cell boundaries are not clear in routine sections of mesenteries, the cytoplasm is lightly acidophilic, the basophilic nucleus is oval and very commonly contains a nucleolus. Mesothelial cells may be classified as different types of epithelia on the basis of form, but functionally they are marked by an ability to differentiate into connective tissue cells and blood cells, a potentiality lacking in all true epithelia.

**Germinal Epithelium.**—An epithelial membrane, usually of cuboidal type, continuous with the mesothelium, is commonly found covering the ovary where it may or may not take part in the germinal activity of the mature ovary in different classes, but in the earlier development of the ovary ova and follicle cells are derived from this epithelial membrane. A similar membrane occurs in the embryonic testes but is reduced to a very inconspicuous membrane in the mature state after the seminiferous tubules are formed and become active in proliferation of sperm.

## LOOSELY ORGANIZED FIBROELASTIC TISSUE

This is probably the most widely distributed type of connective tissue and also contains the component elements to be found in other types. It is well exemplified by subcutaneous tissue which is easily accessible for study. When the skin is removed from a freshly killed animal, a moist, white, filmy tissue is seen lining the undersurface of the skin. It tears easily as the skin is removed; part remains attached to the skin and part adheres to the underlying tissues of the body. It has been called *areolar* tissue because open spaces may be seen among the fibrous intercellular elements when spread out on a slide. In the normal state of the tissue, however, these spaces are filled with a tissue fluid. Study of this tissue clearly reveals cells and fibers, but the tissue fluid does not appear in routine preparations although special methods will demonstrate it.

TISSUE FLUID.—During embryonic development the first intercellular material formed about the differentiating connective tissue cells is an apparently homogeneous fluid substance, the tissue fluid or tissue juice. This continues to occur in variable amounts in all tissues, but is a very important element in the loose fibroelastic tissue which supports all other tissues and carries the vascular supply. In this tissue the tissue fluid receives secretions and other products of metabolism from epithelia and other tissue cells in any given region; receives materials from and gives materials up to the blood by way of the capillaries; and is drained by lymphatic capillaries. The tissue fluid of a given region very closely approaches the lymph of that region in its composition. The inconspicuous tissue fluid should be kept in mind as a vitally important element in the transfer of all metabolic products to and from all cells.

Fibers.—The fibrous elements are divided into three types; white or collagenous, yellow or elastic, and argyrophil or reticular fibers.

Collagenous Fibers.—These fibers are almost transparent in the living tissue and they yield a gelatinous material called collagen when boiled in water. Fixed and stained spreads show a network of fibers extending in all directions. Study shows that the strands are bundles of microscopic fibrils, the larger strands containing more fibrils than the smaller ones. These fibrils are presumably held together in bundles by a cement substance which dissolves when fresh material is soaked in lime water. The fibrils do not branch but their organization into bundles is such that the bundles branch to form networks. In dilute solutions of alkalies and such acids as acetic, the fibrils become swollen. In preparing slides to show them fixing solutions containing acetic acid should be avoided since it causes swelling and distortion of the collagenous material. They are stained by eosin and other acid dyes but stand out sharply with aniline blue. Their properties appear to show some variation in different regions of the same animal as well as in different animals.

They do not stretch, but through their arrangement in networks adapt themselves to expansions of the tissue by changes in the meshes. (Fig. 26.)

**Elastic Fibers.**—In fresh spreads, homogeneous threads or small bands of varying size occur as distinct, refractive, and non-fibrillar

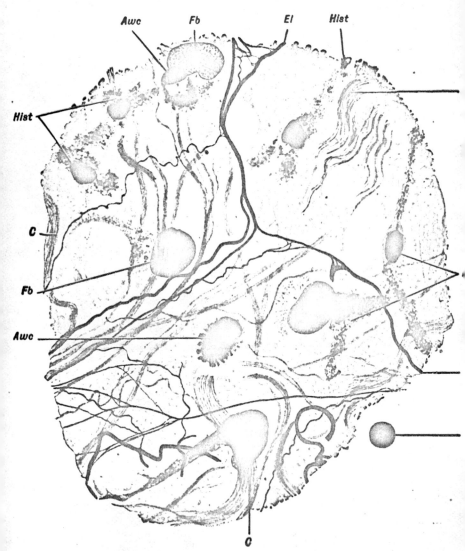

Fig. 26.—Section through slightly edematous, subcutaneous, loose, irregularly arranged connective tissue from the thigh. *C*, Collagenic fibers; *EL*, elastic fibers; *Hist*, histiocyte; *Fb*, fibroblast; *Awc*, ameboid wandering cells; *Erc*, erythrocyte for size comparison. Iron-hematoxylin stain. ×950. (Maximow-Bloom, Textbook of Histology, W. B. Saunders Company.)

elements which branch and form a network. These fibers are decidedly elastic; stretch under tension but resume their original form when released; and if broken the ends curl. They are composed of a compound called elastin which is not affected by boiling in weak acids or alkalies. Grouped in large numbers these fibers appear yellow in color. They are not usually stained by hematoxylin or eosin but specific stains such as resorcin-fuchsin and orcein are used for demonstrating them. Through combination with one another elastic fibers form prominent bands or fenestrated membranes in the walls of large arteries.

**Argyrophil Fibers.**—By use of silver techniques a fine network or reticulum of branching fibers with an affinity for silver can be demonstrated continuous with collagenic fibers not having an affinity for the silver. These silver attracting fibers are called *argyrophil* or *precollagenic* fibers, since collagenous fibers may be preceded by them. Despite such intimate associations of the argyrophil fibers with the collagenous fibers and fibroblasts of loose fibroelastic tissue they are also considered as part of another tissue type, the reticular tissue, to be considered later.

**Fiber Formation.**—The location of fiber formation, whether inter- or intracellular, once subject to much controversy, appears definitely settled as intercellular, that is, they are formed in the tissue fluid through the action of the fibroblast. The fibers are intimately associated with the fibroblasts in all locations but appear as separate intercellular products among which the cells act as independent elements.

**Cell Types.**—Cell types are not easily seen in fresh mounts, nor is it possible to demonstrate clearly all the types in any one preparation. They are often studied by means of *intravitam* staining whereby small amounts of harmless dyes, such as neutral red and trypan blue, are introduced subcutaneously into a living animal from which a small amount of the subcutaneous tissue is later carefully removed for study. In such cases, certain cells take up the dyes in a characteristic fashion.

*Fibroblasts* (*Fibrocytes*).—Derived directly from mesenchyme, these cells become larger, elongated, and flattened. They have long cytoplasmic processes but the cytoplasm is clear and stains only faintly with acid dyes, thus making the cell outline indistinct in preparations. The nucleus is relatively large and oval with lightly stained diffuse chromatin materials. (Figs. 26, 27.) A nucleolus is usually present. In some preparations furrows appear on the surface of the cells presumably as a result of their close association with fibers. Early investigators concluded that these cells produce the material forming the fibers, and the terms fibroblast and fibro-

cyte were applied to them. Their long processes appear to be in contact with similar processes of neighboring cells but the cells act as independent units rather than as a syncytium. They appear capable of multiplying into more fibroblasts and may develop into osteocytes. Fibroblasts resemble endothelial cells in sections but the latter may be distinguished by their association with the vascular lumen; under certain conditions the endothelium and mesothelium may give rise to fibroblasts.

Fɪɢ. 27.—Photograph of a spread of subcutaneous tissue of the cat, showing histiocytes and nuclei of fibroblasts. 1.9 mm. obj. and 5× oc.

*Histiocytes (Fixed Macrophages).*—This type of cell may be almost as numerous as the fibroblasts in some locations. It is smaller and has a few blunt cytoplasmic processes. (Figs. 26, 27.) The cytoplasm is more granular and stains with acid dyes, so that the cellular outline is visible. The nucleus is relatively small, oval or bean-shaped, with a dense chromatin content which causes it to stain darkly and stand out clearly in preparations. A nucleolus is not usually present. Ordinarily these cells are at rest, but under inflammatory conditions they migrate in the tissue spaces by ameboid motion, a type of movement not exhibited by the fibroblasts. The histiocytes are also characterized by a potential phagocytic activity. Their numbers increase at points of infection and inflammation and during active phagocytosis they engulf bacteria, colloidal dyes, and other particulate matter. Under conditions of active phagocytosis they are known as *macrophages* and become amœboid, wandering cells in inflamed areas. (Fig. 26.)

*Pigment Cells.*—Elongated cells with irregularly branching cyto-plasmic processes containing pigment granules occur commonly in loose fibroelastic connective tissue and are known as *chromatophores.* (Fig. 28.)  The origin of these cells is not entirely clear; but in amphibia and birds they arise from neural crest cells and migrate to various areas normally pigmented in these forms.  Such pigment cells are of limited occurrence in mammals but do occur in the choroid coat of the eye and occasionally below the epidermis.  In lower vertebrates similar cells are abundantly and widely distributed in the dermis and in many internal organs.  (Fig. 28.)

Fig. 28.—Photograph of chromatophores in the connective tissue of a section of cleared unstained lung of the bullfrog.  16 mm. and 5× oc.

In fish, amphibians, and reptiles the pigment cells in the skin take part in the color changes exhibited by many species.  Such changes are con-sidered as due to alteration in the distribution of the granules or contraction and expansion of pigment bearing processes of the chromatophores.  Some of these cells are motile and changes in color pattern have been shown due to loss of cells from or their migration into a given region.  Pigment cells containing the black melanin granules are called *melanophores;* those with yellowish lipoidal granules are called *xanthophores;* and those with reddish lipoidal granules are designated *erythrophores.*  Crystal bearing cells, *iridiocytes,* are responsible for iridescence and are common in fish integu-ments.  No single species necessarily offers examples of all these types of cells.  By combination of chromatophore arrangements to effect absorp-tion of different light bands, green, blue and other colors are produced.  In addition to the color patterns associated with protective coloration and secondary sexual characters, pigment cells may play a part in protection against injury from ultra-violet rays in many forms.

*Fat Cells.*—These cells are characterized by a storage of fat droplets until the cell becomes distended to a spherical shape, with its nucleus and a thin layer of cytoplasm pushed to the periphery.

(Figs. 29 and 30.) Such cells occur singly or in small groups along capillaries. An abundant accumulation of fat cells composes adipose tissue which will be considered separately.

Fig. 29.—Diagram showing accumulation of fat in development of a fat cell.

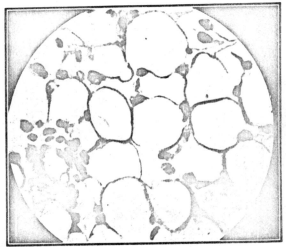

Fig. 30.—Fat cells in a section of loose fibroelastic connective tissue of dog mesentery. Photomicrograph. 1.9 mm. obj. and 5× oc.

*Mast Cells.*—This type of cell occurs in most vertebrates along blood-vessels in mesenteries and subcutaneous tissue but varies in distribution and abundance. It is characterized by cytoplasmic granules of mucoprotein that stain selectively with basic aniline dyes. The cytoplasm of these cells is completely filled with granules, which in some animals are water-soluble. In mammals the cells are usually irregularly rounded, but in other classes long cytoplasmic processes may be present. When neutral red is used as a vital stain, the cytoplasm appears filled with dark red granules. Toluodine and polychrome methylene blue stain the preserved granules from blue to purple in prepared sections. Their origin is debatable, although probably from mesenchymal cells. A secretory function has been assumed and believed associated with production of heparin.

*Undifferentiated Mesenchymal Cells.*—Many cells scattered through this type of tissue, especially along the small blood-vessels, are assumed to have retained an undifferentiated mesenchymal nature and retain their ability to multiply and give rise to other cell types. The reticular cells also represent a type of undifferentiated cell and their location is similar to that of these cells.

*Blood Cells.*—In addition to cellular elements composing the connective tissue, there may be varying numbers of extravascular blood cells, particularly lymphocytes and heterophil leukocytes. These migrate from the blood stream into the tissue fluid, especially under conditions of inflammation subsequent to injury or infection.

**Function.**—Loose fibroelastic connective tissue forms a strong elastic material which is light and flexible and adapted to holding together other tissues which are especially concerned with secretion, absorption, movement, storage and conduction. It is the chief tissue for the support of the blood-vessels and the capillary networks supplying nutrition and oxygen to the tissues involved in secretion and excretion. Furthermore, food, various secretions and oxygen must pass from the capillaries into the tissue fluid of this tissue before reaching other cells. Likewise, secretions and such wastes of metabolism as urea, carbon dioxide and water pass through the tissue juice on their way to the capillaries prior to elimination. Thus, the element of the tissue not usually demonstrated in preparations plays an extremely vital part in metabolism. The cells and fibers of this tissue play important rôles in repair following injuries and infections by the production of scar tissue and the disposal of débris by phagocytosis. Immunological reactions are also closely associated with various cellular elements in this tissue as will be noted under the macrophage system.

### Serous Membanes

The peritoneum, pleura and pericardium are thin layers of fibroelastic connective tissue covered with mesothelium. The cellular elements are of the same type as those composing the loose fibroelastic connective tissue of other regions but are more numerous. The mesenteries (Fig. 31) are folds of peritoneum composed of thin membranes of connective tissues with mesothelium on both surfaces. Histiocytes and white blood cells, especially heterophils, are found in increased numbers in inflammation of these membranes. Fat cells may accumulate about the blood-vessels in certain regions to form considerable masses. (Fig. 30.) A watery, somewhat viscous fluid, the serous exudate, covers the surface of serous membranes and lubricates the surfaces of organs as they move over one another.

### Mucous Connective Tissue

This embryonic type forms the bulk of the umbilical cord and also develops in many regions of embryo preceding the differentiation of fibroelastic tissue. In the fresh condition, as seen in the umbilical cord, it is a homogeneous jelly-like material. The abundant gelatinous intercellular material reacts to stains for mucoproteins and with fixation appears granular. Within this matrix is a network of collagenous fibers and scattered

large stellate cells whose long branching processes make contacts with adjacent cells. The nucleus is oval or roughly spherical, has a granular chromatin content and usually a nucleolus. (Fig. 32.) The cytoplasm is

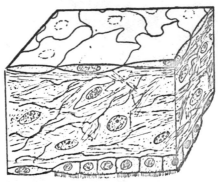

FIG. 31.—Stereodiagrammatic representation of a serous membrane (mesentery) showing arrangement of mesothelial cells to cover each surface. Simple cuboidal or ciliated cuboidal cells frequently cover such membranes in classes below mammals.

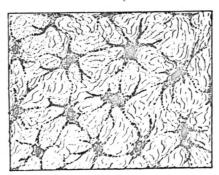

FIG. 32.—Mucous tissue from the umbilical cord, large stellate fibroblasts are embedded in a ground substance containing mucus and a network of collagenous fibrils.

acidophilic but cell boundaries are not sharply outlined by a membrane. In structure and reactions the cells of this tissue are fibroblasts in early stages of differentiation.

## RETICULAR TISSUE

Although this is customarily indicated as a separate type, the argyrophil intercellular fibers have already been mentioned in the development of loose fibroelastic tissue. An argyrophil network immediately adjoins epithelial membranes and continues with the deeper loose fibroelastic tissue. However, both argyrophil fibers and reticular cells occur in lymph organs and blood forming tissues where a characteristic network or reticulum is formed.  It requires silver preparations or special techniques to demonstrate the branching network of argyrophil fibers as distinct from collagenous since both stain with acid dyes in routine preparations.  The network of reticular cells with branching processes can be observed associated with the sinuses of the medulla or central region in routine preparations of lymph glands of mammals.  These cells may be studied to better advantage if the lymphocytes which congest these organs are partially washed out in preparing the tissue.  The nucleus is oval and contains a network of darkly staining chromatin granules. (Fig. 33.)  A nucleolus is not usually present.  The cytoplasm is acidophilic and the boundaries of the cell can be observed except where processes of adjoining cells meet.  These cells may retain potentialities of development very similar to those noted for embryonic mesenchyme and may act as the mesenchymal cells of the adult.

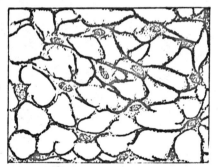

Fig. 33.—Diagram of reticular tissue found in the lymph node, showing the association of the cells and the fibers which appear following silver treatment.

Since the argyrophil, reticular fibers appear to precede the collagenous type in histogenesis, the reticular tissue may be considered as the finer, less differentiated continuations of the loose fibroelastic tissue, an intermediate condition between it and mesenchyme. The wide distribution of reticular tissue in close association with and transition to the loose fibroelastic type makes it difficult to demonstrate except by special preparations.

In addition to the possible potentialities of differentiation found in the mesenchyme the reticular cells are of particular interest in their ability to become phagocytic, as do the histiocytes, and transform into macrophages which, in turn, may then differentiate into fibroblasts.  This transition occurs in regions of injury and inflammation where collagenous scar tissue is ultimately formed.  Reticular cells in myeloid and lymphoid centers may become stem cells for the various blood cells.

### The Macrophage System

The abundantly distributed macrophages in various tissues and organs have been designated as the reticulo-endothelial or macrophage system.

The early inclusion of endothelium was based on assumption that endothelial cells were involved in phagocytic activity but the so-called system properly includes only such cells as can be demonstrated phagocytosing and storing vital dyes circulating in very weak concentrations. By the use of such vital dyes as trypan blue and carmine, macrophages may be demonstrated in fibroelastic connective tissue (histiocytes), in sinuses of lymph and myeloid regions (reticular cells or *littoral cells*), along the blood capillaries of the liver (*Kupffer cells*) and various endocrine glands (reticular cells). The monocytes of the blood also belong to this system since, as phagocytic elements, they may become extravascular macrophages inseparable from others. The macrophage system plays an important part in removing foreign particles from circulation and likewise disposes of worn-out and disintegrating tissue cells. Macrophages also appear to be directly involved in immunological reactions as experimentally demonstrated by their accumulation in controlled localized reaction regions, where they are derived from reticular cells and also from lymphocytes.

## ADIPOSE TISSUE

This is a modification usually associated with loose fibroelastic tissue in which large numbers of cells have become active in fat storage. (Fig. 34.) The fat-storing cells are considered by some to

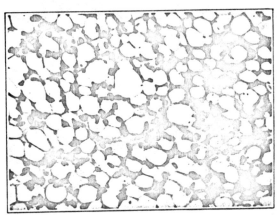

FIG. 34.—Adipose tissue of the fat body of Amblystoma. Photomicrograph. 16 mm. obj. and 5× oc.

be directly derived from fibroblast-like cells, on the basis of observations in tissue cultures of adult fibroelastic tissue; others believe them to be more directly derived from undifferentiated mesenchyme cells called *adipoblasts;* still others present evidence indicating the reticular cell and macrophage. However derived, these cells occur in large or scattered masses among the other elements of loosely organized fibroelastic tissue along capillaries and small blood-vessels.

Droplets of fat accumulate within the cytoplasm until each cell becomes distended by a single spherical drop of fat so that the protoplasm forms a thin peripheral layer in which a deeply staining nucleus is flattened. (Fig. 29.) When a number of fat cells are formed close together, the spherical form of each is modified at points of contact, so that the cells appear as polyhedral bodies resembling a mass of small soap bubbles. In such groups the different portions of the cell membrane may be seen by changing focus. In ordinary routine techniques preparing tissue for examination, the fat is dissolved out and the cells are left as empty shells in the final preparation. The fat may be preserved by using osmium tetroxide, which colors it black, and carried through to the final preparation. Other solutions, such as Sudan III which gives to the fat a dark orange color, can be used to demonstrate fat preserved by frozen sections of formalin treated tissue. Fat cells accumulated in small or large masses can be observed in the fibroelastic tissue of sections of the skin, the mesenteries, the supporting tissues of the thymus, kidney and intestinal tract. The fat stored in these cells is liberated by metabolism and used as a source of energy. The cells then resume a condition in which only scattered droplets appear in the cytoplasm until the storage is repeated.

Fat is commonly accumulated during the summer season by hibernating animals and used during the winter dormant season. In such animals, the fat of adipose tissue may contain pigment and the tissue is organized into a lobulated compact structure. Microscopically, fat cells of such tissue are smaller than the usual type and have numerous small globules of fat instead of the single large drop. These cells may superficially resemble the cells of the liver or adrenal cortex in routine preparations.

## DENSELY ORGANIZED COLLAGENOUS AND ELASTIC CONNECTIVE TISSUE

Under this heading there are irregularly arranged tissues with the components found in the loose fibroelastic type but having collagenous and elastic intercellular material present in far greater quantity. In some locations interlacing collagenous fibers predominate and the proportionately few cells present are mainly fibroblasts. This type forms part of the dermis of the skin and part of the wall, the submucosa, in some regions of the alimentary tract.

A dense tissue in which elastic fibers predominate occurs in the fenestrated membranes which form part of the wall of the large arteries.

A regularly arranged dense tissue usually has either collagenous or elastic fibers predominating. In the sclera of the eye a dense collagenous tissue is present. The dermis of many animals, as exemplified by Necturus (Fig. 13), is composed of a tissue with densely packed collagenous fibers regularly arranged. A group of structures having a regular arrangement of the fibrous elements are classified as tendons and ligaments.

**Tendons.**—Tendons are composed of closely packed bundles of collagenous fibers arranged parallel to each other to form a tough but inelastic cord connecting muscles to bones or cartilage. The entire tendon is surrounded by a sheath of loosely and irregularly arranged fibroelastic connective tissue which extends into the tendon to ensheath bundles of fibers. A characteristic feature of tendons is the location of fibroblasts which are the only cells present. Entire cells cannot be identified in sectioned preparations, but their nuclei appear as deeply stained elongated oval structures. They are located in the region between adjacent bundles of fibrils. (Fig. 35.) The cell form is modified by the compression of the closely packed fibrils; the cytoplasm extends out between the adjacent bundles so that in cross-sections of tendon each cell appears to have several flat wings extending to meet those of cells in other rows. In longitudinal sections the fibrillar composition of the bundles is indicated by faint longitudinal striations. (Fig. 40.)

Fig. 35 —A cross-section of calf's tendon showing the black nuclei of the fibroblasts with lighter cytoplasmic extensions among the collagenous bundles. Photomicrograph. 4 mm. obj. and 5× oc.

**Ligaments.**—Ligaments are tough fibrous bands which structurally resemble tendons but are usually less regularly arranged and may contain elastic fibers in considerable quantity. Ligaments commonly connect two bones where they form a joint. One in particular, the *ligamentum nuchæ*, prominent in large quadrupeds such as cattle, is especially rich in elastic fibers. It forms a strong elastic support connecting the skull with the spinous processes of the cervical and thoracic vertebræ. It is composed of bundles of elastic fibers paralleling each other and harnessed together with loosely organized fibroelastic tissue. Such a structure does not fatigue easily and admirably supplies the demands of grazing animals.

Not all ligaments connect bone with bone. In other locations, as in the case of the uterus of mammals, a broad ligament extending from the peritoneum connects with the uterus and supports it on either side. The round or utero-ovarian ligament is a short fibrous cord extending from the uterus to the ovary on either side. Elastic cords form the ligament flava of the vertebræ and also the vocal cords.

## CARTILAGE

Special dense varieties of connective tissue forming skeletal parts have cells and fibers but the tissue fluid is changed to a solid substance encapsulating the cells or forming a heavy intercellular matrix.

*Pre-cartilage* or *chondroid* tissue is composed of a mass of closely packed ovoid cells, each encapsuled by a small amount of matrix.

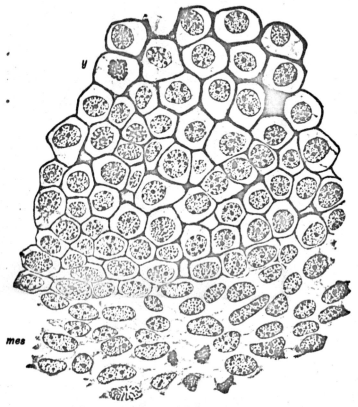

Fig. 36.—Development of cartilage from mesenchyme in a 15 mm. guinea-pig embryo; *mes*, Mesenchymal syncytium which gradually merges into the protochondral tissue (*y*) with interstitial substance. Note mitoses. 750 × (A.A.M.) (From Maximow & Bloom, courtesy of W. B. Saunders Co.)

Such a tissue is an embryonic stage in the formation of true cartilage where the intercellular matrix becomes more abundant. Where chondroid tissue will form, mesenchyme cells proliferate to form a mass of closely packed cells. These become rounded out and larger in size, and are separated by a scanty amount of tissue fluid in which mucoproteins and collagenous fibrils can be demonstrated.

A thin capsule of chondromucoid, a basophilic material which stains metachromatically with polychrome methylene blue or toluidine blue, then forms about the cells so that a structure of considerable firmness results. Examples of chondroid tissue, or *pseudocartilage* as it is also called, may be observed associated with the larval skeletons of the Lamprey and Amphibia, as well as being an early or embryonic stage in cartilage differentiation of other forms. The amount of the intercellular solid matrix varies from a thin rim about the cells to quantities characteristic of cartilage. (Figs. 36 and 37.)

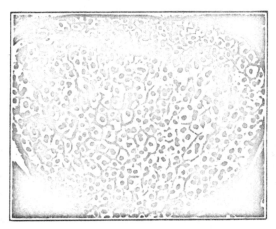

Fig. 37.—Photograph of a vertebra of a newt, showing encapsulated vesicular chondroid cells within the bony vertebral tissue. 16 mm. obj. and 5× oc.

*Cartilage* forms the entire skeleton of the elasmobranch fishes and a considerable part of the skeleton of ganoid fishes. It is still a prominent element in the skeletal framework of Amphibians and, though not so prominent in the adult reptile, bird and mammal, it is the material of which the embryonic skeleton of these forms is first composed. Preliminary to cartilage formation, mesenchyme cells accumulate and differentiate into fibroblast-like cells called *chondroblasts*. The early stellate shape of the mesenchyme is lost and the chondroblasts become ovoid and closely packed. Intercellular substance is at first acidophilic in reaction and contains fine collagenous fibrils. The matrix accumulates a chondromucoid material and a basophilic reaction becomes pronounced. A compact mass of cartilaginous tissue is formed by multiplication of the early chondroblasts and increase in the amount of intercellular matrix. A sheath derived from the early mesenchyme develops about the periphery. This sheath, the *perichondrium*, is composed of fibroblasts and numerous collagenous fibers. It is involved in cartilage formation but may eventually become a relatively inactive limiting sheath or transform to periosteum in long bones. In the early stages the perichondral cells multiply along the periphery of the forming cartilage and differentiate into cartilage cells surrounded by matrix. As fibroblasts, the perichondral cells are flattened but with differentiation into chondroblasts they become rounded and about them matrix gradually accumulates until they are embedded as *chondrocytes* in spaces called *lacunæ*. At first the intercellular material may be primarily collagenous and acidophilic, but as chondroid material is deposited the reaction becomes basophilic and the collagenous fibers may be obscured. The cells in the interior of the early cartilaginous mass also divide and the newly formed cells, in turn, are surrounded by an intercellular matrix. The chondrocytes are usually rounded and separated by matrix, but in the cartilage of some fishes cytoplasmic processes may extend through the matrix to adjoining cells.

On the basis of the composition of the intercellular material, four types of cartilage are commonly distinguished, namely, *hyaline, calcified, elastic* and *fibrous,* although there are all gradations from the early chondroid or embryonic condition to any of the four named.

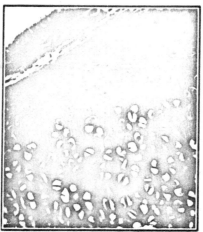

Fɪɢ. 38.—Section through the trachea of a cat with the ciliated epithelial membrane in the upper left; the tunica propria continues into the perichondrium of the hyaline cartilage. Photomicrograph. 4 mm. obj. and 5× oc.

**Hyaline Cartilage.**—In the living condition this widely distributed type is translucent and appears clear or slightly bluish. The matrix is composed of chondrin but when the apparently homogenous solid chondroid matrix is dissolved by treating with trypsin and potassium permanganate, colla-

genous fibers can usually be demonstrated. Cartilage may be regarded as a specialized form of connective tissue in which the matrix represents a solid organization of most of the tissue fluid. (Figs. 38 and 51.)

Throughout cartilage matrix the chondrocytes occur singly or in clusters in the lacunæ. Chondrocytes in the interior of the embryonic cartilage are still active in mitotic division, and each of two daughter cells resulting from a division may be súrrounded by matrix until they are separated into lacunæ and then divide in turn. Or the newly formed daughter cells may remain close together with only a slight amount of matrix separating them and one or both may divide again so that three or four chondrocytes may be clustered together with relatively thin adjoining walls. (Fig. 38.) Different methods of division may occur and result in the production of other types of cell clusters. The nuclei stain deeply and are relatively small. The cytoplasm is acidophilic in routine preparations and appears to be rich in fluid, for in the dehydration necessary to make permanent preparations it often shrinks far away from the wall of the lacuna to which it is closely applied during life. By special techniques fat and glycogen may be demon-

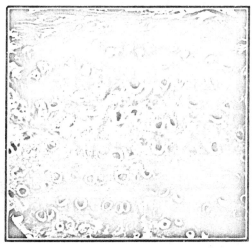

Fig. 39.—A section of Meckel's cartilage of the dogfish, showing the collagenous bundles of the perichondrium above continuing into the hyaline matrix. A region of calcified cartilage occurs in the lower part of the picture. Formalin fixed and Mallory stained material. Photomicrograph. 4 mm. obj. and 5× oc.

strated in the cytoplasm of the chrondrocytes. Embryonic cartilage increases rapidly by division of the chondrocytes throughout the matrix but later growth is associated with formation of new cells and cartilage in peripheral regions. In regeneration following injury, cartilage cells adjoining the area and fibroblasts of the inner zone of the perichondrium become active in new cartilage formation, by division, to form young cartilage cells which differentiate and become surrounded by matrix. Regeneration appears to be dependent upon the presence of perichondrium. Bloodvessels and nerves extend into the outer portion of the perichondrium but not into the matrix so that nutritive materials received by the central cells must reach them by diffusion through the inner perichondrium and the matrix.

Cartilage proper usually is markedly basophilic, but perichondrium takes acid stains. The intermediate region of developing cartilage, about the periphery, shows a transition from the acid-staining condition of the perichondrium to the basophilic intercellular matrix, which obscures the acidophilic collagenous fibers. Bundles of collagenous fibers extend from the perichondrium into the cartilage, but are usually obscured by the hyaline matrix. (Fig. 39.)

**Calcified Cartilage.**—The hyaline cartilage that forms the skeleton of some elasmobranchs becomes impregnated with calcium salts to form a much harder and more rigid support than does hyaline cartilage. A similar deposit of calcium also occurs in epiphyses of amphibian bones and as a regressive stage preliminary to endochondral ossification in long bones, as may be observed in the study of endochondral bone development. (Figs. 39 and 44.)

**Elastic Cartilage.**—In the fresh condition this type has a yellow tinge due to the presence of the elastic fibers in the intercellular material which may be relatively scant among very numerous chondrocytes. The elastic fibers form a coarse network continuing with the perichondrium. The fibers are not readily observed in the matrix of routine preparations and require special techniques to demonstrate them. Elastic cartilage occurs in the external ear of mammals and in the smaller bronchi.

**Fibrous Cartilage.**—In this type there is a predominance of collagenous fibers and the relatively scant basophilic matrix occurs surrounding the lacunæ. This type occurs in intervertebral discs and articular cartilages, and is commonly present where tendons insert into cartilage. (Fig. 40.) An example of transition from tendon to cartilage may be studied in sections of the insertion of the tendon of Achilles of the frog. A chon-

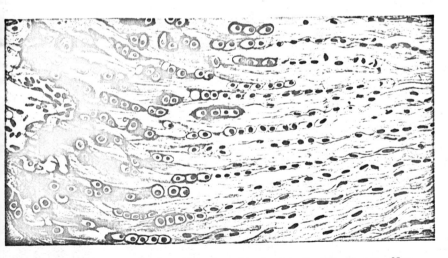

FIG. 40.—Low power drawing of insertion of tendon into the tibia of a rat. Note the direct transformation of the rows of tendon cells (left) into cartilage cells surrounded by deeply staining cartilaginous matrix. Hematoxylin-eosin-azure II. From a preparation of F. C. McLean. (Drawn by Miss A. Nixon.) (From Maxinow & Bloom, courtesy of W. B. Saunders Co.)

droid or pseudocartilage is also present in this region and development of collagenous fibrous material among the chondroblasts shows a gradation to a fibrous cartilage near the insertion of the tendon into cartilage.

## BONE

Although some bones arise directly from differentiation of mesenchyme cells of the embryo, the skeleton of the majority of vertebrates is first laid down as cartilage and is later replaced by bone. In each case the nature of the bone formed is the same, but the processes involved are separated into a direct or *intramembranous ossification*, and an indirect or *endochondral ossification* in which the bone is preceded by a cartilage mass. *Osteoblasts* are specialized connective tissue cells, derived from mesenchyme by way of reticular cells or fibroblasts, associated with the development of the bony matrix which consists of small bundles of collagenous, osteogenic, fibers made rigid by impregnation with calcium salts. As the deposit of collagen accumulates and becomes impregnated with calcium, the osteoblasts gradually become embedded in it and the spaces they occupy in the matrix are called *lacunæ*. The embedded cells are called *osteocytes* and, unlike the cartilage cells, retain the cytoplasmic processes found in fibroblasts and reticular cells. These processes of their cytoplasm extend in small channels, the *canaliculi*, to make contact with adjacent cells and vascular connective tissue.

**Intramembranous Ossification.**—The flat bones of the head, and dermal bones generally, develop directly from an accumlation of mesenchyme tissue in which ossification begins at one or more points. Mesenchyme cells at these points differentiate into osteoblasts about which acidophilic collagenous fibers form an intercellular substance. (Fig. 41.) Calcium salts then begin to impregnate this intercellular fibrous material and accumulate until the first small spicules of the bony matrix are enlarged to form a spongy mass composed of networks of spicules or broader trabeculæ through which a vascular supply extends. The osteoblasts surrounding the spicules or trabeculæ resemble an epithelial membrane and their continued activity results in growth of the spicules in thickness and length. With increasing deposits of matrix, the portion of the osteoblast adjoining the spicule becomes surrounded by matrix and gradually the entire cell is embedded as an osteocyte in a lacuna. Processes of these imprisoned cells radiate from the lacunæ through canaliculi in the matrix to make contact with cytoplasmic processes of adjoining osteocytes, osteoblasts or peripheral connective tissue. With the appearance and early activity of these ossification centers, the mesenchyme surrounding the developing spongy plate condenses

5

into a dense fibrous membrane, the *periosteum*, which closely resembles the perichondrium in structure.  Osteoblasts show a differentiation from the fibroblasts of the innermost region of the periosteum in a manner similar to that of the chondrocytes from the early perichondrium.  Parallel bony plates, or lamellæ, are formed about these osteoblasts, a process known as periosteal ossification.  ·Blood-vessels formed in the connective tissue between

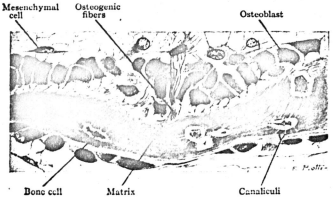

Mesenchymal cell     Osteogenic fibers     Osteoblast

Bone cell     Matrix     Canaliculi

FIG. 41.—Bone formation detail of osteoblasts and bone cells.  (Bremer-Weatherford's Textbook of Histology, courtesy of the Blakiston Company.)

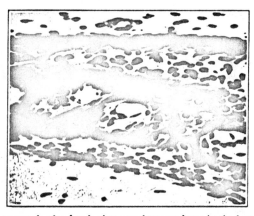

FIG. 42.—Photograph of a developing membranous bone in the head of an embryo cat.  The mesenchyme cells are concentrated in the peripheral region to be occupied by the periosteum.  A number of cells are imprisoned in an acidophilic fibrous material in which calcium salts are depositing.  In the 3 small central spaces primary marrow cavities are forming and contain blood elements and osteoblasts.  4 mm. obj. and 5✕ oc.

the spicules of bone connect with vessels in the periosteum, and other mesenchyme cells in these regions among the spicules give rise to reticular tissue, adipose cells, and developing blood cells, which together represent the embryonic *bone marrow*.  (Fig. 42.)

As a result of ossification to this point, upper and lower (or inner and outer) plates of compact bone are connected by a central region of spongy bone where trabeculæ of bone are separated by marrow tissue composed of blood-vessels, connective tissue and developing blood cells. This early bone is not permanent, for a moulding of the mature bone involves resorption of much of the first bone formed. During the resorption giant multinucleated cells called *osteoclasts* appear in pockets called *Howship's lacunæ* along the lamellæ undergoing resorption. They represent fusion of osteocytes liberated in the process of matrix destruction during which organic and inorganic materials are resorbed simultaneously. Observations of the ossification process in long bones record reversion of osteoclast elements to osteoblasts or into reticular cells; and experiments with vitamin deficiency and hormones involving resorption of long bone matrix suggest that the osteocytes released by resorption processes are capable of becoming osteogenic again with return to adequate diet and hormone balance.

The flat dermal bones may grow indefinitely in reptiles but in the case of head bones growth continues until adjacent bony plates meet and their interlacing edges fuse.

**Endochondral Ossification.**—In this type of bone formation, as exemplified by the long bones, a hyaline cartilage forerunner roughly outlines the bone which is to replace it, and after its removal the resultant bone formation is fundamentally the same as in intramembranous ossification. Ossification activity is preceded by a calcification of the hyaline matrix in the center of the cartilaginous piece, followed by resorption of some matrix and the enlargement of the cartilage lacunæ so that they appear arranged in rows separated by long irregular bars of matrix. (Fig. 43.) Two things happen simultaneously. With the initiation of calcification within the cartilaginous piece, there also occurs a change along the periphery where the inner cells of the perichondrium become osteogenic and give rise to osteoblasts, and this outer fibrous sheath surrounding the cartilage thus becomes the periosteum. In the same manner as in the plates of dermal or intramembranous bones, osteoblasts are differentiated from the periosteum and become associated with the deposit of periosteal (in this location spoken of as *perichondral*) lamellæ of bone. Budlike vascular tufts from the inner cellular region of the newly differentiated periosteum burrow into the cartilage to initiate development of a primary marrow tissue.

Within the center of the cartilage, some of the matrix is destroyed and is resorbed so that a number of cartilage lacunæ coalesce and the tufts of primary marrow tissue extend into the pockets thus formed. The fate of the chondrocytes freed by this resorption process is uncertain; possibly they become fibroblasts or reticular cells as do freed osteocytes, or they may disintegrate and be removed by phagocytic connective tissue and blood cells introduced with the marrow. The periosteal invasions of tissue carry in osteoblasts and vascular elements which continue to extend into the cavities developing in the cartilage. At first, the osteoblasts deposit bony matrix on calcified cartilage spicules not resorbed in the early dissolution

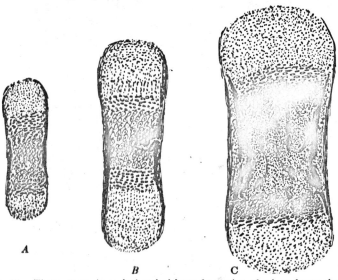

*A*            *B*            *C*

Fig. 43.—Three stages in endochondral **bone** formation of a long bone; the **bone** shown in black, older and resorbing cartilage stippled with large lacunæ; epiphyseal cartilage regions in coarse stipple.

process and then at many other points form spicules of bone in the same manner as in intramembranous bone formation. (Fig. 44.) The dissolution of cartilage progresses toward either end of the cartilage piece and the invading osteogenic marrow tissue deposits bony spicules until the major portion of the cartilage region has been replaced by a lattice-work of spicules and trabeculæ forming a spongy bone. In the development of all bones there is a resorption of much of the early bony matrix in the course of growth and moulding of the mature bone. During these resorption and moulding processes, tubular channels become hollowed out and the osteogenic tissue projecting into them deposits secondary bony matrix in the form of concentric lamellæ, one within the other, surrounding a central cylindrical cavity containing some osteogenic tissue, blood-vessels, and nerve fibers. Such a series of lamellæ with the cavity just described is called an *Haversian system;* the lamellæ are *Haversian lamellæ* and the central cavity is the *Haversian*

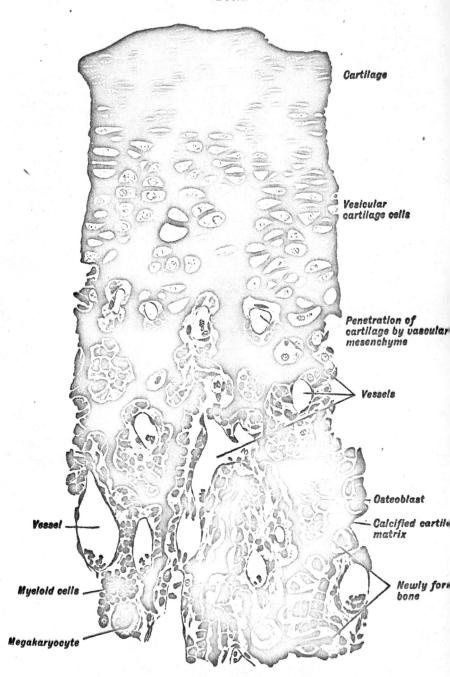

*Cartilage*

*Vesicular cartilage cells*

*Penetration of cartilage by vascular mesenchyme*

*Vessels*

*Osteoblast*

*Calcified cartil* *matrix*

*Vessel*

*Newly forr* *bone*

*Myeloid cells*

*Megakaryocyte*

Fig. 44.—The zone of endochondral ossification in a longitudinal section through the tibia of a cat embryo of 12 mm. Eosin-azue stain 220 ×. A.A.M.) (From Maximow & Bloom, courtesy of W. B. Saunders Co.)

canal. (Figs. 47 and 49.) These systems primarily run the length of the shaft but branches make connections between adjacent systems. Growth in thickness of a long bone is made possible through resorption which increases the central marrow cavity as new bone is added as *periosteal* (or *external circumferential*) lamellæ. Resorption also extends into primary Haversian systems and periosteal

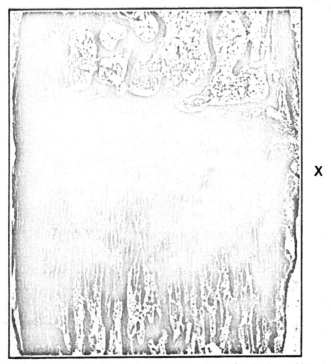

X

FIG. 45.—Photograph of a longitudinal section of the developing rabbit femur. Part of its diaphysis (below) and an epiphysis (above) show endochondral bone formation. In both, the cartilage is resorbed and replaced by spongy bone; in the epiphysis the final bone is irregular and spongy, but in the diaphysis Haversian systems are formed. Growth of the intervening hyaline cartilage region and progressive resorption of it and replacement by bone make possible growth in length of the bone. In the epiphysis there is a network of broad bony pieces and large marrow cavities; in the diaphysis there are more numerous thinner bony spicules separated by narrow cavities. The majority of the bony strands here are deposited paralleling the length of the bone along lines indicated by the paralleled columns of cartilage cells which are resorbed as the marrow tissue extends. Figure 46 shows the right portion, *X*, of the section in greater detail. 32 mm. obj. and 5× oc.

bone, the osteogenic tissue in the channels so formed gives rise to new Haversian systems. Lamellar remnants of older Haversian and periosteal lamellæ are called *interstitial lamellæ*. When the spongy bone is entirely removed, the central shaft region is occupied by

marrow alone and develops an internal lining of *endosteum*, which resembles the periosteum in structure and gives rise to *endosteal* or *internal circumferential lamellæ.* (Fig. 48.)

FIG. 46.—Photograph of a portion of the diaphysis shown in Figure 45. The arrangement of the cartilage cells, the resorption of the matrix between the adjacent cells and the extension of marrow tissue are shown in studying from top toward the bottom. In the central and lower portion bony spicules have been deposited by the osteoblasts; at the right (dark portion) the periosteum is depositing layers of bony matrix in the same manner as in the case of membranous bone. A projection of vascular tissue (light area beginning in middle of right margin) is shown extending from the perichondrium through the periosteal bone into the central marrow tissue 16 mm. obj. and 5× oc.

Many small canals without lamellæ, *Volkman's canals*, carry vascular tissue into Haversian canals from the periosteal and endosteal surfaces. Tightly attaching the periosteum and endosteum to the underlying bone are bundles of collagenous fibers, *Sharpey's fibers*, which continue from these sheaths to become embedded in the bony matrix.

Growth in length of endochondral bones is brought about by the continued formation of cartilage at the epiphyseal extremities of

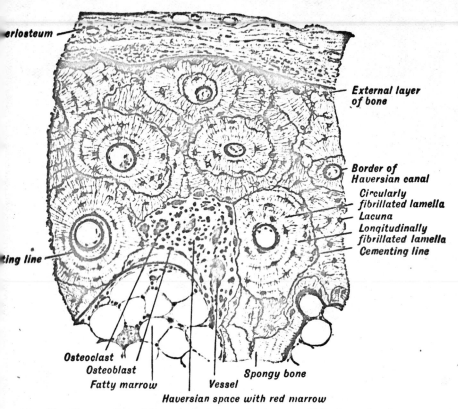

*erlosteum* — 

**External layer of bone**

**Border of Haversian canal**

**Circularly fibrillated lamella**

**Lacuna**

**Longitudinally fibrillated lamella**

**Cementing line**

*ting line* —

**Osteoclast**
**Osteoblast**
**Fatty marrow**
**Vessel**
**Spongy bone**
**Haversian space with red marrow**

FIG. 47.—Cross section of the second phalanx of a human middle finger showing replacement of spongy bone by compact bone. 110 ✕. After Schaffer. (From Maximow & Bloom, courtesy of W. B. Saunders Co.)

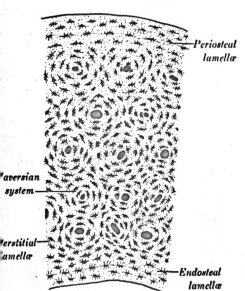

*Periosteal lamellæ*

*'aversian system* —

*'erstitial 'amellæ*

*Endosteal lamellæ*

FIG. 48.—Diagram of cross-section of shaft of a long bone.

FIG. 49.—Photograph of a portion of a cross-section of an Haversian system, showing the lacunæ and canaliculi occupied by the osteocytes in living bone. The alternating dark and light lamellæ indicate differences in their fibrous organization. 4 mm. obj. and 5✕ oc.

the shaft and its progressive replacement by bone. Between birth and maturity calcification centers appear in the epiphyses and invasion of osteogenic tissue results in the formation of spongy bone, except at the end surfaces where cartilage remains as a pad for the joint. Ossification in the epiphyses gives rise to fewer Haversian systems and more abundant spongy bone. Each bony epiphysis is separated for some time from the adjoining shaft by a plate of cartilage for resorption and replacement. Growth in these regions finally ceases, calcification occurs, resorption and bone formation fuse the shaft (diaphysis) and both epiphyses so that a continuous bony structure is formed and growth in length ceases. (Fig. 50.) The marrow of the shaft becomes yellow through accumulation of fat but in epiphyses remains red and actively hemopoietic.

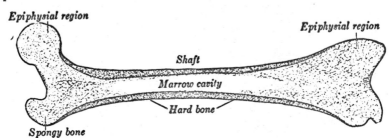

Fig. 50.—Diagram of a long bone.

In case of endochondral bone formation in the small lower vertebrates, the process of bone deposition appears to be primarily peripheral (periosteal or perichondral), little or no spongy bone being formed in the course of cartilage resorption of the shaft which becomes progressively filled with marrow tissue as the cartilage is resorbed. A tube of periosteal bone forms the early shaft of a frog femur or other long bone and each epiphyseal end is plugged by a piece of calcified cartilage which overlaps the bony tube projecting into it. (Fig. 51.) Formation of an endosteum accompanies the hollowing out of the shaft and gives rise to endosteal lamellæ. The moulding of the bone through resorption and formation of new systems is essentially similar to the process typical of mammals but relatively few Haversian systems are present since these bones are very thin shells. The marrow contains large numbers of eosinophils in the region of cartilage resorption, and abundant fat cells occur throughout the central marrow cavity.

The fused bones of the Amphibia, as represented by the radia-ulna or the tibia-fibula of the frog, have separate cartilage primordia and early ossification processes form a sheath of perichondral bone about each. An arch of bone develops from the peripherally located periosteum of each shaft to fuse medially while resorption breaks down the cartilage and first bone in the region where the bones face each other. Eventually a single large shaft is formed with a common marrow cavity corresponding to the central region of the diaphysis of each bone. Distally there is a gradual lack of such complete fusion and two distinct epiphyseal regions are present.

Bird bones are likewise relatively thin tubes of periosteal and endosteal bone with a few Haversian systems and with spongy bone limited to the epiphyseal regions. The marrow contains myeloid tissue and lymphoid nodules in far greater quantity than in the frog, and air sacs from the lung also invade the marrow cavity of many bird bones.

Developments and structural arrangements in compact and spongy bone have been demonstrated closely related to the stresses and strains imposed and show marked modifications with changing conditions. Growth changes in bone may be measured by feeding madder, which colors bony matrix formed after its feeding. X-ray studies are also used to demonstrate structural features in bone.

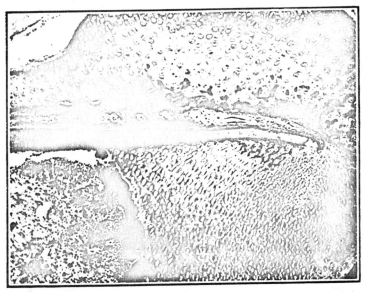

Fig. 51.—A longitudinal section through the epiphyseal region of the frog's femur, showing the cap of hyaline cartilage with dark areas of calcification, the shaft of bone projecting into the cap, and the inner core of cartilage in the process of resorption accompanied by extension of the marrow cavity. Photomicrograph. 32 mm. obj. and 5× oc.

Mature bones are composed of about 30 per cent organic and 70 per cent inorganic material. The inorganic material consists chiefly of calcium phosphate, with small amounts of calcium carbonate, magnesium phosphate, and sodium chloride. When fresh bones are boiled in water, a gelatinous organic substance, called ossein, is obtained and is similar to the collagen derived from other types of connective tissue. If fresh bones are placed for a long period in a weak solution of nitric or hydrochloric acid, the inorganic material is removed to leave a flexible decalcified bone which may be sectioned. This method is used for preparing material to be sectioned for histological study. To study untreated compact bone for lamellar arrangement it is necessary to grind down thin pieces until they are trans-

lucent enough to permit observation of lamellæ, lacunæ and canaliculi; this method does not demonstrate cellular components.

## Joints

The junction of bones with each other may be by one of three types of joints, one permitting of no movement is called synarthrosis, a joint with limited movement in an amphiarthrosis and the one permitting of free movement is called a diarthrosis.

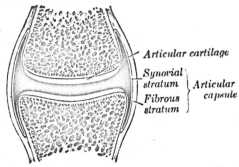

*Articular cartilage*

*Synovial stratum*

*Fibrous stratum* } *Articular capsule*

Fig. 52.—Diagrammatic section of a diarthrodial joint. (Gray's Anatomy.)

In the synarthrosis the tissue between the developing bones may form a dense collagenous region or suture tying the bones together and its later ossification results in fusion of two bones as in the case of head bones. In an amphiarthrosis, ligaments develop which tie the bones together and permit of very limited movement as in the vertebræ.

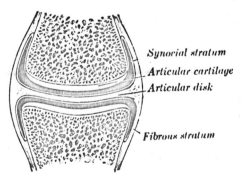

*Synovial stratum*

*Articular cartilage*

*Articular disk*

*Fibrous stratum*

Fig. 53.—Diagrammatic section of a diarthrodial joint, with an articular disk. (Gray's Anatomy.)

The diarthrosis is the general type of joint occurring throughout the skeleton where free movement of adjoining bones occurs. In this type, the connective tissue between the developing bones remains more loosely organized and forms a fluid-filled cavity about the articulating hyaline cartilage ends of the adjoining bones  Such a joint cavity is bounded, externally by a dense fibrous tissue which continues with the perichondrium of adjoining epiphyses. An inner more vascular fibroelastic connective tissue forms the *synovial membrane* lining the cavity and may project thin folds, the *synovial villi*, into the cavity. A heavy fold or plate involving the outer heavy fibrous coat may project between the articulating surfaces of the bones to form a *meniscus*, which commonly develops into a fibrocartilage tissue where pressures are great.

Immediately adjoining the synovial cavity the surface of the synovial membrane is composed of an irregular layer or layers of fibroblasts and histiocytes. The *synovial fluid* is mainly water in which salts, albumin, some fat and mucoid materials occur. Blood cells and histiocytes and fibroblasts occur in the fluid in variable numbers but are normally scarce. The origin of the fluid may be from the tissue juice of the adjoining synovial membrane, there being no special secretory areas clearly defined, and its drainage may be facilitated by the villi.

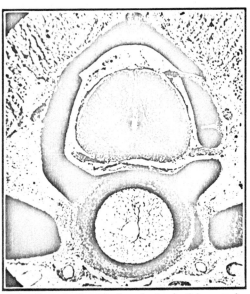

Fig. 54.—A section through the spinal cord of a dogfish pup, showing the dorsal and ventral roots, a spinal ganglion, the vertebral cartilages, and the notochord surrounded by a sheath of fibroblasts which will give rise to the cartilage forming the centrum. Photomicrograph. 32 mm. obj. and 5× oc.

## Notochord

The origin of this structure in the early embryo, whether from ectoderm, endoderm or mesoderm, is not clear-cut and presents variations in development within different classes  Whatever its embryonic origin with regard, to the germ layers, it appears early in embryonic development as a cord composed of a few cells just above the gut and below the forming neural canal. (Fig. 24.) The early cells multiply and a fluid content accumulates until a single large vacuole distends each cell and pushes the cytoplasm and nucleus to the periphery in a manner very similar to conditions observed in fat cells. Sheaths varying in number and composition with different animals surround this rod of large distended cells. There is usually an inner layer of epithelial-like cells immediately surrounding the notochordal cells, and this cellular layer is surrounded by an elastic membrane. An outermost sheath is formed from mesodermal contributions and is composed of a thick layer of fibroblasts with associated fibrous

tissue in varying quantities. (Fig. 54.) Eventually this outer sheath is involved in formation of vertebral cartilage. The degeneration of the notochordal tissue is accompanied by loss of cell boundaries and replacement by the encircling cartilage. This progresses most rapidly among the mammals where the notochordal tissue is least developed and is a transient feature of the embryo and fetus. Among the fishes, the notochord is well developed and remains over a considerable period while the cartilaginous parts develop about it and slowly take over most of the region occupied by it.

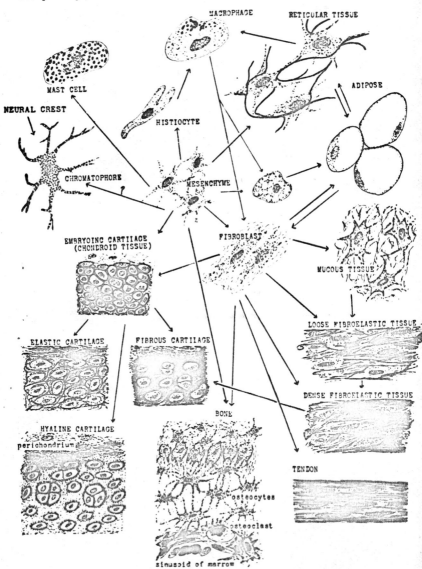

Fig. 55.—Chart showing derivations of connective tissues.

# CHAPTER IV

# THE BLOOD

BLOOD might well be considered under connective tissue as a type in which the intercellular material, the plasma, is a fluid carrying a variety of free cells. The blood cells originate from mesenchyme during embryological development and in later development they are intimately associated with the connective tissue, especially the reticular type. Both the fluid and the cellular elements circulate through the body in endothelial-lined vessels and act as media for metabolic exchanges. The blood also plays a vital part in integrating and regulating the activities of the other tissues through the endocrine secretions which it carries.

## THE PLASMA

Although the plasma ordinarily presents no structural features in histological preparations, its physiological importance should not be overlooked. Biochemical and biophysical studies show the plasma to be composed largely of water with numerous substances in solution. Various salts, sugar, proteins, and fat are held at relatively constant concentration levels in the blood. During circulation they are made available to the cells of the body by diffusion through the capillary walls into the tissue fluid at the same time that local secretions and metabolic wastes are entering the blood through the capillaries from the tissue juice. Since some knowledge of the rôle of the plasma in relation to processes concerned with the internal environment of the organism is essential to an understanding of the functioning of the tissues and organs, the student is advised to consult the references given for this chapter.

## THE BLOOD CELLS

The cells of the blood are divided into two main groups: the *erythrocytes*, or red blood cells, and the *leukocytes*, or white blood cells. In addition to these there may be small cytoplasmic bodies, the *platelets* in the case of mammals and *spindle cells* or *thrombocytes* in lower forms.

**Erythrocytes.**—These cells take their name from the red color they give the blood *en masse*, but single cells have a pale greenish yellow color. In mammals the erythrocytes are enucleated, biconcave discs, but in other vertebrates they are true cells, usually

(78)

flattened ovals in shape, with a central nucleus causing a cellular bulge. There is great variation in their size in different species, as evidenced by the following list: Amphiuma (Fig. 56), about 80 microns in diameter; the frog, 22.3 by 15.7 microns; the lizard, 15.8 by 9.9 microns; the rabbit, diameter about 6.9 microns; the cat, 6.3 microns; the musk deer, 2.5 microns; and man, 7.5 microns. In many species, especially those with nucleated erythrocytes, there may be some variation in size in the same individual.

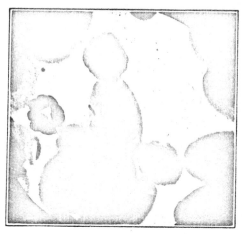

Fig. 56.—Photograph of blood cells of Amphiuma, showing erythrocytes and heterophils. 1.9 mm. obj. and 5× oc.

When a drop of fresh mammalian blood is spread out in a thin film on a glass slide, the erythrocytes tend to collect in groups called rouleaux, strings of biconcave discs. The formation of such strings indicates a certain cohesiveness in the limiting membranes. Two components of these cells have been distinguished, a stroma or framework which is an optically homogeneous colloidal substance, and hemoglobin which is a conjugated protein composed of globin and a colored compound of iron called hemochromogen. The hemoglobin may be discharged by the process known as hemolysis from cells experimentally subjected to various chemical and physical agents; when this occurs in the circulating blood, as it does in the case of certain pathological conditions, the hemoglobin is eliminated from the plasma in the kidneys and passes out with the urine.

The surface of the red cell is somewhat more dense than the interior protoplasm. It is semipermeable and in osmotic equilibrium with the solutions normally present outside and is said to be isotonic with them. Mammalian plasma has about the same osmotic

pressure as an 0.85 per cent sodium chloride solution, which is
considered isotonic with the protoplasm within the red corpuscle
while frog plasma is similar to a 0.7 per cent sodium chloride solution.   If distilled water is added to a drop of fresh blood on a slide,
microscopic observations show the erythrocytes increasing in size as
they absorb water.   If the swelling is allowed to continue the cells
become spherical, and hemolysis occurs.   This change is a result of
endosmosis, since the solution has a concentration less than that of
the protoplasm within the red cells.   Such a solution is said to be
hypotonic.   A reversal of this process occurs if the external medium
is more concentrated, or hypertonic.   Water is then extracted
from the red cells which become wrinkled or crenated.   Such distortions commonly occur in improperly prepared blood films and
tissue sections.

Oxygen diffuses through the membranes of the respiratory surfaces into the tissue juice and then through the endothelial walls of
the capillaries.   As the erythrocytes circulate slowly through the
capillaries investing the alveoli of the lungs, or through the capillaries in the gills and skin of aquatic animals, the hemoglobin unites
in a weak chemical combination with oxygen to form oxyhemo-
globin.   In this form oxygen is carried to the various tissues of the
body and is given up.   The surface area of all the red cells may
be computed on the basis of individual cell size and the estimated
number of red cells in the body.   In the case of man, estimates
from 2500 to 4500 square meters have been worked out, areas
many times that of the body.   Depending largely upon the severity
of service, there is a limit to the functioning of the red cells.   When
the colloidal composition ages beyond a certain point a granular condition results and the red cells are destroyed.   Dead cells and their
remnants are removed from the circulation in the spleen and liver
and new cells arising in the blood-forming centers take their places.

The reasons given for the segregation of hemoglobin in special cells
or corpuscles, a condition characteristic of vertebrates and rarely
found in animals of the lower phyla, is that capillary walls are so
constructed that if the hemoglobin were free in the plasma it would
leave the capillaries and be eliminated from the circulation, as
occurs in malaria where red cells are destroyed.   Furthermore, the
retention of hemoglobin within the capillaries, should it be free in
the plasma, would necessitate the capillary walls being so constructed as to prevent its passage.   If this were so, various other
substances whose passage through such walls is essential would
also be retained.   In its present arrangement the hemoglobin held
in the red cells is surrounded by a fluid stroma whose constantly

balanced properties permit it more efficient functioning than would be possible if it were free in the plasma of the blood where the sodium chloride concentration would interfere with its function.

**Leukocytes.**—These elements of the blood are called white blood cells and all are nucleated. Special stains make possible a differentiation of five distinct types which can be separated into two classes. One class lacks granules in the cytoplasm and its cells are known as *agranulocytes;* the other class, the *granulocytes,* includes those cells with a distinctly granular cytoplasm.

AGRANULOCYTES.—Two types of cells are differentiated in this class, lymphocytes and monocytes, although there are numerous apparently transitional forms and variations.

*Lymphocytes.*—Lymphocytes are small cells about as large as the red cells in mammals, but smaller than the erythrocytes in many lower vertebrates. The cell body is round in form, with a relatively large spherical nucleus and only a thin rim of basophilic cytoplasm. The nucleus has a darkly staining chromatin network and usually a nucleolus. The cytoplasm takes a light blue tint with various blood stains which are usually composed of methylene blue and eosin.

Variations in the size of lymphocytes are common and three sizes, large, medium, and small, are often designated. The small lymphocytes are usually meant when lymphocytes are mentioned without any qualification as to size. The medium and large lymphocytes are limited to the lymph glands and bone marrow, occurring but rarely in the circulating blood under normal conditions. The lymphocytes cannot be looked upon as fully differentiated cells, for they are believed to have the ability to develop not only into lymphocytes of various sizes and become stem cells (hemocytoblasts) for development of blood elements, but also differentiate into monocytes which may become extravascular macrophages and then fibroblasts. The lymphocytes are primarily extravascular and leave the circulating blood, soon after entering it from lymphoid or myeloid centers, by pushing their way between adjoining endothelial cells of capillaries to invade the adjoining tissues. Their invasion may carry them into the lumen of the alimentary tract and large numbers are lost in this manner. They are found in large numbers associated with inflammation and phagocytic action has been attributed to them which is doubtful. Although nothing very definite can be said of their rôle as lymphocytes, as wandering elements capable of differentiation into other cell types their rôle is important. Their source is mainly the lymph nodes and the spleen in mammals, but in lower forms they may have their origin in the same regions as the other blood cells.

6

*Monocytes.*—Monocytes are larger than lymphocytes, with a spherical or indented, more lightly staining nucleus located eccentrically in the basophilic cytoplasm. These cells have a marked motility intravascularly and are actively phagocytic for foreign materials, including cell débris and bacteria. They transform into macrophages when actively phagocytic and may differentiate into fibroblasts after they pass from the capillaries into surrounding connective tissues. Many of the features of enlarged monocytes, macrophages, and fibroblasts make clear differentiations of types

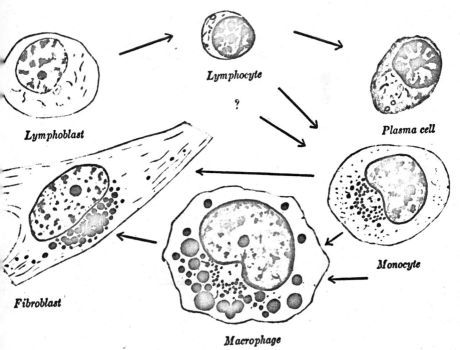

*Lymphocyte*

*Lymphoblast*

*Plasma cell*

*Fibroblast*

*Monocyte*

*Macrophage*

Fig. 57.—Interrelations of non-granular leukocytes. (Cowdry's Textbook of Histology.)

impossible. Various gradations of cells from typical lymphocytes to monocytes are found and indicate their source as the lymphocyte.

Under conditions of chronic inflammation, cells derived from lymphocytes are present. These cells, called *plasma cells*, have an eccentric nucleus in which the chromatin material radiates from the center like the spokes of a wheel. (Fig. 57.)

GRANULOCYTES.—These cells are differentiated in hemopoietic centers as end-products, usually not possessing an ability to multiply or give rise to other cell types but capable of ameboid movement to

varying degrees. Three types of cells (heterophil, eosinophil, and basophil) are separated on the basis of the nature and reaction of the specific cytoplasmic lipoidal granules each develops. Among the mammals the various granulocytes are larger than the red cells but in lower forms they are usually smaller.

*Heterophils (Neutrophils).*—The cytoplasm of this type is filled with numerous variably sized small granules which show considerable variation in reaction to dyes in different animals; in some cases being primarily acidophilic (as in the rabbit), in others reacting to both acid and basic dyes. In man the granules are uniformly small and take a light lavender stain (therefore called *neutrophils*) with the usual blood stains (Wright's, etc.). The nucleus has several small deeply staining lobules connecting by thin strands, a condition termed polymorphic, and the term *polymorphonuclear leukocyte* is often applied to these cells. Increase in the degree of lobulation of the nucleus and decrease in cytoplasmic granules are associated with aging of this and other types of granulocytes. The heterophils are the most motile of the three types and frequently migrate from the blood into adjoining connective tissues, especially following infections and injuries involving inflammation. They are capable of marked phagocytic action, both in and outside of the blood stream, and while thus engaged are termed *microphages* in contrast to the larger macrophages. Great numbers of these cells appear in areas of infection and numerous dead ones occur in pus and serous exudates from inflamed regions. In such sites they have been considered as giving rise to a substance stimulating fibroblast activity and connective tissue formation.

*Eosinophils.*—These cells have less markedly polymorphic or even spherical nuclei and numerous uniformly large acidophilic granules which may partially obscure the nucleus in film preparations. Eosinophils are less motile than the heterophils, are frequently found in extra-vascular locations, especially below the epithelium of the stomach and intestine, and may have slight phagocytic action for some bacteria. They are found in greater numbers following parasitism by worms and under other conditions suggesting the possibility of a rôle in detoxification. Reports on conditions present during resorption of the larval gut during metamorphosis in Amphibians indicate these cells as active phagocytosing elements. Centers of production for this type of granulocyte appear abundantly in the connective tissue of the gut and other organs of fish and Amphibia but become limited to myeloid centers in higher forms.

*Basophils.*—As the name implies, this type has basophilic cytoplasmic granules which are relatively large and numerous and considered as composed of a mucoprotein. The nucleus is slightly lobed or even spherical, is located centrally, and stains lighter than the cytoplasmic granules which may obscure it in preparations. Basophils are rare in man but occur in greater numbers in lower vertebrates. It has less motility than either of the other types of granulocytes and little is known concerning its function although invasion of foreign materials may produce an increase in their number. They closely resemble the mast cells found in loose fibro-elastic connective tissues but are not considered as the same cell or from the same sources; the basophil arising in myeloid centers and the mast cells differentiating from undifferentiated mesenchymal cells in connective tissues, particularly in serous membranes and subcutaneous tissue.

**Platelets.**—In addition to the red and white cells of the blood there are found in mammals certain cytoplasmic elements called platelets. These are much smaller than the red cells and in smears take the blue basic dye and appear in clumps or masses. They are thought to be associated with blood clotting. Their origin is traced to large giant cells in the bone marrow, known as *megakaryocytes*, which are thought to extend pseudopodia into the marrow sinuses where they are cut off and give rise to the platelets.

**Megakaryocytes.**—These are giant cells found extravascularly in the red marrow of mammals. Their cytoplasm is lightly basophilic and homogeneous except after special staining which brings out small basophilic granules. The nucleus is lobulated in such a manner that the cell appears multinucleated. Blunt cytoplasmic extensions give an irregular cell outline and the protrusion and loss of such processes into the sinusoids give rise to the platelets. Origin of the megakaryocyte is traced to the hemocytoblasts in the marrow; degeneration of these giant cells is followed by their removal by macrophages of the marrow. (Figs. 58 and 59.)

**Thrombocytes or Spindle Cells.**—Platelets are not found in the blood of vertebrates below mammals, but a cellular element, the spindle cell or thrombocyte, is thought to have an analogous rôle in blood clotting. These cells are about the size of the red cells or lymphocytes and have a heavily staining spherical or oval nucleus in which a nucleolus is usually not present. The cytoplasm is clear and varies in its reaction from relatively neutral to lightly acidophilic. The cells appear oval or spindle-shaped in outline but in film preparations several cells fuse and give the appearance of a cytoplasmic mass with several nuclei. These cells resemble lymphocytes in early stages and originate from lymphocytes or hemocytoblasts.

**Blood Films.**—In preparation for making blood films carefully clean several slides, then place a drop of freshly drawn blood on one of the slides, touch it with the edge of another slide and draw the blood across the slide. Do not push the blood. The spreading of the film should be done immediately after the blood is obtained and the film dried by gentle heating above a flame or simply waved in the air several times.

To stain the film Wright's stain is commonly used; this is an alcoholic solution of a compound dye with methylene blue and eosin. Enough of the stain is added to the film to completely flood it and left for one minute; then an equal amount of distilled water is added to the stain, the slide is rocked to mix the fluids, and the diluted stain is left for three minutes; after this time the slide is thoroughly rinsed in distilled water and set on edge to dry.

Such stained and dried films may be kept so or covered by adding some gum damar and a cover-glass. Films that are too thick or are stained too heavily will be a dark greenish or blue in color. Good films should have a pink color macroscopically. Too heavily stained films can be improved by a bath in 95 per cent alcohol to remove some or all of the stain; in the latter case the film may be restained.

Imprints from bone marrow and the spleen freshly removed and gently rested upon a slide may be treated as are blood films.

**Blood Cell Formation.**—Hemopoiesis is the name given to the process of blood cell formation, and a study of it in different groups of vertebrates shows some variation in its location. Embryologically, blood cells as well as the blood-vessels originate in mesenchyme, occurring first as isolated masses or cords, called *blood islands,* in the wall of the yolk sac. The peripheral cells of these masses become flattened and form the endothelium of the vessels, while the central cells become free, rounded elements, surrounded by plasma and form the first blood cells. Other similar centers arise from the mesenchyme of the embryo proper and with subsequent development a vascular network is formed that gradually gives rise to a system of blood-vessels and developing blood cells. During the early stages blood cells are formed by division of the primitive blood cells in the vessels and to a lesser extent from the surrounding endothelial cells. After this early embryonic stage, blood cells cease to proliferate in the vessels, and proliferation becomes localized in various centers developed from mesenchyme in different regions of the body. A study of the vertebrates, beginning with the fish and progressing through to the mammals, presents a series in which evolution of blood-forming centers may be traced and compared with similar stages in the embryonic development of mammals.

The earliest hemopoietic center to appear may be found in the case of the "hagfish," a cyclostome, where a diffuse arrangement of proliferating and differentiating blood cells occurs in the connec-

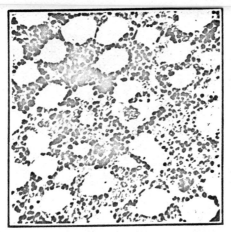

FIG. 58.—Photograph of bone marrow from a rabbit with a **megakaryocyte in the center** of the field and lower right. Scattered fat cells appear as **clear ovals** among the strands of differentiating blood cells. 4 mm. obj. and 5× oc.

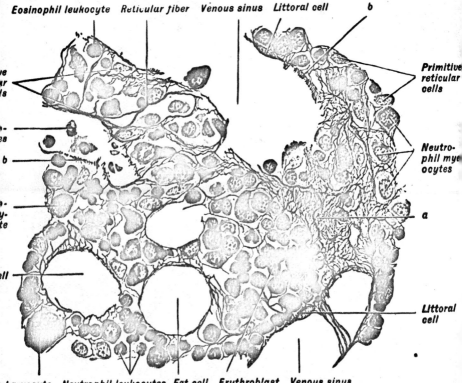

*Eosinophil leukocyte    Reticular fiber    Venous sinus    Littoral cell    b*

*Primitive reticular cells*

*Neutrophil myelocytes*

*a*

*Littoral cell*

*akaryocyte    Neutrophil leukocytes    Fat cell    Erythroblast    Venous sinus*

FIG. 59.—Bone marrow from the upper epiphysis of a femur of a child of six years. The fibrous network of the wall of a vessel is seen from the surface at *a* and in cross section at *b*. Bielschowsky stain. 500 ×. (A.A.M.) (From Maximow & Bloom, courtesy of W. B. Saunders Co.)

tive tissue of the gastro-intestinal tract. In other forms, blood-forming tissue becomes more localized and concentrated in certain regions of the tract, as in the primitive "spiral valve" of the lamprey. A still further condensation in the cyclostomes gives a spleen that is bound into the wall of the stomach or intestine. Such centers are supported by a network of connective tissue in which the blood cells are proliferating in close association with sinusoidal capillaries leading into the venous system. In ganoids, the spleen is an extra-enteral organ attached to the mesentery; the submucosa of the intestinal tract may still retain the capacity to develop granulocytes, but red cell formation centers in the spleen: In the higher fishes and in larval amphibia, the spleen becomes the main center for blood cell formation but mesenchyme cells in other localities, such as the capsule of the gonads, kidneys, and in the liver, also give rise to areas of blood cell formation. Separate sites along the gut also occur where accumulations of lymphocytes alone are produced in loose fibroelastic connective tissue. These accumulations, or nodules, are designated as lymphoid tissue while that giving rise to the red cells and granulocytes is termed myeloid. With the shift of hemopoiesis to the bone marrow there is an accompanying marked development of lymphocyte production in lymphoid tissue located along the gut and also in the marrow and spleen. In birds and mammals the spleen becomes primarily lymphoid; and accessory lymph structures, nodes, are developed along the lymph vessels, especially in mammals.

Blood cell formation in the circulating blood normally occurs only during early embryonic life; in later development and in the adult state hemopoietic centers arise and only the differentiated blood cells normally appear in the circulating blood. Whether the formation of blood cells in the hemopoietic centers is extra- or intravascular has been a controversial subject but there is agreement as to a very intimate association between hemopoiesis and peculiar sinusoids of such centers.

Sinusoids.—These are broad channels located between arterial and venous capillaries, but their very permeable walls are composed of flattened cells which can be demonstrated as actively phagocytic, a feature not characteristic of endothelial cells but true for reticular cells. Closely associated reticular cells forming the adjoining connective tissue stroma of the marrow are considered as possible sources of blood stem cells. The relationship of the myeloid areas to the vascular channels is not readily determined from routine sections and interpretations vary. In accordance with one explanation, blood cell formation occurs in pockets among reticular cells closely adjoining but not continuous with sinusoids and when the blood cells are differentiated they migrate through the sinusoidal wall into the blood stream which is very sluggish at this point. This represents an extravascular type of hemopoiesis. Another interpretation considers red cell production (erythropoiesis) as occurring within the sinusoids, that is, intravascularly. Stem cells (hemocytoblasts, lymphocytes, and reticular cells) are described as accumulating or migrating into the sinusoids where they multiply and cause a temporary blockage of the blood stream which moves very slowly, at best, through these passageways. A period of multiplication is followed by differentiation of red cells which gradually are drawn into the venous blood stream of adjoining capillaries and the sinusoids become open to circulation again. The granulocytes are considered as forming from stem cells present in or migrating into the reticular stroma adjoining the vascular system. Following multiplication and differentiation of the stem cells in such extravascular location, mature granulocytes migrate into the blood by passing through the sinusoidal walls. Thus, reds are considered derived intravascularly and the granulocytes extravascularly. (Fig. 59)

Lymphocyte production is localized in nodules of lymphoid tissue where lymphocytes are produced in a reticular stroma and pass into reticular sinusoids before passing into either venous or lymph capillaries. In the spleen and marrow, lymph nodules occur in the reticular stroma and lymphocytes enter the blood stream by way of the sinusoids. Lymphocyte production is considered as extravascular in its location whether it occurs in the connective tissue of the gut, in the spleen, in the marrow, or in the special lymph glands or nodes prominent in mammals.

The series of transitions from the stem cells to the various differentiated types of blood cells is difficult to follow and there is no complete agreement on any given line of development. The following is a very abbreviated sequence in the differentiation of the erythrocytes, granulocytes, and lymphocytes. (Fig. 60.)

*Erythrocyte Differentiation.*—The hemocytoblasts are generalized cells similar to large lymphocytes and are the stem cells from which erythrocytes and granulocytes develop. They may have an ameboid appearance. Their cytoplasm is non-granular and basophilic; the nucleus is large and oval with a coarse chromatin network.

Certain hemocytoblasts differentiate into round *erythrocytoblasts* with a spherical nucleus, and following a series of mitoses, accompanied by increasing differentiation they become erythrocytes. In the erythrocytoblast stage the cytoplasm reacts to both acid and basic dyes. As the hemoglobin increases the basophilic reaction diminishes, and in the *normoblast* stage the cells have considerable hemoglobin in the cytoplasm and the nucleus is relatively smaller. These changes become more prominent with further mitoses, until mitotic activity comes to an end. In mammals the nucleus is extruded from the cell body, which then passes into the vascular circulation. Series of stages from hemocytoblasts to newly formed erythrocytes may be found in red marrow.

*Granulocyte Differentiation.*—Other hemocytoblasts undergo mitoses to form cells in which a differentiation of another kind takes place and gives

rise to one or another of the three types of granulocytes. An early stage is recognized as the *promyelocyte*, of which three forms can be distinguished on the basis of lipoidal cytoplasmic granulation. The nuclei are spherical or reniform at first, but each type undergoes further mitoses with further differential granulation of the cytoplasm and lobulation of the nucleus until neutrophil myelocytes, eosinophil myelocytes, and basophil myelocytes are formed. Each of these types undergoes its own special development leading to the formation of completely differentiated neutrophils, eosinophils, and basophils which enter the circulating blood by way of the sinusoids.

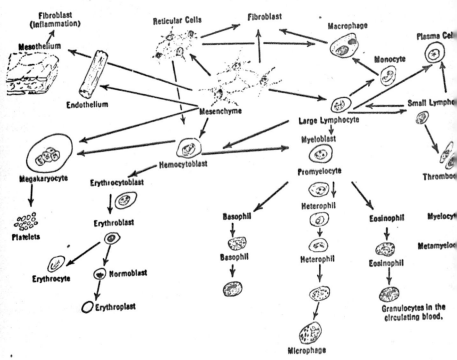

Fig. 60.—Table showing derivation of blood cells.

*Lymphocyte Formation.*—The production of lymphocytes is localized in nodules of lymphoid tissue widely distributed throughout the body. Each of these nodules is usually composed of a lighter central area occupied by large lymphocytes with lightly basophilic cytoplasm; these large cells and the adjoining intermediate size undergo mitosis and produce cells which are the small lymphocytes occupying the periphery of the nodule. The small lymphocytes with their small amount of homogeneous basophilic cytoplasm pass into the adjoining lymph or blood streams as potential sources of larger lymphocytes, monocytes, and as extravascular migrants may become blood stem cells.

**The Destruction of Blood Cells.**—The different types of blood cells apparently have differing periods of life. Some are relatively short

lived, as the erythrocytes of mammals which have an estimated life
of about thirty days, but others may live over much longer periods.
It has been observed that many red cells are phagocytized by the
macrophages in the red pulp of the spleen; in certain pathological
conditions so many are destroyed that the red pulp becomes brown
in color. Old granulocytes are phagocytized by macrophages in the
liver and spleen. Some lymphocytes migrate from the capillaries
into tissues where they may degenerate or become blood stem cells
(hemocytoblasts); others migrate through epithelial membranes
of the digestive system or ducts of the excretory, genital and respiratory systems to be lost from the body.

# CHAPTER V

## THE MUSCLE TISSUES

THE most outstanding functional feature of muscle tissue is the capacity to contract and consequently it plays an important part in all movements of an organism. Associated with the functional features are intracellular threadlike structures, the *myofibrillæ*, embedded in a more fluid cytoplasm, the *sarcoplasm*. The fibrillar structure is not evident in living tissues but appears in fixed and stained material. A protein called myosin has been extracted from muscle fibers and by electron microscope observation it has been shown as bundles of parallel filaments composing the myofibrillæ. Three types, smooth mucle, cardiac muscle, and skeletal muscles are distinguished. Both cardiac and skeletal muscle fibers have alternating dark and light cross-striations, in contrast to the smooth muscle in which such striations do not appear.

### SMOOTH MUSCLE

This type shows a very close association with connective tissue and is widely distributed through the vertebrates, occurring in the wall of the alimentary tract, in the arteries and veins, and in numerous other ducts. It is apparently the least differentiated type of muscle, is involuntary, and appears widely in invertebrates in places where, from vertebrate studies, skeletal muscle would be expected. The histological unit is easily identified as the smooth muscle cell which is fusiform in shape, though varying greatly in length and breadth.

Embryologically, mesenchyme cells in the region where smooth muscle will develop begin to elongate and a multiplication of such cells, called *myoblasts*, gives rise to a network and finally sheets of smooth muscle cells. The reticular and loose fibroelastic connective tissue network associated with these differentiating and later fully developed muscle cells is derived from mesenchyme cells similar to those giving rise to the myoblasts. Even in the adult vertebrate it is believed that smooth muscle cells may be derived from undifferentiated mesenchyme, or reticular cells, especially in association with the formation of new blood-vessels.

The myoblasts become more and more elongate with development and appear still connected laterally by cytoplasmic processes, as were the mesenchyme cells from which they were derived. Long

very fine threads, the myofibrillæ, appear enmeshed in the sarcoplasm of prepared material. Coarse fibrils developed in the embryonic stage apparently undergo longitudinal splitting and give rise
to more numerous and much finer fibrils of the fully differentiated
cells. Also the lateral connections are no longer apparent and the
cells appear as independent units structurally but functional characteristics have been presented as support for retention of delicate
lateral processes and a syncytial structure in fully differentiated
tissue. The fully developed cells are fusiform and have an elongated
oval nucleus occupying a central position. (Fig. 61.) The size of the
cells varies in different species and in different regions in the same
species.

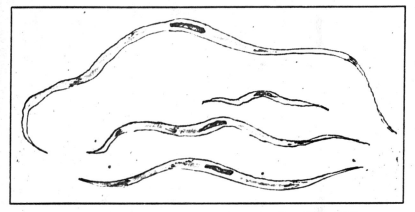

Fıg. 61.—Diagram of isolated smooth muscle cells. (Churchill.)

In the mature organization the cells are connected with each other
by a reticulum of fine argyrophil fibers which may be demonstrated
by silver techniques. Increase in cells may be effected through
development of embryonic cells left among the mature cells or by
division of the mature cells which apparently retain their ability
to divide by mitosis. In general, the myofibrillæ of this type of
muscle are difficult to distinguish in routine sections; the entire
cytoplasm appears as a homogeneous acidophilic material. The
non-fibrillar sarcoplasm is represented by a lighter area at either
end of the nucleus where the myofibrils diverge in passing. By
soaking pieces of tissue composed of smooth muscle in weak acid or
alkaline solutions it is possible to observe isolated smooth muscle
cells.

Smooth muscle cells are variously organized. In the connective
tissue of the villi or folds of the intestine a few isolated smooth

muscle cells occur; associated with hairs are small bundles which form the arrector pili muscles; in more complex organizations the cells are arranged in bundles or sheets. When organized into groups or muscle coats, the tapering portions of the cells overlap and a network of reticular fibers extends between adjacent cells and continues with the surrounding fibroelastic connective tissue. When such sheets or bands of smooth muscle are cut in longitudinal section, the characteristic spindle shape of the cells is evident, but in cross-sections roughly circular sections of different sizes appear adjacent to each other and nuclei appear only in those sections passing through the central region of the cells. (Fig. 62.)

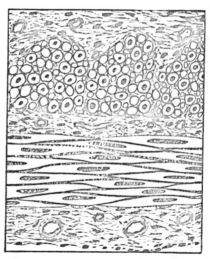

**Fig. 62.**—A longitudinal section through the intestine: the internal circular smooth muscle coat shows cells in cross-section and the outer longitudinal coat has cells cut longitudinally. Loose fibroelastic connective tissue separates the two coats and extends in among groups of muscle cells. A serous membrane forms the outermost coat of the organ.

In the wall of the alimentary tract from the lower esophagus to the anus or cloacal opening there are usually two distinct sheets of smooth muscle; an inner coat of muscle cells encircles the tube, and an outer coat has cells arranged lengthwise. (Fig. 63.) Constrictions of the inner coat decrease the lumen, and constrictions of the longitudinal coat cause a shortening of the tube at the points affected. During life, waves of contraction pass along these coats simultaneously and cause the peristaltic movements essential in the functioning of the digestive system.

Sometimes when pieces of the intestinal wall are fixed, indications of the contraction wave have been preserved. Small band-like swellings, which stain more deeply, cross the muscle sheet at regular intervals, and involve different portions of adjacent cells.  When the intestine or other organ involved is greatly distended, the muscle sheets appear much thinner than in the relaxed state.  With relaxation after such expansions the cells slide back into their former position and form a thicker coat.  Capillaries extend through the connective tissue network surrounding the bundles or sheets of

Fɪɢ. 63.--Photograph of cross-section and longitudinal section of smooth muscle in wall of frog's stomach.  4 mm. obj. and 5× oc.

muscle cells and follow their disposition as do the sympathetic nerves controlling their involuntary action.  In the repair of smooth muscle there are evidences of some degree of mitotic activity on the part of fully formed cells, but in cases of extensive injury lesions are closed by scars of connective tissue.

### SKELETAL MUSCLE

As the name implies, this type is associated with skeletal parts. The unit of structure is the fiber which is an unbranching, elongated, multinucleated cylinder of varying length.  Their origin is traced to myoblasts derived from mesodermal cells in the myotomes.  Each fiber is a syncytium; distinct cellular limitations are not evident and many nuclei are distributed along the length of each fiber. These fibers do not break into semblances of cells upon treatment with dissociating fluids.  The development of the elongate multinucleated fibers is held by some to occur by repeated divisions of the nuclei of myoblasts without accompanying division of the cytoplasm, which increases in quantity and elongates.  Others believe they arise through fusion of the ends of adjacent myoblasts.

Both may be true. Preparations show a few coarse fibrils first about the periphery. This is followed by an increase in number of smaller fibrils which gradually fill the fiber during development. The nuclei of the myoblast are central at the first appearance of fibrils, but later in development they may be localized in the peripheral region or become distributed throughout the fiber. In the lower forms, as represented by the dogfish, coarse fibrils occur in a peripheral region and leave a relatively prominent central core of sarcoplasm and nuclei even in the mature tissue. (Fig. 64.)

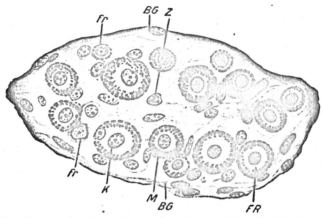

Fig. 64.—Cross section through an embryonic muscle bundle of a sheep. *BG*, Cells of the primordium of the perimysium; *FR*, muscle fiber in cross section; *fr*, muscle fibers in cross section with a single layer of primitive fibrils; *K*, nucleus in the axial sarcoplasm; *M*, primitive muscle fibers; *Z*, cells of the jelly-like tissue. 740 ×. After Schaffer. (From Maximow & Bloom, courtesy of W. B. Saunders Co.)

**Muscle Organization.**—Individual fibers are surrounded by a thin sheath of connective tissue, the *endomysium*, composed of fibrous and cellular elements of loose fibroelastic and reticular tissues. (Fig. 65.) Continuing with the endomysium is an *internal perimysium*, a sheath of similar but more abundant tissue, which surrounds bundles or *fasciculi* of fibers. An *external perimysium* or *epimysium* is the external, heavier sheath which encloses large numbers of fasciculi to form a muscle. Fibrocytes, histiocytes and undifferentiated mesenchymal cells in the connective tissue sheaths play a part in the repair of lesions of skeletal muscle which does not exhibit marked powers of regeneration. The capillaries and nerve fibers as well as the larger blood-vessels and nerve trunks are supported in the connective tissue networks.

Individual fibers may be observed in fresh skeletal muscle by teasing with needles, but it is difficult to find uninjured ends of such fibers. In fixed and stained preparations, fibers are seen to end in various ways. Some are rounded and blunt, others taper off within their connective tissue sheath which becomes continuous with other similar sheaths within the muscle or with tendinous tissue by which muscles are attached to bones, cartilage, or other structures.

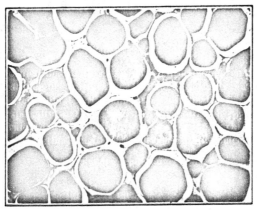

Fig. 65.—Photograph of a cross-section of skeletal muscle of the turtle, showing fibers surrounded by endomysium. Capillaries may be seen between some fibers. 16 mm. obj. and 5× oc.

*Sarcolemma.*—The fibers are clearly limited within their endomysial sheath by a continuous, thin, transparent membrane, known as the *sarcolemma*. In injured regions of teased fibers the fibrillar contents are often broken and separated, making it possible to observe this membrane more easily. Its origin has been disputed; some believed it to be formed by the connective sheath; others attributed its presence to the activity of the protoplasm of the muscle fiber itself. The latter seems more likely, for it has been shown to have none of the reactions of collagen or reticulum of connective tissue and appears in pure tissue cultures of muscle.

*Myofibrillæ.*—Within the sarcolemma the fibers are composed of a fluid protoplasmic substance, the *sarcoplasm*, and numerous highly developed myofibrils which run the length of the fiber parallel to each other. The fibrils appear to originate in the peripheral sarcoplasm of the developing myoblasts. With development of the fiber, the myofibrils increase in number until they occupy all but a central region in which nuclei are located in undifferentiated sarcoplasm; finally the entire fiber is filled with myofibrillæ and nuclei may be scattered or limited to the sarcoplasm below the sarcolemma. The sarcoplasm may be reduced to a small amount uniformly distributed among the fibrils, or groups of fibrils may be separated conspicuously by regions of intervening sarcoplasm. Such groups

of fibrils are called *sarcostyles* and are apparent in cross-sections as *Cohnheim's areas.* The separation of such groups from each other depends upon the amount of intervening sarcoplasm and in some muscles they are not easily discovered. Fixation may also play some part in producing these decidedly localized groups of fibrils.

Each fibril appears as a continuous thread of protoplasm, composed of plates, or discs, of alternating kinds of material. Observations with the electron microscope reveal the same striations observed with the ordinary microscope and adds the observation that

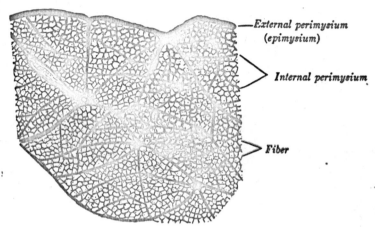

—*External perimysium (epimysium)*

*Internal perimysium*

*Fiber*

Fig. 66.—Diagram of a cross-section of a skeletal muscle.

the myofibrillæ are composed of bundles of parallel myosin filaments which are indicated as the contractile units. The discs show better when the muscle tissue is soaked in dilute aqueous solutions of acids and alkalies. A number of bands have been identified; only four are easily demonstrated and ordinarily only two of these are outstanding and are responsible for the conspicuous dark and light bands forming the cross-striations characteristic of this and cardiac muscle. The relatively broad, dark, refractive band stains with hematoxylin and is called the "$Q$" or anisotropic band. Alternating with these are the less refractive pale discs that ordinarily remain unstained; these are the "$J$" or isotropic bands. Each of these bands is divided by another narrower band of opposite character. The "$Q$" band is thus seen to have an indistinct light band, the "$M$" band, running through its center; and the "$J$" band has a distinct thin dark band, the "$Z$" band, or intermediate disc, running through its center. These latter bands represent differences in the densities of the "$Q$" and "$J$" bands. The "$Z$" band appears continuous with the sarcolemma and separates the fiber and fibrils

7

into small structural and functional units called *sarcomeres*. The myosin filaments adhere also in the "*Z*" disc region. Various theories of muscle contraction have arisen based on the different peculiarities associated with the parts of these sarcomeres. The dark "*Q*" discs are doubly refractive, poor in extensibility, poor in water content, do not shrink, and stain darkly in hematoxylin. The lighter "*J*" discs are singly refractive, pale, rich in water content, extensible, shrink in reagents, and do not stain well, if at all.

**Nuclei.**—The nuclei of skeletal muscle fibers are oval in shape, but their size and location varies, depending upon the animal. In lower

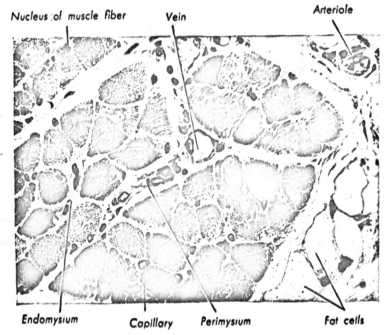

Fig. 67.—Cross-section of skeletal muscle. Human tongue. Hematoxylin and eosin. Photomicrograph. × 425. (Bailey's Textbook of Histology, courtesy of Williams and Wilkins Company.

vertebrates the nuclei may be central but are more commonly scattered throughout the fiber with a tendency, in some cases, to be located more abundantly in the peripheral sarcoplasm below the sarcolemma. In mammals the nuclei are most commonly located in the sarcoplasm directly below the sarcolemma, but in some muscles of the red type they may be scattered more generally through the fiber. The nuclei vary from an oval to a fusiform shape, but are disposed lengthwise in the fiber in either case.

**Dark and Light Muscles.**—Two types of muscle may be distinguished macroscopically, the red or dark and the light or white muscles. Both types may enter into composition of the same muscle or certain muscles may be composed almost exclusively of a single type, as in the case of the white muscles forming the breast of chicken and the red muscles of the legs; likewise the dorsal muscles of fish are dark while the lateral ones are light. The red type is associated with muscles carrying on repeated contractions over long periods; their fibrils are coarser, sarcoplasm is more abundant, and the nuclei are central or scattered peripherally. The location of the pigment, whether in the fibrillar material or in the sarcoplasm, is not definitely known. The pale muscles are associated with quicker and stronger, though less extended contractions; fibrils are abundant, sarcoplasm is relatively scanty, fibrils are finer than in red type, and pigment is absent.

The sarcoplasm filling in between the fibrils may vary greatly in amount and the density and size of the fibers also show variations not only with the species but also in the same individual. A muscle may increase in size with use; such increase is due to increase in size, not number, of fibers. Largest fibers are found in Amphibia; the smallest occur in birds and mammals.

**Blood-vessels and Nerves.**—The nerve supply from the cerebrospinal nerves places this type of muscle under voluntary control in contrast to the other two types of muscle. Capillaries form a meshwork with the longer capillary portion running lengthwise of the fibers, and short and thicker cross-pieces, or ampullæ, extend across the fibers and may dilate with blood when the muscle is contracted.

**Regeneration.**—If a muscle is seriously injured its destroyed portion is replaced by scar tissue, but if the sarcolemma and nuclei of a fiber are not destroyed the nuclei with surrounding sarcoplasm are reported to give rise to myoblasts which reform the fiber or give rise to new fibers. Origin of new fibers by budding occurs in early stages and lower vertebrates but the regeneration in higher forms (especially mammals) appears doubtful and the usual result following injuries is the development of connective tissue scars.

**Attachment.**—The manner of attachment of skeletal muscles to tendons was thought by some to involve a continuation of the myofibrils with the collagenous fibrils of the tendon but the more probable association involves a continuation of the connective tissue of the fibers (endomysium) and the muscle (internal and external perimysium) with the collagenous material of the tendon which, in turn, continues with that of the periosteum or perichondrium. Silver preparations demonstrate the argyrophil fiber net-

work immediately surrounding the muscle fiber to be continuous
with the same fibers among the collagenous fibers of the tendon or
periosteum.

## CARDIAC MUSCLE

Beneath the foregut of the embryo, an endothe'ial tube surrounded
by mesenchyme is the forerunner of the heart and the base of its
connecting vessels, to which this type of muscle is limited.   The
processes of the early mesenchyme cells appear to continue with the
adjacent cells to form a syncytium, and from these the cardiac
muscle is derived by continued multiplication, gradual elongation,
and differentiation of intracellular fibrils.   The developing cells, or
myoblasts, form coarse fibrils, the cardiac myofibrils, in the peripheral
sarcoplasm.   The cells grow in length but preserve their fiber-like
form and lateral attachments with adjoining myoblasts.   The myofibrillæ increase in number and become more numerous in the peripheral region, leaving a central portion with a core of undifferentiated
cytoplasm and the nuclei.   With development the fibrils show striations resulting from alternate differences in composition; these
appear as dark and light bands which occur at the same level in all
the fibrils of a given fiber, so that the whole fiber has a striated
appearance.   The same bands or discs compose these striations as
in the case of skeletal fibers.   In the lower vertebrates the myofibrils
are less numerous and form a peripheral layer, but in higher forms
they are scattered throughout, except in a limited central region
occupied by the nuclei.   Each fiber is limited by a thin membrane,
the sarcolemma.   A thin sheath of loose fibroelastic and reticular
tissue carries a capillary supply among the fibers of the heart in
higher vertebrates, but among the fishes and amphibians fibers are
separated from the blood in the heart only by the endothelium and a
delicate reticular network, a condition resembling the embryonic
state of higher forms.

The general picture of a longitudinal section of cardiac muscle is
that of a network of long fibers in which the nuclei are in the center
at regular intervals.   The clefts between fibers are small in the
higher vertebrates but are easily seen in lower forms, such as the
dogfish and frog.   A cross-section shows sections of the fibers irregular in outline where the branching occurs, but in other portions the
size is more uniform and the outline quite regular.   This is in contrast with cross-sections of smooth muscle, where the outlines are
regular but the size varies with the region of the cell cut, and the
uniformity of the larger skeletal fiber outlines.   After treatment in
dissociating fluids, cardiac muscle can be shaken into separate

units resembling single cells. They are roughly rectangular in shape, with parallel sides and very uneven ends. (Fig. 68.) One or both ends may have short stubby branches that connected it with adjacent fibers. Each of these units is cross-striated and shows longitudinal fibrillæ. It is not certain that the apparent ends are actually boundaries of cells; they may be artifacts brought about by dissociation. The isolated units of cardiac muscle correspond to cells since each has a nucleus and a surrounding portion of cytoplasm. However, the most reasonable conclusion drawn from the lack of definite cell boundaries, and the fact that the myofibrils extend continuously through several such units, is that the cardiac muscle is a syncytium.

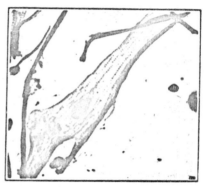

Fig. 68.—Photograph of an isolated portion of cardiac muscle of the frog, showing a fiber with a central nucleus, striated myofibrils, and branches. 4 mm. obj. and 5× oc.

At times even in fresh heart tissue, and particularly after certain techniques, peculiar bands, the *intercalated discs*, may be observed extending partially or interruptedly, like steps, across a fiber. These discs were formerly thought to represent functional end-boundaries of the cells, but this seems unlikely since some of them pass across a fiber at the level of the nucleus and others delimit portions of a fiber without a nucleus. They usually present a staircase appearance and the separate steps do not overlap. Some investigators interpret them as places where the fibers were in a state of contraction. They were commonly found in older cardiac tissue and from this the inference has been drawn that they possibly represent lines where norma functioning is breaking down, but they have been observed in young tissue also and are interpreted as points of possible growth or representing boundaries of functional activity. The exact nature of these structures remains to be demonstrated.

The blood for cardiac muscle is supplied directly from the clefts between the fibers in the case of the lower vertebrates, as may be observed in the dogfish or amphibian heart. In mammals, however, there is a rich capillary network carried between the fibers by the interpenetrating connective tissue. The syncytial organization of the heart is probably directly concerned with the rhythmical contractions so characteristic of it. It is also essential that a free circulation takes place regularly, for interferences in the blood flow affect the normal rhythmical activity. Cardiac muscle contractions are shorter in duration than the resting phase and under normal conditions fatigue rarely occurs. Regeneration does not occur in cardiac muscle and enlargements of the heart in some adult animals result from increase in the size of the muscle fibers, not their number, or from increase in the connective tissue present.

Fig. 69.—A longitudinal section of human cardiac muscle, showing the central nuclei in the light areas and intercalated disks as dark irregular lines crossing the fibers. 1.9 mm. obj. and 5 x oc.

**Neurogenic and Myogenic Theories of the Heart-beat.**—Although this appears to be primarily a functional problem, histological discoveries have had much to do with clarifying it. The heart of an elasmobranch has two chambers: an auricle and a ventricle. The sinus venosus draining blood from the body carries this blood into the auricle from which the blood passes into the ventricle whose contraction drives it into circulation through the body. In action, the sinus contracts first, then the auricle, then the ventricle, then the bulbus arteriosus. In this order, one after the other, repetition occurs rhythmically. It appears that whatever the nature of the stimulus is, it begins in the sinus wall. The amphibian heart has two auricles and one ventricle; reptiles have two auricles and the beginning of two ventricles; birds and mammals have two auricles and two ventricles. In each case the old elasmobranch heart organization is represented roughly by tissue at the junction of the vena cava with the right auricle, and careful

observation shows that the rhythmic contraction of these higher hearts begins at this tissue and is followed by contraction of the auricles and ventricles.

The heart is provided with branches of sympathetic nerves which have a sensory function, and with branches of the tenth cranial (the vagus) over which the impulses regulate the speed of the rhythmic beat. There is no

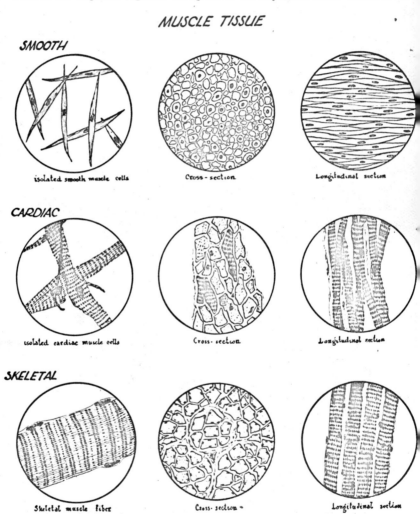

## MUSCLE TISSUE

**SMOOTH**

isolated smooth muscle cells · Cross-section · Longitudinal section

**CARDIAC**

isolated cardiac muscle cells · Cross-section · Longitudinal section

**SKELETAL**

Skeletal muscle fiber · Cross-section · Longitudinal section

FIG. 70.—Diagrammatic chart of muscle types.

evidence, however, that either set of nerves is concerned with the origin and continuance of the rhythm. Rhythmical contractions of so-called hearts of invertebrates are effected by nerve impulses, and the occurrence of nerves in vertebrate hearts suggested that the heart-beat was due directly to nerve stimuli. However, this explanation does not apply to vertebrate hearts; the embryo heart beats rhythmically before nerves have developed in it, and when the heart of a cold-blooded vertebrate is removed from its body, rhythmic beating may be continued for many days if proper conditions are maintained. Also, small pieces of heart of the chick or rabbit live, grow, and contract in tissue culture where it has been observed that nucleated portions corresponding to separate cells may contract independently.

The myogenic theory, on the other hand, has much in its favor. According to this idea, the stimulus arises in cardiac tissue and is transmitted by this tissue to various contracting portions. The question then arises as to whether impulses pass over ordinary muscle fibers or whether there are special fibers for this function. Such fibers have been found in mammals, where a small mass of especially modified fibers occurs at the junction of the superior vena cava and the right auricle. These fibers, known as *Purkinje fibers*, have fewer, peripherally located fibrils and a relatively abundant sarcoplasm. This mass is called the sino-auricular node and is the place where the automatic rhythmic contractions begin. The impulses continue over the auricle *via* a network of the same type of fibers, branches of which become continuous with typical cardiac fibers. The auricles are separated from the ventricles by rings of connective tissue around the openings between them and here Purkinje fibers converge to form the auricular-ventricular node, a second mass of modified cardiac fibers. This node is located near the ventricles and Purkinje fibers extend on into the ventricles. Impulses beginning at the junction of the vena cava with the auricles cause the latter to contract, and the impulses continuing into the ventricles cause a progressive contraction in them also. The rest period between each cycle of contraction is longer than the contraction period. The heart is refractory during this rest period and does not respond readily to stimuli. Its sensitivity to stimuli increases toward the end of the rest period. An interference with impulses to the ventricles causes a failure in rhythmic activity or may set up independent ventricular rhythms, in which case the heart fails to function properly.

# CHAPTER VI

## THE NERVE TISSUE

ALL cells are, to a certain extent, irritable and conductive; that is, they receive stimuli from external sources and transform them into impulses which are conducted to a portion or the whole of the cell to stimulate some reaction by that portion or by the entire cell. Among the metazoans generally, an association of special cells has evolved from ectoderm to form the nerve tissue, which functions primarily as a receiver of stimuli from and conductor of impulses to other tissues. The vital unit of this tissue is the nerve cell, or *neuron*, which takes on varied forms but invariably has one or more cytoplasmic processes making contact with closely adjacent or more remote cells or tissues of the body. Typically, each cell has a large nucleus surrounded by a cytoplasmic mass from which slender processes grow out for varying distances to form nerve fibers. Each neuron is a separate unit; but the processes of one come into contact with those of other neurons by an association called a *synapse* so that impulses pass from one nerve cell to another; and by chains of neurons impulses may be conducted over considerable distances. In this manner, stimuli are received in various nerve centers and responses are effected in other cells or tissues. Little is known concerning the exact nature of stimuli, or how they are transformed into impulses, or how the latter are transmitted along nerve cells, but the essential part played by these cells in coördinating the other tissues of the organism has been proven repeatedly by careful experimentation. The nerve cells and their processes are organized into organ centers such as the brain, spinal cord, and ganglia, but the processes alone form the nerves which are organized into an interconnecting system associating the various tissues and organs with the nerve centers and making integrated action possible.

**Histogenesis of Nerve Tissue.**—The foundation of all the nerve tissue appears in the developing embryo as a thickened region of ectoderm, the *neural plate*, along the mid-dorsal line. Following rapid and unequal growth of the cells of this plate, a neural groove is formed and deepens until the thickened folds fuse dorsally to form a neural tube which lies below and separate from the ectoderm. (Fig. 24.) The cells of this neural tube give rise to the major part of the nerve tissue. The anterior portion of the tube forms the brain and the posterior portion the spinal cord. Between the neural tube and the ectoderm a longitudinal band of cells appears on each side to form the neural crest which segments to form the cranial and spinal ganglia.

The newly formed neural tube is composed of elongated epithelial cells giving an appearance of stratification although, actually, tapering ends of each of these cells contact both boundaries of the tube. Mitotic figures are common, especially in the lateral regions bordering the lumen of the tube. The prevalence of mitotic figures in this region is explained by migration of nuclei toward the lumen before division takes place and migration

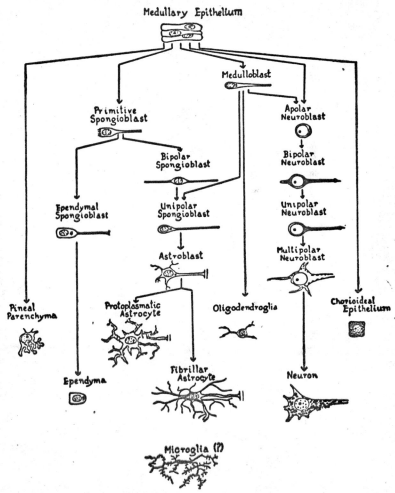

FIG. 71.—Schema showing the histogenesis of the nerve and neuroglia cells. (Bailey, Textbook of Histology, courtesy of Williams & Wilkins Co.)

of newly formed nuclei away from the lumen. These early undifferentiated cells of the tube and similar ones of the crest undergo two lines of differentiation; one group becomes the primitive nerve cells or *neuroblasts* which give rise to the nerve cells of the brain, spinal cord and craniospinal ganglia; and the other group of undifferentiated cells becomes the *spongioblasts* which give rise to the neuroglial elements. Migratory elements distribute

themselves into various parts of the body where many form the sympathetic ganglia, some are associated with the origin of chromatophores, while others become chromaffin cells associated with endocrine secretion. Invading the developing neural regions are mesenchymal cells which give rise to supporting connective tissue and vascular elements. (Fig. 71.)

The neuroblasts lose contact with the lumen boundary of the early tube and become characterized by a cytoplasmic process with a swollen end, the *growth cone*, which grows outward from the cell body to extend into other regions of the developing central nervous system or out among the other developing tissues and organs of the body to terminal points of innervation such as muscle, integument, or glands. Similar processes of neuroblasts in the spinal ganglia migrate into the developing cord to make associations with neuroblasts there. Additional processes, the dendrites, make their appearance after the development of the first process, which is usually an axon, and these commonly remain in the neighborhood of the cell body. In the case of spinal ganglion neurons, both types of processes may extend long distances from the cell body. An elaborate system of nerve cells is gradually differentiated and their processes are closely associated by contact (synapse) to establish an integrated system.

Associated with the differentiation of the neuroblasts is an accompanying differentiation of the spongioblasts into the neuroglial cells which are packed among the nerve cells of the central nervous system, ensheath the ganglion cells (*satellite cells*), and migrate along the peripheral processes of nerves to form a sheath, the *neurilemma*.

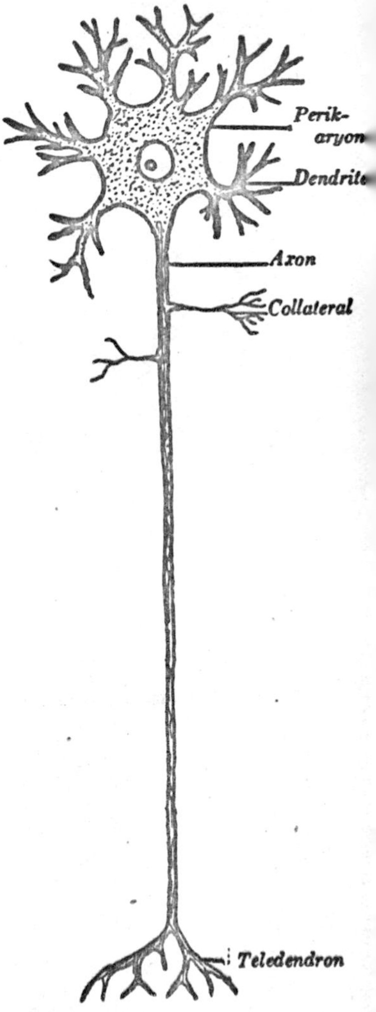

## THE NEURON

A description can be divided into a consideration of the cell body or *cyton*, which consists of the nucleus and surrounding portion of cytoplasm, *perikaryon*, and the cytoplasmic processes which extend out from it as a single *axon* and numerous *dendrites*. (Fig. 72.)

Fig. 72.—Diagram of a neuron.

**The Cell Body (Cyton).**—The size of this portion of the neuron varies from a few to several hundred microns in diameter. The limiting surface is a denser cytoplasm but not as distinct a cell membrane as found in other types of cells. There is considerable variation in shape, some cell bodies are spherical, others oval, pyriform, fusiform, or stellate. Such variations are largely due to the number and location of the cytoplasmic processes.

*Nucleus.*—The large spherical nucleus is bounded by a distinct nuclear membrane. Its chromatin material is generally scant, as compared with that of other cells and appears concentrated at the periphery and about a prominent nucleolus. Fine protoplasmic granules staining with both basic and acid dyes occur abundantly. In some neurons several nucleoli may be observed but a single one is most common. Mature neurons differ from other cells in that they do not undergo mitosis.

Fig. 73.—Spinal ganglion cells of the cat, showing numerous Nissl bodies. Each cell is surrounded by a number of small nuclei belonging to the satellite cells which form a sheath about each neuron. Photomicrograph. 1.9 mm. obj. and 5× oc.

*Nissl's Bodies.*—There are irregular masses of basophilic material occurring in the cytoplasm and have been called *tigroid bodies,* and *chromophil* substance. (Fig. 73.) Special techniques are often used to make them stand out clearly, but even routine preparations may show them scattered through the cytoplasm. It is believed that these bodies contain iron and store oxygen, and that their presence is essential to the functioning of the nerve cell. In living cells the substance of which they are composed may be in a diffuse state and their appearance as definite bodies may be due to fixation, since different fixatives result in differences in their form. Modifications in their appearance occur with changes in the conditions of the nerve cells. In pathological conditions or following lesions they decrease in number and often disappear entirely.

*Neurofibrils.*—Very fine threadlike elements, *neurofibrillæ*, have been observed and recorded within a fluid cytoplasm (*neuroplasm*) of the living neuron. Others have recorded a similar picture due to lining up of mitochondria which in prepared material appear more scattered and not to be confused with the neurofibrillæ. Special techniques using silver impregnation also demonstrate the occurrence of such fibrils in permanent preparations but routine methods of preparing tissues fail to show them clearly, if at all. At first they were thought to be the primary means by which impulses were transported, but there seems to be little proof as to their function, though they appear as characteristic features in nerve cells.

*Golgi Apparatus.*—By special techniques, using osmium tetroxide or silver, a blackened network appears in the cytoplasm usually concentrated about the nucleus. This apparatus of Golgi disappears in cells subjected to injury.

*Mitochondria.*—Tiny filaments, rods and granules appear scattered through the cytoplasm and may be demonstrated in living cells with Janus green B. Certain methods also preserve them in fixed and stained preparations. Little is known of their functional significance.

**Cytoplasmic Processes.**—It is customary to recognize two types of processes extending from the cyton, namely, axon and dendrities. There is no Nissl substance in the axon which is a slender extension of uniform diameter and has a smooth clean surface. Usually the axon (*axis cylinder, neurite*) arises from a particular place in the cyton marked by a conical extension called the *axon hill.* Slender *collateral branches* may arise at right angles along its course. The axon ends distally in a brush of finer branching processes known as the terminal arborization or *teledendron.* The dendrites are thicker, irregularly branching processes which contain Nissl substance and other cytoplasmic elements generally present in the perikaryon. A polarity also characterizes these processes, the axon carries impulses from the cyton while the dendrite carries them toward the cyton from which each arises.

**The Reflex Arc.**—The simplest physiological organization of neurons is called a reflex arc. It involves at least two neurons, as in the following example: A stimulus on the skin is translated into a nerve impulse in the peripheral terminus of a dendritic process of neuron A. (Fig. 74.) The nerve impulse travels centrally to the cyton of this neuron, which is located in a spinal ganglion. From this cyton the nerve impulse passes over its axon into the gray matter of the cord to terminate in the ventral horn. Here it connects with the dendrites of neuron B, and passes into the cyton of this second nerve cell. From cyton B the impulse travels into the axon which extends outward in the spinal nerve to muscle tissue and stimulates the muscle to contract. Most reflex reactions involve more than two neurons. This is especially true of higher mammals, where volition exercises control over simpler reflex mechanisms.

**The Synapse.**—Neurons are associated with each other through the synapse, at which point the terminals of the axon of one neuron come into contact by contiguity with the dendrites or cell body of another neuron. Such association may be effected by basketwork of neurofibrillar processes

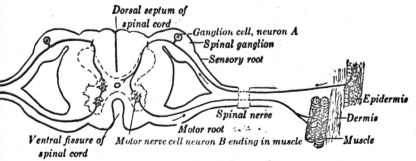

FIG. 74.—Diagram illustrating a reflex arc.

from the terminal end of one neuron fitting against the dendrites or cyton of the neuron receiving the impulse. An alternative type of neuron association, involving continuity of processes at these points, had many supporters at one time but both living and prepared materials of vertebrates have demonstrated the neurons as independent structural units associated only by contact at the synapses.

## TYPES OF NEURONS

Neurons located in different regions of the nervous system have definite functional demands made upon them, and associated with their functioning is a certain arrangement of their processes so that several types of cells may be classified as follows: *unipolar cells*, neurons with a single process which arises from one side; *bipolar cells*, in which a single axon and a single dendrite process project from opposite ends of the neurons: *multipolar cells*, in which numerous processes project from different regions of the cytons; and *ganglion cells*, in which two different processes, axon and dendrite arise from one side, a *pseudo-unipolar* condition.

**Unipolar Cells.**—During the early differentiation of the neuroblasts, a unipolar condition develops when a single process grows out from the cell body. This condition does not usually remain throughout development, for one or more additional processes are developed from different portions of the cyton, and change the cell into a bipolar or multipolar type when differentiation is complete. In lower vertebrates the unipolar condition is believed to remain in some completely differentiated neurons of the brain, spinal cord, and ganglia. (Fig. 71.)

**Bipolar Cells.**—In these neurons a single axon and dendrite are developed and project from opposite ends of the cyton. This condition is found in the embryological development of the multipolar

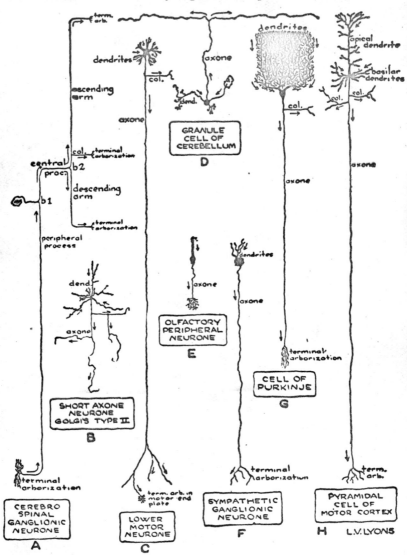

Fig. 75.—Some of the principal forms of nerve cells. The direction of conduction is shown by arrows. (Bailey, Textbook of Histology, courtesy of Williams & Wilkins Co.)

cells of the brain and spinal cord; in the spinal and cranial ganglion neurons before they are completely differentiated, and is true of completely differentiated neurons found in the retina and parts of the ear. (Fig. 75.)

**Multipolar Cells.**—This type of cell is by far the most numerous and the most easily demonstrated. Although beginning its development with a single cytoplasmic outgrowth, it eventually develops one axon process and several dendritic processes. The shape of these cells is, therefore, dependent upon the number and arrangement of the dendrite processes. Examples are found in the pyramidal cells of the cerebrum, the Purkinje cells of the cerebellum, and the motor cells in the ventral horn of the spinal cord.

*Pyramidal cells*, characteristic of the cerebral cortex, have a pyriform or pyramidal shape with a long thick branching dendrite extending from the narrow end and a number of shorter dendrites arising from the sides and base. A single slender axon arises from the base and extends down

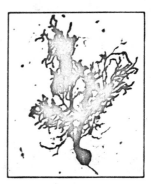

Fig. 76.—Photograph of a pyramidal cell from the cerebral cortex of a cat with two protoplasmic astrocytes surrounding the largest dendritic process. The axon leaves the base of the pyriform cell body. 4 mm. obj. and 5× oc.

Fig. 77.—A photograph of a Purkinje cell from the cerebellum of the cat, showing many branched dendritic processes and a single fine axon process. Golgi technique. 4 mm. obj. and 5× oc.

into the white matter of the brain. Another variety of this cell has a short axon which branches near its origin and extends only a short distance from the cell body, a condition which has led to considering them association cells. (Figs. 75 and 76.)

*Purkinje cells*, characteristic of the cerebellar cortex, have pyriform cytons, but have only one or two main dendrites which subdivide to form a thick bushlike thicket of processes. An axon arising from the base of the cell body extends into the white matter. (Figs. 75 and 77.)

*Motor neurons* of the spinal cord have irregularly stellate shapes due to the origin of dendrites from many points. (Fig. 78.) The axon, which often extends long distances, is a single, slender, and smooth process of the cell body. (Fig. 75.)

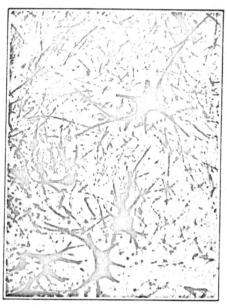

Fig. 78.—A photograph of multipolar cells from the ventral horn of the cat's spinal cord. The nucleus occupies the light central area of each. Cajal method. 4 mm. obj. and 5× oc.

**Ganglion Cells.**—Ganglion cells, characteristic of the craniospinal ganglia, have regular pyriform or spherical cytons due to the single process leaving them. The processes are not readily studied in routine sections but the cells can be observed to have a large nucleus and a prominent nucleolus in a dense acidophilic cytoplasm commonly packed with basophilic Nissl's granules. (Fig. 73.) A sheath of neuroloyal cells is indicated about the cytons by numerous small nuclei. Embryologically the cells produce two processes, a bipolar condition, but in fully differentiated cells a single process extends from the cyton. This single process usually branches to form two axon-like processes, one extending to the periphery, regarded as a dendrite, and the other passing into the dorsal horn of gray matter of the cord and regarded as an axon. (Fig. 75.)

### NEUROGLIA

Although the neurons are the outstanding components of nerve tissue, essential neuroglial elements are associated with them in the

8

composition of the central nervous system, of the ganglia, and of the peripheral fibers. Several of the common types of neuroglial elements differentiated from the spongioblasts of the early embryo will be described. Although some of the characters of neuroglia may be determined in routine preparations, like the neurons, they are also better observed by special silver techniques.

**Ependyma.**—These represent the early indifferent cells left as a membrane about the lumen of the brain and spinal cord. In the course of development the long tapering process into the neural tube is almost lost and there remains a columnar cell with cilia, usually projecting into the lumen. (Fig. 79.) The acidophilic cytoplasm

Fɪɢ. 79.—Diagrammatic representation of the ependymal cells lining the centra canal of the spinal cord.

is homogeneous and no fibers are associated with these cells. In certain regions of the brain there are vascular invaginations called *choroid plexus* over which the ependymal cells lose their cilia (except in fishes) and become cuboidal. The ependymal cells have been demonstrated to give rise to a fluid secretion in tissue cultures and presumably contribute to the cerebrospinal fluid, particularly in the choroid plexus.

**Astrocytes.**—These are stellate cells closely associated with the blood-vessels supplying the gray and white matter and are the largest type of neuroglial element. The nucleus is large and oval with scanty chromatin and no nucleolus. The cytoplasm is lightly acidophilic and cellular outlines are not clearly visible in routine preparations. Fibers, called *glia fibers*, associated with these cells may be demonstrated by special techniques but are not visible in routine preparations. Two types of astrocytes, separated as fibrous and protoplasmic, can best be studied in silver preparations which demonstrate glia fibers. *Fibrous astrocytes*, also called spider cells,

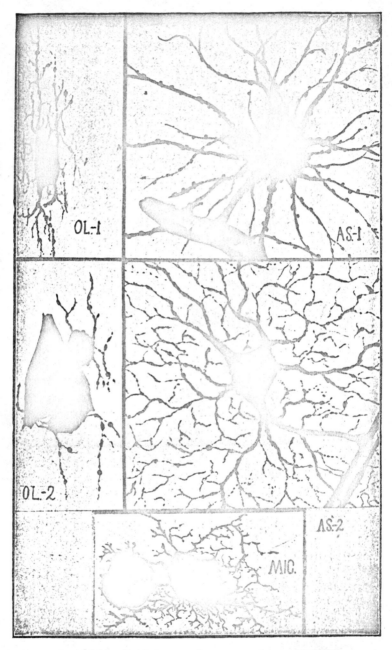

Fig. 80.—Interstitial cells of the central nervous system. *AS-1*, Fibrous astrocyte with perivascular feet on vessels; *AS-2*, protoplasmic astrocyte; *MIC*, microglia; *OL*, oligodendroglia. (Penfield and Cone, Cowdry's Special Cytology, courtesy of Paul B. Hoeber.)

are characterized by long, usually unbranched processes with embedded glia fibers. They occur most abundantly about the myelinated fibers of the white matter in the brain. *Protoplasmic astrocytes,* also called mossy cells, have many short stubby branching processes and associated fibers. Their cytoplasm is granular and they are most abundant in the gray matter. (Figs. 76 and 80.)

**Oligodendrocytes.**—These are smaller cells than the astrocytes and have fewer and more delicate processes. Their nuclei are smaller and round, have more chromatin and no nucleoli. The cytoplasm is acidophilic and granular but no glia fibers are associated with their cytoplasmic processes. These cells occur packed closely about fibers, together with the astrocytes, within the brain and cord. Very similar, if not the same, cells migrate to become the satellite cells, closely surrounding the cytons (Fig. 73) of the ganglia and the elongated and flattened cells forming the *neurilemma* sheath about peripheral nerve fibers.

**Microglia.**—These cells are derived from the mesenchyme cells which invade the developing nerve centers and are the smallest cellular elements in nervous tissue. They have delicate irregular processes capable of withdrawal and the cells are capable of ameboid movement. Their nuclei are the smallest and stain the most deeply of those found in sections of the brain or cord. The microglia may become phagocytic and during this activity become enlarged.

**Functions of Neuroglia.**—The ependymal cells lining the lumen of the cord are ciliated and may function as aids in circulating the fluid in the lumen while those covering areas of the choroid plexus are secretory and may play a part in formation of cerebrospinal fluid.

The astrocytes, which act as supporting elements for the neurons, may also play a part in the healing of injuries and in the formation and maintenance of the myelin.

The oligodendrocytes, as such, in the central nervous system and the satellite and neurilemma cells are considered to coöperate with the neurons in the formation of the myelin sheaths. A nutritional and insulating relationship to the neurons is suggested for these cells and also for the astrocytes.

The microglia, as motile elements with phagocytic powers, play a part similar to the macrophages of other regions.

## THE NERVE FIBER

In the immediate region of the cyton of the brain and cord, and often over considerable distances of the gray matter, the nerve processes are bare but as they pass from the region of the cyton, or gray matter, they are usually surrounded by one or two sheaths directly derived from or associated with neuroglial cells. In the white matter of cord or brain a lipoidal substance called myelin surrounds the fiber. This appears as a clear halo in cross-sections of routine preparations but can be preserved and blackened by osmium preparations. (Figs. 81 and 82.)

As fibers leave the brain or cord during development to become components of the cranial and spinal nerves, neuroglial cells migrate to form a *sheath of Schwann*, or *neurilemma sheath*, consisting of a series of encircling single, flat, nucleated cells under which myelin

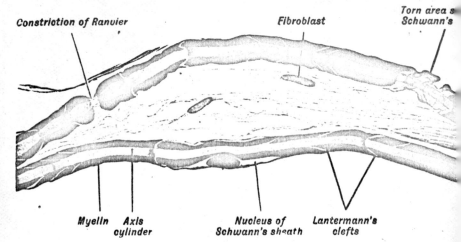

Constriction of Ranvier        Fibroblast        Torn area s Schwann's

Myelin    Axis cylinder        Nucleus of Schwann's sheath    Lantermann's clefts

FIG. 81.—Two myelinated fibers of the sciatic nerve of a frog; treated with osmic acid and picrocarmine and teased. 330 X. (A.A.M.). (From Maximow & Bloom, courtesy of W. B. Saunders Co.).

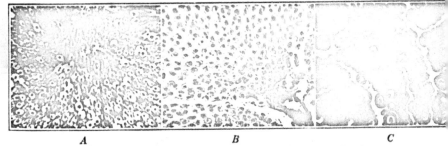

A                    B                    C

FIG. 82.—Cross-section of myelinated peripheral nerves, showing appearance following different treatments. *A*, Fixed in Bouin; stained in eosin and hematoxylin. The myelin is dissolved away. *B*, Prepared with silver impregnation to show the axis cylinder. *C*, Fixed with osmium tetroxide and preserving the myelin. Photomicrographs. 4 mm. obj. and 5X oc.

accumulates to form a second sheath between the fiber and the neurilemma. Surrounding most peripheral nerve fibers is a delicate sheath of connective tissue, the *endoneurium*, derived from mesenchyme of the region through which the fiber passes. (Fig. 81.)

The neurilemma cells vary in length, being longer and larger in the case of fibers of large neurons. Where the ends of these cells meet they appear to be in contact with the axon, so that at these depressions, or *nodes of Ranvier*, the myelin is interrupted. The portion between two adjacent nodes is called the internode and represents the length of the neurilemma cells. In the middle of each internode, at some place on the internal periphery of the neurilemma, a nucleus is surrounded by a small amount of granular protoplasm. Between the nodes of Ranvier the myelin sometimes exhibits funnel-like interruptions, called *incisures of Lantermann*, which some observers regard as artifacts. (Fig. 81.)

In the central nervous system some fibers appear to be embedded in neuroglia but lack myelin. Furthermore, many axons of the nerves from sympathetic ganglia have no myelin and are surrounded by a sheath of neurilemma in which there are no nodes of Ranvier. These are known as fibers of Remak.

## HISTOLOGY OF A PERIPHERAL NERVE

Peripheral nerves originating from the brain and spinal cord emerge through foramina of the skull or vertebræ and pass to out-

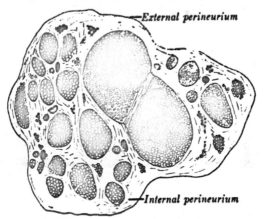

*External perineurium*

*Internal perineurium*

Fig. 83.—Drawing of cross-section of a peripheral nerve. Two large and a number of smaller fasciculi of fibers are shown. External and internal perineurium are shown around and between the bundles.

lying parts. Such a nerve consists of a great many hundreds of fibers, each composed of an axon, myelin, neurilemma, and endoneurium. The fibers are arranged in bundles, or fasciculi, of varying size, bound together by loose fibroelastic connective tissue, and the entire nerve is supported by similar tissue. (Fig. 83.) The connective tissue surrounding all the fascicules is called *epineurium*, or *external perineurium*, and continues in between the bundles to merge with a connective tissue around each bundle, the *internal perineurium*. There is also a loose delicate extension of connective tissue which surrounds single fibers to form the *endoneurium*.

As the nerve extends out from its central origin, it branches, and each branching represents a sorting out of bundles and a gradual diminution in number of fibers in a bundle. The connective tissue of a nerve has a special nerve supply, called the nervi nervorum, and a vascular supply, the vasi nervorum.

**Degeneration of Nerves.**—Degeneration changes appear soon after a peripheral nerve is severed. Before this occurs, however, there is an almost immediate chemical change which extends in both directions from the lesion. This effect is known as traumatic degeneration and extends centrally to reach the cytons of the neurons involved. The Nissl substance disintegrates and disappears. Although the cytons are affected by the lesion they possess the power of recovery. This recovery phase soon follows and extends out along the nerve fibers as far as the lesion. But the portion of the nerve distal to the lesion does not recover and disintegration of the myelin and axon progresses outward from the lesion. A great increase in neurilemma nuclei has been observed to accompany these changes. In about three days after the lesion is made, the nerve no longer conducts and the structure innervated by this particular nerve is no longer served. If the nerve supplies certain muscles, these will be paralyzed, since motor impulses are no longer being sent to them. Paralysis will be permanent unless the nerve regenerates.

**Regeneration of Nerves.**—If soon after the lesion is made, the cut end of the peripheral portion of the nerve is brought into contact with the cut end of the central portion and kept in this position, then the neurilemma cells which absorbed the broken-down axon and myelin material will form protoplasmic bands. These protoplasmic bands serve as tracks along which the sprouting ends of the cut central portion of the axon will grow, and the developing new axons will find their proper terminations. It is very important to have no large masses of scar tissue formed by connective tissue at the lesion where the cut ends of the injured nerve are brought together. Regeneration is more rapid in young animals than in old and also more rapid in warm-blooded types. Degeneration proceeds centrally in some cases, and involves cytons and dendrites. No fiber regeneration of such cells takes place. Nor is there any cyton replacement in the central nervous system. The phenomenon of degeneration has been of great value in aiding the determination of the origin and distribution in the central nervous system and peripheral termination of groups of nerve fibers. An experimental lesion is made involving a small area in the spinal cord or brain. Proper time for degeneration of the nerve fibers concerned is permitted to elapse. The animal is then killed. The cord and brain are removed and serial sections made following the proper technique devised for the purpose. Disintegrating fibers and cytons have a distinctive appearance and enable the investigator to follow the route of the degeneration and thus determine the origin of the fibers occupying the region of the cord involved in the experimental lesion.

## NERVE ENDINGS

The reception of external stimuli by nerve cell processes and the transforming of these into nerve impulses necessitate some organization of the other tissues located at each of these end-points. As examples, there are specialized sense organs such as the eye and ear, and other less complex organizations such as the lateral line and taste-buds where neuro-epithelia receive physical and chemical stimuli and transmit them to associated nerve endings. The stimuli received in such receptors arouse nerve impulses which are transmitted by the sensory neurons to others ending in effectors. Such effectors are organizations of the nerve endings with other tissues, such as the muscles and glandular epithelia, which they stimulate into action. The eye and ear are *exteroceptors* in that they receive stimuli from outside the body. There is another group of internal receptors, the *enteroceptors*, or visceral receptors which receive internal stimuli. Still other receptors, the *proprioceptors*, supplement the internal and external receptors and lead to a regulation of the reactions set into play by the impulses conveyed to the effectors. A few of the many devices for receiving and affecting stimulation will serve as examples of the interrelation of the neurons with other tissues. Those nerve endings receiving stimulation are called sensory; those effecting stimulation of other tissues or cells are the motor endings.

**Sensory Endings.**—The free ending of fine nerve branches demonstrated between and close to epithelial cells are associated with both sensory and motor impulses. Morphologically, the free ends of sensory and motor nerves are similar.

In glands, the terminal ends of sympathetic fibers form a network just outside the basement membrane; some branches pass through this, forming another net around the bases of the gland cells, and some small branches extend between the gland cells. Some of these act as receptors and others as effectors regulating secretion. An arrangement of free endings similar to this is present in stratified squamous epithelium, as, for example, the epidermis, where it is sensory. Organs of special sense have epithelial cells, derived from ectoderm, which are especially sensitive to particular types of stimuli. In the postero-dorsal region of the nasal passage, among the protective cells of the membrane, are special olfactory cells which connect basally with nerve fibers of afferent neurons forming part of nerve pathways to the olfactory center of the brain. There are special cells in the cochlea of the ear which connect with processes of neurons belonging to the auditory branch of the eighth nerve, and so form part of a pathway to the auditory center in the brain. These pick up vibrations which become translated as sounds. The rods and cones of the retina are stimulated by light waves and connect with a bipolar cell proximally connecting with other neurons which extend in toward the brain.

Sensory end-organs, called *neuromuscular spindles* are formed about a group of smaller, pale skeletal muscle fibers and are separated by connective tissue from the surrounding fibers. (Fig. 84.)

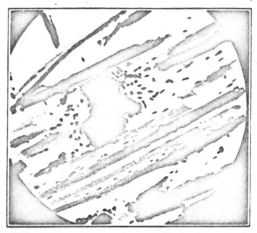

FIG. 84.—Photograph of neuromuscular spindle in skeletal muscle of the cat. The terminal arborization of a nerve fiber is wrapped about skeletal muscle fibers and acts as a sensoreceptor. Silver impregnation. 4 mm. obj. and 5✕ oc.

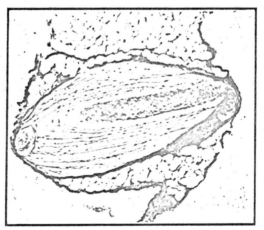

FIG. 85.—Photomicrograph of a section of a cat's mesentery, showing a Pacinian corpuscle surrounded by fat cells. 16 mm. obj. and 5✕ oc.

The distal end of an afferent nerve breaks up into fine threadlike branches which are coiled about these special fibers. When the muscle as a whole has contracted, the sensory nerve of the muscle spindle is stimulated, and this is relayed to a nerve center. In this way arises consciousness of degree or extent of flexure in the appendages.

Distributed widely through fibroelastic connective tissue are special sense organs called *Pacinian corpuscles*. These are small ovoid structures consisting of concentric overlapping layers of connective tissue, rich in tissue fluid, covering an inner, more cellular core in which is embedded the flat or branched and coiled end-process of a nerve. (Fig. 85)

**Motor Endings.**—A motor nerve as it ends in a skeletal muscle passes in through the external and internal perimysia to the muscle fibers. The end of each nerve fiber breaks up into a teledendron and the myelin disappears. The neurilemma at the end of the fiber

Fig. 86.—Motor end-plates in skeletal muscle fibers of the frog prepared with gold chloride; some are contracted and one plate is expanded. Photomicrograph. 4 mm. obj. and 5× oc.

appears to merge with the sarcolemma of the muscle fiber to which that particular teledendron is connected. Each branching terminal network passes into a shallow pool of sarcoplasm just under the sarcolemma, where it forms a platelike net known as a *motor end-plate*. These plates show contracted and expanded conditions corresponding with physiological state. Each muscle fiber has at least one motor end-plate and the nerve impulse reaching this organ causes the muscle to contract. (Fig. 86.)

In smooth and cardiac muscle, one or more small swellings of the terminal branches of sympathetic fibers form simpler motor endings closely associated with the smooth or cardiac fibers.

## GANGLIA

A ganglion may be defined as a small aggregation of neurons (cytons and processes) outside the central nervous system. (Fig. 87.) Each dorsal root of a spinal nerve possesses a spinal ganglion. The

dorsal root of such a nerve is sheathed in external perineurium. This connective tissue covers the ganglion and extensions from it continue internally, partly separating masses of cytons and fibers. The cytons are large spherical cells of different diameters. Within each is a large nucleus which usually contains a nucleolus. Around each cyton may be seen a row of nuclei, indicative of a sheath of so-called satellite cells, which are homologous with oligodendrocytes and neurilemma cells. Elsewhere are clumps of fibers, usually

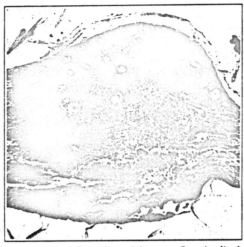

Fig. 87.—Photograph of spinal ganglion of the cat. Longitudinal section, showing groups of ganglion cells separated by fiber tracts. The loose fibroelastic connective tissue sheath is partly torn away from the ganglion. 32 mm. obj. and 5× oc.

with myelin and neurilemma. The processes of the cytons are not visible in routine sections but by silver impregnation methods the craniospinal neurons have been demonstrated to have an appearance of unipolar condition. The cyton has a single process which branches to form two axon-like processes, one extending peripherally, being functionally a dendrite, and the other passing as the axon into the gray matter of the dorsal horn of the cord. Embryologically, these cells produce two processes, a bipolar condition, but these later join in a common outlet and then branch so that they are referred to as *pseudo-unipolar* cells. Surrounding each cyton of the ganglion is a sheath of satellite cells which continue out over the process as neurilemma cells. A connective tissue capsule about the satellite cells continues with the endoneurium of the fibers.

Outside the cord and brain are several sympathetic ganglia of such size and uniformity of location that they have received anatomical names. But in addition to these which can be located by dissection, there are a great many small ganglia that can be seen only in microscopic preparations. The cells of sympathetic ganglia are multipolar and have long axons and dendrites which may, in some cases, extend out beyond the capsule cells to form connections with adjacent cells. In other cases the dendrites are entirely within the capsule. Connective tissue surrounds the ganglion and penetrates among the fibers and cells. Myelin does not usually surround the sympathetic fibers but a neurilemma sheath is present.

## THE CENTRAL NERVOUS SYSTEM

A study of the central nervous system is beyond the scope of any introductory study of microscopic anatomy and must be left to neuro-anatomy. A brief consideration will be given to general features of the spinal cord, the cerebrum and cerebellum, and the connective tissue membranes, the *meninges*, supporting these structures.

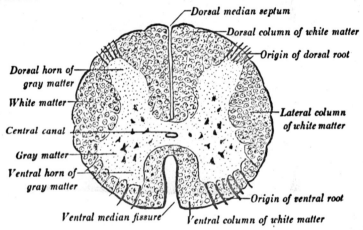

FIG. 88.—Diagram showing regions of the spinal cord.

**Spinal Cord.**—In the spinal cord the gray matter is internal and surrounded by white matter. The cord may be almost divided into two halves by a deep *median dorsal septum* and a shallower, wider *median ventral fissure*. However, the two halves are connected by a white and gray commissure. The gray matter resembles the letter "X" or letter "H." The narrower dorsal horns of gray matter extend almost to the periphery. (Fig. 88.) The ventral horns are much wider and do not extend to the ventro-lateral surface. The dorsal median septum extends down to the gray commissure, and the latter contains the canal of the spinal cord which is lined by ependymal cells. Ventral to the gray commissure is a white commissure. The white matter between the dorsal septum

and the gray horn adjacent to it is known as the *dorsal funiculus* or column of white matter. Ventral and lateral to the dorsal horns on either side is the *ventro-lateral column* or funiculus. The latter white matter may be subdivided into a ventral column between the ventral fissure and the gray matter of the ventral horn adjacent to it. The white matter dorsal and lateral to this is known as the *lateral column* of each side. The white matter consists of myelinated and unmyelinated axons, and neuroglia but no neurilemma. The surface of the cord is immediately covered with a connective tissue sheath, *pia mater,* and this extends into the white matter as short vascular septa. Studies of various kinds have shown that the axons of the white matter occur in strands of well-defined location. The axons of the dorsal columns carry sensory impulses up the cord; those of the ventral columns carry motor impulses down the cord; and the lateral columns are subdivided into tracts, some of which are sensory and some motor. The gray matter of the cord consists of: neuroglia; axons entering from the columns; entire short neurons; cytons, dendrites, and the initial portions of axons which extend further beyond the gray matter into the ventral roots of spinal nerves and on out into such nerves. The neurons of the gray matter are multipolar in type and have already been described. Axons of some gray matter neurons extend out into the white matter and are incorporated as part of a white column.

**Cerebrum and Cerebellum.**—The brain, like the spinal cord, has a region of gray matter occupied by cytons, axons, dendrites, and neurolgia; and a white matter occupied by the axons, dendrites, and neuroglia only. The cerebrum and cerebellum may be readily recognized by the type and arrangement of cells, even in routine preparations, where nuclei are most prominent and cytoplasmic portions are not clearly outlined. However, special preparations are essential to properly demonstrate the nerve and neuroglial elements. In the cerebrum, the pyramidal cells occupy the cortical region and are clearly outlined together with supporting neuroglial elements in silver preparations, but in routine preparations the large characteristic nuclei indicate the pyramidal cells and the smaller surrounding ones indicate the location of the neuroglial cells. The invading connective tissue with an accompanying vascular supply can be observed in both types of preparations. In the cerebellar region, the Purkinje cells are diagnostic features in silver preparations but in routine ones their prominent cytons are located between an outer finely granular acidophilic layer with few nuclei (the *molecular layer*) and an inner region (the *granular layer*) rich in nuclei. The molecular layer contains the dendritic branches of the Purkinje cells, a few association neurons, and supporting neuroglial elements; the granular layer contains numerous association neurons, whose processes form a basketwork about the Purkinje cyton, and many neuroglial cells.

**Meninges.**—The brain and spinal cord are suspended within a cartilaginous or bony capsule by several connective tissue membranes derived from mesenchyme; their development is least among the lower classes and best represented in the mammals where the following divisions may be observed. (Fig. 54.) The outermost, the *dura mater*, is a thick fibroelastic sheath which attaches to the surrounding skeletal capsule of bone across a space, the *epidural*

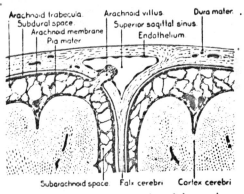

Fig. 89.—Schematic diagram of a coronal section of the meninges and the cerebral cortex, showing the relation of an arachnoid villus to the dural venous sinus. (Weed, Am. J. Anat.; courtesy of the Wistar Institute.)

*space*, in forms below mammals. A narrow cleft, the *subdural space*, contains fluid and separates the dura from an inner membrane, the *arachnoid*, which is a thinner connective tissue membrane. A few strands connect the arachnoid and dura but numerous delicate *arachnoid trabeculæ* extend across a *subarachnoid space* to join the innermost membrane, the *pia mater*, which immediately surrounds the brain or cord. The subarachnoid spaces among the arachnoid trabeculæ are filled with fluid, the *cerebrospinal fluid*, a term applied also to the fluid within the ventricles of the brain and the canal of the cord in the formation of which the ependyma is thought to play a part, particularly in the choroid plexus. Drainage of this fluid is effected through villi of the arachnoid extending into veins of the dura. Abnormal conditions in the central nervous system causing inflammation of the meninges (*meningitis*) lead to failure in drainage and accumulations of fluid in the ventricles of the brain which may cause hydrocephalic conditions. The composition of the cerebrospinal fluid and its content of blood cells are used in diagnoses of neural pathology.

# CHAPTER VII

## THE VASCULAR SYSTEM

As already observed in the study of blood and connective tissue, groups of mesenchyme cells begin the development of the vascular system in various regions of early embryos. The central cells of such an area become rounded and separated by a fluid intercellular plasma. The peripheral cells of these early blood islands unite to form an endothelial tube enclosing the free primitive blood cells and the plasma. The thin walls about these spaces are interconnected with others, so that gradually a network of endothelial-walled tubes forms the first capillary system. Some of the early capillaries develop into arteries, others into veins, and a tubular part is later differentiated into the heart. In the development of an artery and a vein, not only is an enlargement of the tube brought about, but there is also an addition of connective tissue and smooth muscle organized in sheaths about the endothelial lining.

### THE CAPILLARIES

These narrow, delicate, endothelial-walled tubes form a vast network in the fibroelastic connective tissue throughout the body. The diameter varies from a minimum of slightly more than the diameter of an erythrocyte to a diameter several times this. (Fig. 90.) In cross-sections of very small capillaries only one or two

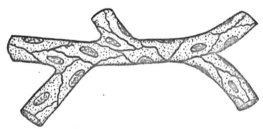

Fig. 90.—Diagram of part of a capillary network, showing endothelial cells.

endothelial cells form the wall, but in larger tubes a number of cells are present. The boundaries of the endothelial cells show as irregular black lines after silver nitrate treatment. The cells are elongated in the direction of the flow in the lumen and each cell has a nucleus in the center of a clear cytoplasm. In fixed preparations, the capillaries contract and in cross-sections the nuclei appear,

( 127 )

to protrude into the lumen, a condition not true of living capillaries where the bore is smooth and relatively constant.

Some investigators conclude that capillaries are intrinsically con-

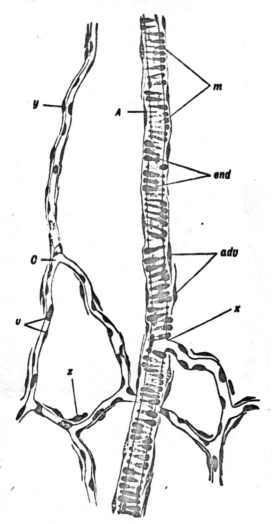

Fig. 91.—Small artery, *A*, and capillaries, *C*, from the mesentery of a rabbit; *m*, muscle cells in the media; *adv*, adventitia; *x*, origin of a capillary from the artery; *y*, pericyte; *z*, perivascular (adventitial) histiocyte; *end*, *v*, endothelial nuclei. 187X. (From Maximow & Bloom, courtesy of W. B. Saunders Co.).

tractile, and others believe that the contractility is due to certain flat irregular cells (adventitial cells, pericytes, perivascular cells) adjoining the endothelium. Another type of cell, the *Rouget cell*, with many processes has been observed encircling some capillaries

and has been demonstrated as contractile when stimulated electrically. (Fig. 92.) All the cellular elements of loose fibroelastic and reticular tissue are closely associated with capillaries so these encircling elements may be derived from fibroblasts or reticular cells and some are probably primitive smooth muscle cells. Another interpretation of change in diameter of capillary lumens places the controlling factor in the rate and volume of blood passed to them by arterioles with contractile muscular walls. Smooth muscle cells organized as motor units under nerve control have been demonstrated in arterial capillaries.

It is well known that plasma and leukocytes from the blood stream pass out into tissue spaces through the thin capillary wall and also that wastes in fluid form and secretions pass from tissue spaces into the stream within the capillary. Some investigators claim that the exchange is facilitated by minute openings where adjacent cells meet, but the endothelial wall is normally unbroken. The chemistry and physics of passage of fluids and white cells from the capillary and back into it are incompletely known but changes in the intercellular cement have been shown to play a part.

Usually the blood-vascular system of a vertebrate is regarded as a closed system in that the erythrocytes do not normally leave it. In every other respect it is an open system. There is a constant passage of digested materials from the intestinal tract through the tissue fluid into capillaries and lymphatics in the folds or villi where they lie near the epithelium. Oxygen diffuses through the wall of the alveoli of the lung into tissue fluid and is taken up by erythrocytes in capillaries adjacent to the air sac wall. Wastes of metabolism also pass from tissue juice into capillaries through the endothelial membranes. The composition of *sinusoids* associated with capillaries in certain regions has already been described in the consideration of blood and lymph formation.

The arrangement of the capillary network is determined to a considerable degree by the disposition of the cells or tissue organization supplied. Capillaries supplying skeletal muscles are long tubules between adjacent muscle fibers and are connected laterally. In the kidney there is a rich capillary network between adjacent urinferous tubules. In each villus of the small intestine there is a basketwork of capillaries within the epithelial wall. Secretory vesicles of the thyroid gland are enclosed in delicate connective tissue in which lies a network of capillaries. The richness of the capillary network is related to the functional activity of the organ supplied. Where great functional activity of the organ is constant, the meshwork is close and its capillaries are large. A good illustra-

9

tion of this is seen in the capillary network about the alveoli of the lung and the tubules of the kidney. The capillary system of the liver and spleen is sinusoidal and will be described when considering these organs. Healing of tissue lesions may involve development of new capillaries and of small arterioles and venules. In case such structures form, they are initiated as buds from existing capillaries.

An examination of the circulation in the web between the toes of the frog's foot reveals a rapidly flowing stream of blood cells in the small arterial branches and a much slower streaming in the network of capillaries. Erythrocytes are carried along like leaves in a stream, some having to bend in making a turn from one channel into another. In some capillaries the flow may be interrupted and then resumed while in others it is continuous. The slow flow through capillaries permits diffusion of food and oxygen out into the tissue spaces and a return of organic wastes to the blood stream from the tissues. As the capillaries unite to form small veins, the speed of the current increases again, but is not as rapid as in the corresponding arteries.

Functional demands often result in the formation of small new temporary capillaries which may then differentiate into larger permanent vessels by increase in their endothelial wall and addition of connective tissue and muscle coats from surrounding fibroblasts and mesenchymal or reticular cells in the same manner that vessels develop embryologically. In capillaries whose flow is interrupted the lumen decreases and if such interruption is permanent the vessel collapses and degenerates.

Foreign particles, such as carbon and carmine, introduced into the blood stream have been demonstrated sticking to the endothelial walls of capillaries before being phagocytosed by histiocytes and reticular cells (macrophages) closely surrounding the endothelium. Presumably the accumulation of foreign particles stimulates a temporary passage of material between endothelial cells to the phagocytes immediately adjoining, since the endothelial cells are not actively phagocytic. Leukocytes, especially heterophils and lymphocytes, may be demonstrated in living tissues migrating between endothelial cells under stimulus of physical irritation or conditions of inflammation. Red cells normally remain within the endothelial membranes except in the sinusoids of certain regions and following injuries which effect changes in the endothelial membranes that permit their passage into surrounding tissues. The passage of components of the plasma and tissue juice from and to capillaries is considered as effected through the intercellular cement as well as through the cells of the endothelial membrane.

The capillaries may be considered as the equivalents of the secretory end-pieces of glands while the arteries and veins function merely as duct systems to and from them and as regulators of blood flow.

## THE ARTERIES

The transition from capillaries to arteries is marked by the gradual appearance of smooth muscle and fibroelastic connective

tissue in a vessel wall until three coats are usually present: an inner, *tunica intima;* a middle, *tunica media;* and an external, *tunica externa,* or *adventitia.* (Fig. 95.) The intima is composed of the endothelial lining with a slight amount of reticular and fibro-elastic connective tissue. The media is characterized by smooth

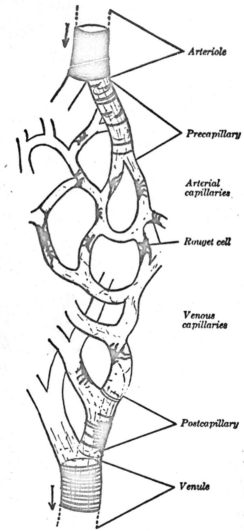

Arteriole

Precapillary

Arterial capillaries

Rouget cell

Venous capillaries

Postcapillary

Venule

FIG. 92.—Diagram of transition from an arteriole to a venule. (Cowdry's Textbook of Histology.)

muscle associated with varying amounts of fibroelastic connective tissue. The adventitia is chiefly fibroelastic connective tissue. Arteries are usually divided into three groups on the basis of size

and composition of the media.   The large or elastic arteries include
the aorta, pulmonary arteries, carotids, and a few others with a
similar structure.   The medium-sized, or muscular, arteries include
other arteries named by anatomists; these vessels agree in structure,
although they vary in size.   To the small arteries belong a great
number that have no special names.   Two more groups might be
added, namely, arterioles and precapillary arterioles.   Although the
composition of all these groups varies, there is a gradation of the
types of construction all along the line, as can be understood best
by studying the smallest arteries first.

**Small Arteries.**—The scattered fibroblasts, reticular cells and
mesenchymal cells adjoining a capillary become more numerous and

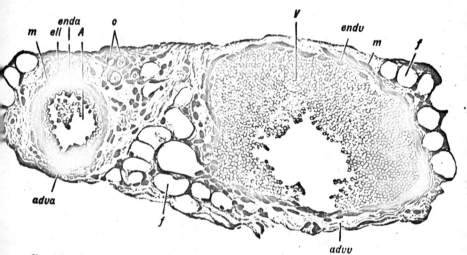

Fig. 93.—Cross section through a small artery (*A*) and its accompanying vein (*V*)
from the submucosa of a human intestine; *adva* and *advv*, Adventitia of the artery
and vein; *c*, cross sections of capillaries; *enda* and *endv*, endothelium of the artery
and vein; *eli*, elastica interna; *m*, muscle cells of the media; *f*, fat cells in the loose
connective tissue. 187 X. (A.A.M.). (From Maximow & Bloom, courtesy of W. B.
Saunders Co.).

are organized into a delicate connective tissue sheath as the lumen
increases.   When the flow becomes continuous and also increased
in volume the elements of the connective tissue sheath become
supplemented by developing smooth muscle cells which encircle the
vessel.   The smallest branches adjacent to capillaries have a small
amount of connective tissue supporting isolated smooth muscle cells
outside the endothelium.   These are *pre-capillary arterioles* and are
branches of larger *arterioles* which have a definite smooth muscle
sheath surrounded by a sheath of fibroelastic tissue.   The small
arteries have thick walls in comparison with the size of the lumen;

the intima has a thin subendothelial layer of fibroelastic connective tissue separated from the media by an *internal elastic lamina,* a membrane of elastic fibers. The media is composed mainly of smooth muscle cells interspersed with elastic connective tissue. (Fig. 93.) The adventitia is composed of fibroelastic tissue and is usually not as thick as the media but much thicker than the intima. With the addition of the muscle tissue the vessels take an active part in controlling distribution of blood by contraction and decrease of vessel lumen and blood volume, or relaxation with accompanying increase in lumen and volume of blood flow.

Fig. 94.—A photograph of a medium or muscular artery of the cat, showing internal and external elastic membranes outlining the muscular and elastic media. 16 mm. obj. and 5× oc.

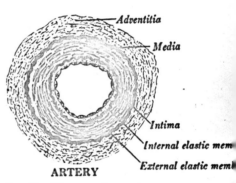

ARTERY

Fig. 95.—Diagram of muscular artery.

**Medium-sized or Muscular Arteries.**—These are larger than the preceding vessels and the predominant tissue of the media is smooth muscle. In the larger branches the proportion of elastic fibers in the media increases. The intima is often poorly preserved, the endothelial cells being indicated by their nuclei which protrude into the lumen. The subendothelial connective tissue is generally inconspicuous but is better seen in the larger vessels of this class. The internal elastic membrane appears as a clear, wavy line and the thick media shows numerous layers of smooth muscle separated by connective tissue. In larger vessels, elastic fibers appear more prominently in the media and an *external elastic membrane* adjoins the adventitia which is as thick as the media or may be thicker, with elastic fibers becoming more numerous toward the media. (Fig. 95.)

**Large or Elastic Arteries.**—These vessels, such as the aorta and the pulmonary arteries, have a relatively thick wall which appears thin in view of the large size of the lumen. When compared with a

medium-sized artery the muscle has decreased in amount and there
is a greater supply of elastic fibers. The intima may be thicker,
especially in older animals, due to the presence of more subendothelial connective tissue. The internal elastic lamina is not evident
and in the media are many layers of fenestrated elastic membranes
which are seen best when orcein or resorcin fuchsin is used as a
stain. (Fig. 96.) Alternating with the elastic tissue are smooth

Fig. 96.—Aorta of the dog,
showing the heavy elastic
media and fibrous adventitia.
Photo-micrograph. 32 mm.
and 5× oc.

muscle and collagenous fibers. The
media is much thicker than the adventitia which is composed of fibroelastic
tissue. At the origin of the aorta and
pulmonary arteries from the heart of
mammals, the walls may be composed
mainly of cardiac muscle. The fibroelastic tissue forming the outer coat of
the adventitia in all vessels merges with
the connective tissue supporting the
vessel.

The main function of arteries is to
conduct blood from the heart to the
capillaries. The contraction of ventricles forces blood into the large arteries
originating from them, and these vessels
already filled with blood are distended by the added supply. When
the force of ventricular contraction is spent, the fluid tends to return
to the ventricles but is prevented by the closing of the valves at
their entrance. Then the distended elastic walls contract as the
stretched elastic tissue recoils. The blood is thus sent on into the
medium-sized arteries where the smooth muscle takes a part in
regulating the volume and rate of flow to the smaller vessels.

A common condition among old or diseased mammals is the presence of
*arteriosclerosis* where arteries may exhibit accumulations of fat and fibrous
elements with subsequent calcium deposits in the intima so that the lumen
is partially obstructed; other arteries show accumulation of mucoproteins
followed by deposits of calcium in the fibrous elements of the media so that
a rigid tube of limited caliber may result.

### THE VEINS

Passing from a capillary toward the heart, there are postcapil-
laries, venules, small veins, medium-sized veins, and large veins,
showing varying structural additions and modifications. Outside
the endothelial lining smooth muscle and fibroelastic connective
tissue form the added tissue in the wall of veins, but there is such
a great variation in structure that each vein must be studied for its

particular type of organization. On the whole, however, it can be said that the wall of any vein is thinner than that of its accompanying artery, and consequently veins often appear collapsed in microscopic preparations. (Fig. 93.) Elastic laminæ are not usually present and in many cases it is difficult to distinguish all three coats. The structure seems to be influenced by gravitational difficulties so there appears to be more muscle in veins of the extremities than in those nearer the heart.

Veins differ from arteries in that they possess valves which are pocket-like extensions of the endothelium with a thin core of intimal

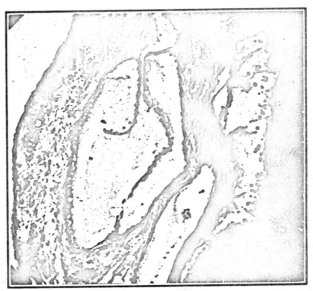

Fig. 97.—A section through the capsule and cortex of a lymph node of the dog to show a valve in an afferent lymph vessel. Photomicrograph. 4 mm. obj. and 5× oc.

connective tissue. Such valves open toward the heart so that a backward flow of blood is prevented. In the connective tissue that supports an artery there is usually a companion vein which has a greater volume and usually appears collapsed in microscopic preparations. In the adventitia of arteries and veins, but not in arterioles and venules, there occur blood-vessels called *vasa vasorum*, which provide a capillary network for the medial and adventitial coats but the intima is believed to receive its supply by diffusion through the endothelium of the vessel lumen. Similarly a nerve supply, known as the *nervi vasorum*, is present. The outer coat of the larger arteries and veins supports a system of small lymph vessels also.

## THE LYMPH VESSELS

In general, these vessels resemble veins in structure but have thinner walls and more valves. (Fig. 97.) Lymph capillaries are larger than blood capillaries, are thin walled, and not commonly seen in ordinary preparations. When preserved uncollapsed, the smaller lymphatics appear as endothelial-lined spaces in loose fibro-elastic connective tissues. In the largest lymphatics, three coats may be differentiated. These vessels are larger than the veins whose distribution they parallel, but their walls of connective tissue with scattered smooth muscle cells collapse and are not prominent in preparations of routine material but may be demonstrated by injected material. Lymphatic vessels may be distinguished from blood-vessels in routine preparations by their content of lightly acidophilic finely granular material (the precipitated plasma elements), the presence of lymphocytes, and absence of red cells.

# CHAPTER VIII

## THE LYMPHATIC SYSTEM

THE lymph vessels develop in a manner similar to, if not as outgrowths of the embryonic venous system. In either case a system of closed endothelial tubes is formed which develops valves and closely parallels the veins in their distribution. According to Drinker and Field, "the lymph capillaries are complete vessels, whose content is identical with the fluid outside them. The barrier presented by their walls is extremely slight. It serves to guide their contents into heavier walled channels from which escape is difficult, and by means of which return to the blood is accomplished. Capillary lymph and tissue fluid are thus considered to exist in a common reservoir, and to this blood capillaries make addition of fluid and by resorption withdraw it." In the formation of the larger vessels, mesenchyme cells surrounding the endothelium develop a connective tissue wall in which some smooth muscle also differentiates.

The smallest blindly ending divisions of these vessels, the lymph capillaries, collect fluid from spaces between the fibers and cells of connective tissue. This fluid passes from the capillaries into the smallest lymph vessels, thence into larger and larger branches, which ultimately join the venous system in the region of the heart. A rhythmic contractivity has been observed beginning with certain bulbous capillaries and occurring in the valve region of larger vessels. Lymph resembles the blood in having a plasma containing free cells, the lymphocytes, but normally lacks erythrocytes and granulocytes.

At intervals along the developing lymphatic system, active mesenchymal elements develop into lymphoid organs in which lymphocytes are produced and are added to the colorless, fluid lymph. Lymphoid organizations are especially well developed in mammals where lymphocyte production is carried on apart from the production of other myeloid cells. Among birds and reptiles, and in the amphibians to a lesser extent, lymphocytes are formed in lymph nodules scattered in various parts of the body, but the spleen is the major lymph organ in these forms. In mammals, particularly, there is a variety of organizations all characterized by the presence of one or more lymph nodules.

Numbers of lymphocytes may migrate into and accumulate in

the subepithelial connective tissue of the digestive tract and other ducts or fibroelastic tissue generally.

## THE LYMPH NODULE

The nodule is composed of an oval or round, densely packed mass of lymphocytes supported in a reticulum of connective tissue. Nodules vary in size and may be located singly or grouped in the subepithelial connective tissue along the extent of the digestive and respiratory tract. Each nodule has a connective tissue framework within whose meshes are lymphocytes in various stages of development. A lighter central area is frequently evident in a nodule, this region is called the *germinal center* and is occupied by

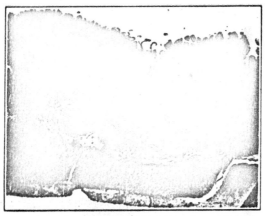

Fig. 98.—A group of nodules (Peyer's patch) below the epithelium of the ileum of the dog. Photomicrograph. 32 mm. obj. and 5× oc.

large lymphocytes, the *lymphoblasts*, which are mitotically active and give rise to new smaller lymphocytes that accumulate toward the periphery of the nodule. Periods of activity may be followed by inactive periods during which most cells differentiate into small lymphocytes and a uniform mass appears in sections of such nodules. The destiny of the lymphocytes is varied, as observed in hemopoiesis, and their potential development is conditioned by their environment. Most become extravascular again after a short period following their migration into lymph or blood capillaries adjoining the nodule and develop into the larger lymphoblast or hemocytoblast progenitor. Some migrate through the epithelium of the gut or other ducts and are lost.

*Peyer's Patches.*—In the ileum of mammals, near its junction with the large intestine, are groupings of many nodules, called Peyer's patches. (Fig. 98.) Some of these extend to the epithe-

lium of the intestinal lumen and also into the submucosal coat. Other similar collections of nodules occur in the connective tissue adjoining the epithelium of the cecum and vermiform appendix.

*Tonsils.*—In mammals, several prominent aggregations of lymphoid nodules, known as tonsils, may be found in the pharynx. They differ in location but have a similar organization. A group composing the *faucial* or *palatine tonsils* is located on each side of the pharyngeal cavity between the pillars of the fauces. The *lingual tonsil* is located beneath the non-papillated epithelium of the upper surface of the tongue posterior to the foramen cecum.

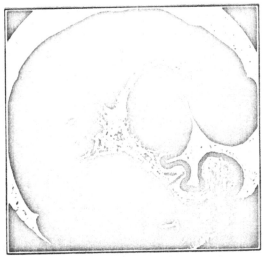

FIG. 99.—Tonsil of the dog   The nodules are closely packed below a stratified squamous epithelium.   Photomicrograph.   32 mm. obj. and 5× oc.

Another group, composing the *pharyngeal tonsil* (these and palatines absent in mouse and rat), lies just below the epithelium in the upper posterior face of the pharynx near the entrance of each Eustachian tube. In all these structures, groups of nodules lie below a stratified epithelial membrane. (Fig. 99.)

Scattered *crypts*, or pits, extend down into the tonsilar tissue from the epithelial surface as shallow pockets, or longer and blindly ending branching ducts, lined by stratified squamous epithelium. The epithelium rests upon a fibroelastic connective tissue continuous with similar tissue forming the coarser framework for the nodules. The lymph nodules are sometimes clearly separated, but may have diffuse lymphoid tissue connecting them due to invasion of the surrounding connective tissue by lymphocytes produced in the nodules. A fine network of reticular connective tissue extends

through the nodules and between them.   Below the lymphoid mass
is a dense fibroelastic connective tissue which merges with similar
tissue associated with the skeletal muscles of the neck.   Tonsil
tissue gives rise to a supply of lymphocytes, many of which may be
lost by passing through the epithelial membrane; others may enter
capillaries associated with the reticulum.   The tonsils commonly
atrophy but may become hypertrophied under conditions of infection.   Their incomplete removal is often followed by regeneration
of lymphoid tissue in the same locality.

## THE LYMPH NODES

The lymphoid structures so far studied are associated with the
lymph capillaries, *i. e.*, they are situated near the beginning of
lymph vessels.   A more elaborate structure, the *lymph node*, or

Fig. 100.—Mesenteric lymph node of the gray squirrel, showing dense cortical
region and lighter medulla.   The connective tissue of the capsule extends into the
medulla at the hilum and forms trabeculæ in the cortex.   Photomicrograph.   32 mm.
obj. and 5× oc.

*lymph gland*, is widely distributed in mammals as an oval or bean-
shaped mass associated with the larger lymph vessels.   Lymph
enters the node by one or more afferent lymph vessels and leaves
by an efferent lymphatic.   Lymph nodes vary in size from a few
millimeters in length to 2 centimeters or more.   They are also
indefinite in number, since they may degenerate or new nodes may
form in the loose fibroelastic connective tissue of certain regions.
Lymph nodes are prominent in the mesentery near the junction of ·
the small with the large intestine and also in the connective tissue
in the region of the axilla and the groin.   (Fig. 100.)

Each node is invested with a capsule of fibroelastic connective
tissue in which smooth muscle cells are usually scattered.   The
capsular tissue is more evident at the *hilum*, or concave depression,

where the efferent lymph vessel, an artery, vein, and nerves are connected with the node. In examinations of stained preparations of mammalian nodes, two regions, an outer *cortex* and an inner *medulla,* usually stand out clearly. (Figs. 100 and 101.)

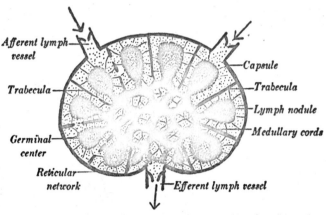

Afferent lymph vessel — Trabecula — Germinal center — Reticular network — Capsule — Trabecula — Lymph nodule — Medullary cords — Efferent lymph vessel

Fig. 101.—Diagram showing structural plan of a lymph node. The cortex in the outer zone containing lymph nodules. The medulla is the central region with cords of lymphocytes.

**Cortex.**—Partitions, or *trabeculæ,* of fibroelastic connective tissue extend from the capsule into the medulla, thus dividing the cortex roughly into compartments. In these compartments are lymphoid nodules usually composed of oval or pyriform masses of lymphocytes. Extending from the coarser connective tissue framework is a finer network of reticular cells and fibers in whose meshes the lymphocytes are held. The reticular cells extend between the nodules and trabeculæ and capsule to form *cortical sinuses.* Afferent lymph vessels entering the capsules break into capillaries connecting with these sinuses through which the inflowing lymph passes into the medulla. The lymphocytes produced in the nodules move through the reticulum into the cortical lymph sinuses through which lymph is slowly passing toward the medulla. The size of the germinal centers varies with the degree of mitotic activity in them, the active nodules having more marked germinal centers. The endothelial lining of the afferent lymph vessels entering the cortex is considered as continuing with reticular cells, here called *littoral cells,* which line the sinuses. (Fig. 102.) Many of these littoral cells become macrophages and remove foreign elements from the lymph as it filters through the sinuses.

**Medulla.**—The internal ends of the fibroelastic trabeculæ form a coarse network between which extends the reticulum of argyrophil fibers and reticular cells. Clustered along the coarser connective tissue network are rodlike masses of lymphoid cells known as *medullary cords*. Between them are interconnecting spaces, the *medullary sinuses*, with which the cortical sinuses are continuous. The medullary sinuses are composed of the same reticular cells found in the cortical sinuses and these cells likewise are capable of ingesting foreign elements. There is a slow distribution or circula-

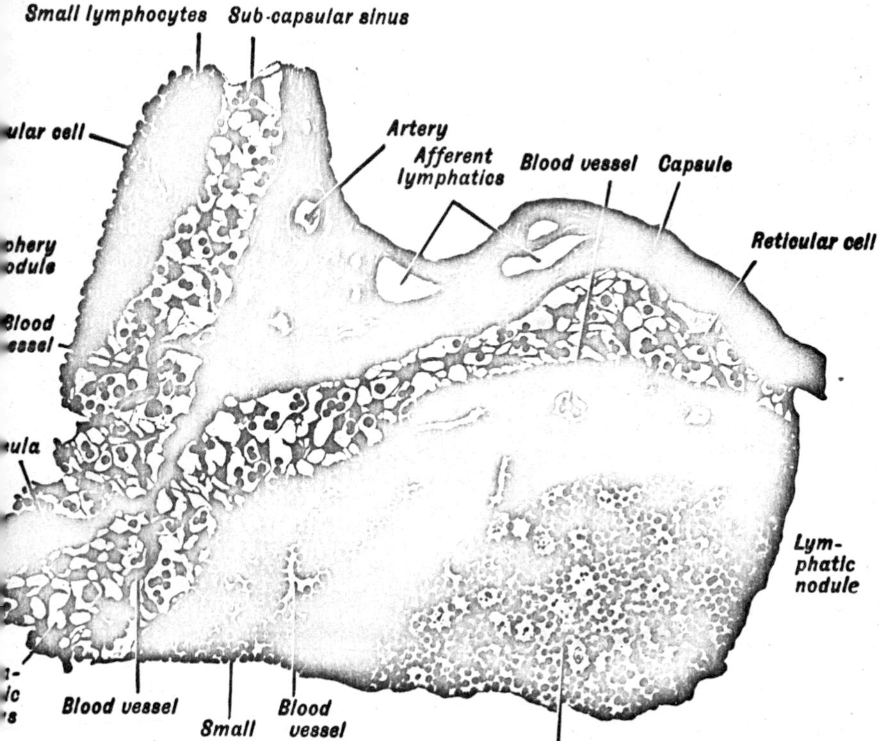

*Small lymphocytes*    *Sub-capsular sinus*

*ular cell*

*Artery*
*Afferent lymphatics*    *Blood vessel*    *Capsule*

*chery odule*

*Reticular cell*

*Blood essel*

*ula*

*Lymphatic nodule*

*Blood vessel*    *Blood vessel*
*Small lymphocytes*

*Lymphocytopoietic center*

FIG. 102.—Portion of cortex of a lymph node of a dog. Hematoxylin-eosin-azure stain. 87 X. (A.A.M.). From Maximow & Bloom, courtesy of W. B. Saunders Co.).

tion of lymph from the lymph vessels at the cortex through the sinuses into the efferent lymph vessels at the hilum. During this passage through the sinuses a number of lymphocytes are added so that lymph leaving the node is richer in cells than when it entered.

Three varieties of lymphocytes (small, medium, and large) have been distinguished in the node, but by far the greater number are the small variety. When mitotic activity ceases the germinal center is filled with lymphocytes of the small variety similar to those in the peripheral portion of the nodule. Then proliferation ceases for

a time and during this inactive period the nodule has a uniform appearance throughout. With renewal of activity the central cells differentiate into actively mitotic large cells (lymphoblasts) and a lightly staining germinal center is again evident in sections. Another function has been attributed to the nodes, namely the destruction of old lymphocytes entering by way of the lymph or vascular supply.

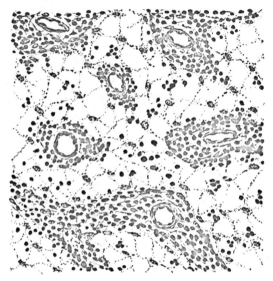

Fig. 103.—Drawing from a section through the medulla of the lymph node of the dog, showing the reticular (littoral) cells of the sinuses adjoining the medullary cords packed with lymphocytes and containing a vascular supply.

Recent experiments give support to the theory that the nodules may also be the site where lymphocytes in process of dissolution are phagocytosed by reticular cells and further that the lymphocytes play a part in antibody formation.

The artery entering at the hilum branches throughout the fibro-elastic connective tissue skeleton, breaking up into capillaries which connect with venules and the latter eventually with the vein or veins which leave from the hilum. Small arterioles in trabeculæ give rise to a capillary net which surrounds the nodules. So far as erythrocytes are concerned, they remain within the vascular system in the node, *i. e.*, there are normally no free red blood cells in the sinuses. Trabeculæ appear to be better developed in peripheral lymph nodes, such as those in the axilla or groin. Nodes within the body cavity have relatively greater medullary regions. Trabeculæ of small nodes are difficult to locate, and in some nodes the cortex is massed chiefly at one end while the medulla is concentrated at the other.

**Hemolymph Nodes.**—Although the lymph node appears limited to mammals, somewhat modified structures, called hemolymph nodes or glands, are found in mammals and birds. In these lymphoid organizations, which structurally resemble the lymph nodes, blood instead of lymph is distributed in the cortex from arterial capillaries and filters through sinuses to be collected by efferent veins. Lymph vessels are limited to the scanty trabecular tissue.

### THE SPLEEN

The spleen is the largest single lymph gland in all forms, but contains no lymph sinuses. It is similar to hemolymph nodes, which are often called accessory spleens, in being associated with the blood-vascular system instead of lymphatics. Its shape and location varies in different vertebrates; among the fishes it may be an irregular mass closely associated with the stomach and intestinal wall; in others, as in the frog, it occurs as a spherical mass in the mesentery supporting the intestine; among the mammals it is a flattened structure near the stomach.

The spleen is surrounded with a capsule of fibroelastic connective tissue and smooth muscle covered with mesothelium, but there is no division into a distinct cortex and medulla. Trabeculæ of connective tissue and smooth muscle extend from the capsule to form a coarse internal framework. A reticulum like that in the nodes extends between the trabeculæ and forms the inner support for the lymphoid tissue, and myeloid tissue when present. The larger arteries and veins supplying the spleen are carried by the trabeculæ.

Examination of slices of fresh mammalian or avian spleen reveals small, whitish masses, the *white pulp*, distributed throughout a red tissue. The white pulp is composed of lymph nodules comparable with those already described in the lymph node but here they form a sheath about arteries. (Fig. 104.) Within each is one or two branches of a small artery, usually eccentric; a feature which serves to identify spleens so organized. The *red pulp* is composed of a reticular network, diffuse lymphoid tissue, and sinusoids filled with blood.

The microscopic structure of a mammalian spleen is clarified by an understanding of the distribution of blood-vessels in it. The main splenic artery and splenic vein enter at the hilum and each vessel divides into branches which are supported by the branching trabeculæ. As the trabeculæ divide, each supports a branch of an artery and an accompanying vein. Small arterial branches leave the trabecular tissue and enter the lymphoid tissue. (Fig. 105.)

The adventitia of such arteries has loose fibroelastic connective tissue in which lymphocytes become aggregated into rodlike or oval masses, the *splenic nodules*. The branches of these small arteries emerge into the red pulp, where they divide into a group of short vessels, the *penicilli*, which have a *pulp*, a *sheathed*, and a *terminal* region. The tunica media of the first division is rich in smooth

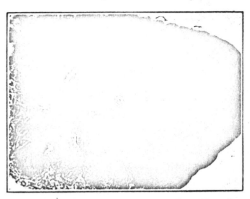

Fig. 104.—Spleen of the woodchuck, showing a member of lymph nodules scattered through the diffuse red pulp. The nodules have light germinal centers and arterial branches appear in their peripheral portion as small, open, white areas. Photomicrograph. 32 mm. obj. and 5× oc.

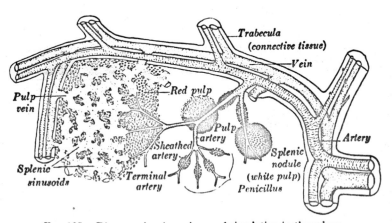

Fig. 105.—Diagram showing scheme of circulation in the spleen.

muscle and is embedded in red pulp; the sheathed portion is devoid of muscle and has a narrow lumen surrounded by connective tissue infiltrated with the lymphocytes and connected with the reticulum of the red pulp; the terminal portion ends as an endothelial tube which unites with the peculiar sinusoids in the red pulp. (Fig. 107.)

10

The sinusoids usually have a wide irregular lumen in contrast to the smaller and uniform caliber of the common capillary. Furthermore, the endothelial cells lining the capillaries become associated with flattened reticular cells which line the sinusoids. Among the reticular cells of the sinusoidal wall are regions where these cells associate with reticular cells forming a network through the red pulp. A loose open framework of reticular cells and fibers thus receives blood from the arterial capillaries before it leaves through sinusoids which join complete endothelial-walled venous capillaries. The venous capillaries continue into venules and veins carrying the blood back into the trabeculæ and out of the spleen. (Fig. 106.)

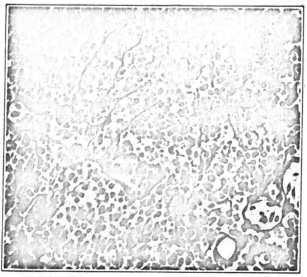

Fig. 106.—Photograph of spleen of Necturus, showing the vascular distribution. the vessel on the left is shown with several branches opening out into sinusoids; Mallory stain. 4 mm. obj. and 5× oc.

The sheathed portions of the penicilli, where the lumen is small, slow down the blood issuing from the small arteries to the splenic sinusoids. The sheathed arteries may act as valves, preventing backward flow of blood. In the red pulp of the spleen and of hemal nodes, openings in the blood vascular system may occur. If so, cells in the blood may pass through the slits in the sinusoid wall into the red pulp proper and cells in the red pulp may pass into the blood stream by way of the sinusoid. In the reticulum and diffuse lymphoid tissue of the red pulp there are the same red and white cells found in the circulating blood. The lymphocytes produced in the nodules enter the reticulum of the red pulp and thus may

pass directly into the blood stream. Also in the red pulp are
numerous giant cells, macrophages presumably derived from reticular cells in which phagocytic activity is pronounced. Foreign elements and disintegrating blood cells are ingested by these cells.
In certain pathological conditions so many red cells are disintegrating and so many are being ingested by macrophages that the
red pulp acquires a brown color.

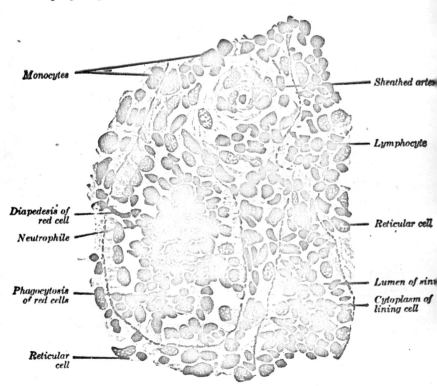

Fig. 107.—Pulp of spleen. × 750. (Redrawn and modified from Maximow-
Bloom's Histology, courtesy of W. B. Saunders Company.)

In embryonic mammals and in lower vertebrates the spleen is
hemopoietic, and although lymphocyte production may still be
localized in nodules these are not so distinctly separated from the
surrounding reticulum in which myeloid elements are packed. Conditions resemble those found in the bone-marrow and the same
question of inter- (extra-) or intravascular origin of cells arises.
Although erythrocytes are produced in the spleen of the embryo
mammal, this power is later transferred to the red marrow of bones.
However, in certain pathological conditions, erythroblasts and the

three types of myelocytes can be found in the spleen, showing that in such cases production of erythrocytes and granulocytes can again occur here.

Some investigators support an open arrangement for this portion of the vascular system—open to the extent that blood with its cells can pass freely, though sluggishly, into diffuse reticular tissue of the red pulp. The splenic sinusoids join complete venous capillaries, which continue into small venules projecting through the red pulp to enter the trabeculæ. In the spleen, blood can leave the vessels and mingle with surrounding cells without clotting. Blood-pressure is very low here, and periodic pulsations of the entire spleen have been observed; a periodic contraction forcing blood from the pulp into the sinuses and veins is followed by a dilatation. The smooth muscle in the capsule and trabeculæ effects this contraction. The connective tissue of the capsule limits the dilatation or the accumulation of too much blood as the contraction of the smooth muscle imparts a gentle pressure forcing the blood back into the veins. The absence of cellular injury when blood enters the red pulp from the sinusoids apparently accounts for the failure of clotting of such extravascular blood. Other investigators support a closed system throughout the vascular network, even in the spleen, and this interpretation requires an extremely permeable sinusoidal wall through which various cells move relatively freely.

## THE THYMUS

The thymus occurs throughout the vertebrate groups as a variable structure beginning as invaginations of the epithelium of the gill clefts or pouches, involving both ectoderm and endoderm, that invade the underlying mesenchyme. In most forms the associated mesenchymal elements develop a lymphoid tissue about the early epithelial elements which compose the primitive medulla. This lymphoid tissue becomes more prominent among reptiles, birds and mammals. The epithelial tissue is usually cut off from the gill pouches during embryonic development. In the lower forms the thymus may remain as a varying number of small masses associated with the gill pouches. (Fig. 121.) In the mammals a common lobulated mass is usually formed and lies along the lower part of the esophagus and extends into the thorax over the pericardium.

In general, a thin-walled capsule of fibroelastic connective tissue surrounds the entire gland and extensions of it carrying a vascular supply divide the gland into small lobules. (Fig. 108.) Under the microscope each lobule appears to be a mass of lymphocytes with a darkly staining peripheral cortex of more dense cells and a central diffuse medulla composed of a fibroelastic and reticular framework containing a vascular supply and few lymphocytes. The medullary portions of adjacent lobules connect with each other. At the border between cortex and medulla there is an abrupt change to the diffuse

distribution of cells in the medulla. Each lobule has a network of reticular cells and fibers continuous with the coarse framework of loose fibroelastic connective tissue. The lymphoid cells are considered by some not to be typical lymphocytes, and as derivatives from embryonic endoderm are differentiated as *thymocytes*. However, their appearance and reactions are so similar that the usual view is that they are lymphocytes derived from mesenchymal elements that migrated into this region.

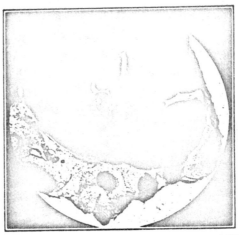

FIG. 108.—Photograph of a section through a portion of a child's thymus gland. Several lobules are shown with cortex and medulla. Note connection of the medullary portions of some adjacent lobules. 32 mm. obj. and 5× oc.

Some of the reticular cells forming a network through the tissue are considered as derivatives of mesoderm into which the epithelial thymic invagination extended and appear very similar to those found in other locations. Other cells forming a cytoreticulum in the medulla appear to be derived from the early epithelial tissue and react differently than true reticular cells.

In the medulla of many lobules, fusiform cells are concentrically arranged to form smaller cell masses known as *Hassall's corpuscles.* In the center of some there may be deposits of calcium and small cysts surrounded by flattened connective tissue cells. The significance of these bodies is debated but they have no features indicative of secretory activity and appear more like regions of degeneration.

The thymus differs from other lymph organs in that it has no nodules and no lymph sinuses.

The thymus may begin to degenerate in the adult mammal, although there is considerable individual variation in the extent to which such involution has proceeded at particular ages. The lymphoid tissue becomes progressively less prominent, and connective tissue containing fat cells occupies much of the structure.

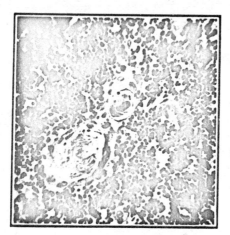

F₁ᴀ. 109.—A photograph of several small Hassall's corpuscles in the thymus of a woodchuck.    4 mm. obj. and 5× oc.

Despite many endeavors to discover the exact function of the thymus, there are as yet no clear-cut results, other than production of small lymphocytes as occurs in other lymphatic structures.

Recent experiments with birds present some evidence for the production of a hormone, *thymovidin*, associated with formation of the albumin and shell of the egg.

# CHAPTER IX

## THE INTEGUMENT

THE covering of the vertebrate body, the integument, is composed of the skin and the various derivatives such as the scales, feathers, hairs, and glands. Since the integument is in direct contact with the environment it is modified for a variety of functions such as protection from injury, prevention of loss of body fluids, resistance to entrance of injurious substances, assistance in the elimination of certain wastes and reception of sensory stimuli leading to adjustment to external conditions. In all vertebrates the skin is divided into two regions, an outer *epidermis* composed of stratified epithelium, and an underlying region of connective tissue, the *dermis* or *corium*.

**Epidermis.**—The epidermis is derived from embryonic ectoderm and is usually divisible into at least two regions. The layer or layers of cells immediately adjoining the corium composes the *stratum germinativum*, or *Malpighian layer*. Cells of this region are in contact with the nutritive fluids carried in the corium, and by growth and division they give rise to new cells that are gradually pushed outward to form a superficial second region, the *stratum corneum*, composed of one or more than one layer of dead or dying cells. As the cells of the stratum corneum are worn away, other cells are added from the stratum germinativum. Invaginations of the stratum germinativum give rise to glands and are involved in or solely responsible for such derivatives as the scales, hair, and feathers. The composition of the epidermis varies not only in different animals but in different regions of the same individual.

**Dermis (Corium).**—The dermis is derived from mesenchyme and differentiates into two regions. The *stratum vasculare* (or *spongiosum*) immediately adjoining the epidermis is composed of reticular and loosely organized vascular fibroelastic tissue which may thrust papillæ, *dermal papillæ*, into the epidermis. Chromatophores when present occur most abundantly in this region below the epidermis. The deeper region, the *stratum compactum*, is composed of dense interlacing fibrous elements mainly paralleling the surface.

The dermis is continuous with a region of looser fibroelastic connective tissue, the *subcutis* or *tela subjunctiva*, which connects the integument with underlying tissues of the body. Adipose tissue appears in relatively large amounts in the subcutaneous connective tissue of most vertebrates. There are marked variations in the details of skin structures in the different classes of animals but this general composition is true for all.

## INTEGUMENT OF FISHES

The epidermis of a fish is usually composed of a stratified squamous epithelium with numerous glandular cells scattered through the intermediate layers. These glandular cells, which may form a very prominent layer in some scaleless fish, secrete a mucus which forms a protective film over the skin surface. The formation of a cuticle, which is characteristic of Amphioxus and an essential element in the exoskeleton of many invertebrates, is of limited occurrence among vertebrates. A basal cuticle does occur and gives rise to the enamel of the teeth and placoid scales. Invagination of the germinativum gives rise to the lateral line and the associated neuroepithelial bodies supplied by sensory nerves.

The dermis is divided into a narrow stratum vasculare of fibroelastic tissue with abundant chromatophores adjoining the epidermis; and a broad stratum compactum of dense fibrous tissue with interlacing bundles of collagenous fibers.

The subcutis is composed of loosely organized fibroelastic tissue which is continuous with the septa between segments and bundles of skeletal muscle.

**Scales.**—Although some fish have integuments composed of an epidermis and dermis fitting the general description above, the majority have additional structures, the scales, derived from elements of one or both of these regions. The four anatomically separated scale types (*placoid, ganoid, ctenoid, cycloid*) have but two histological types of derivation. One type, represented by the placoid, differentiates the scale from elements contributed by both epidermis and dermis; the other, represented by the ganoid, ctenoid and cycloid, produces the scale from dermal elements alone.

**Placoid Scales.**—Among the Elasmobranchs, as represented by the dogfish, a multiplication of dermal fibroblasts occurs at intervals immediately adjoining the epidermis and small papillæ are formed. Each papilla projects above the level of the corium and carries the covering columnar cells of the germinativum into the overlying layers of the stratified squamous epithelium. This early papilla increases in size and length and bends posteriorly in the epidermis. The dermal fibroblasts form a cellular layer along the periphery of the papilla below the columnar cells of the adjoining germinativum. Between these two cellular layers an acidophilic fibrous material forms in close association with the fibroblasts and becomes impreg-

nated with calcium salts in a manner similar to that of bone formation.˙ This bony tissue, or *dentine* as it is called here, increases but,
unlike bone, the modified fibroblasts, called *odontoblasts*, associated
with its formation do not become surrounded by the matrix but
cytoplasmic processes from them do. In this way a layer of
odontoblast cell bodies lines the inner surface of the dentine and

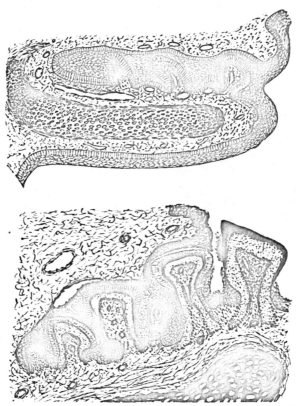

Fig. 110.—Two stages in the development of the placoid scale as found in sections
through the dental lamina of the dogfish; enamel in black, dentine in stipple; the
vascular pulp with a layer of odontoblasts facing the dentine, Meckel's cartilage with
lacunæ. Early stage as found in a 6 inch pup on the top; later stage found in an
18 inch specimen shown in bottom figure.

their processes extend into it through canaliculi called *dentinal
tubules*. The fibroblasts at the base of the early papilla become
similarly active to form a broad *basal plate* of dentine associated
with the *spine* being formed by the papilla. The vascular connective tissue of the stratum vasculare of the dermis extends as the
*pulp* through the basal plate and occupies the central area of the
spine. (Fig. 110.)

While this growth has been taking place in the dermal portion of the scale, the columnar cells, called *ameloblasts*, of the stratum germinativum of the epidermis covering the spine papilla have been forming a basal cuticle immediately adjoining the dentine. This cuticular contribution becomes impregnated with calcium salts to form the *enamel* of the scale. The spine of the mature scale ruptures through the overlying layers of the epidermis, the covering enamel epithelium is lost and the enamel covered portion clear of the integument surface bends posteriorly from the basal plate of dentine. (Fig. 111.)

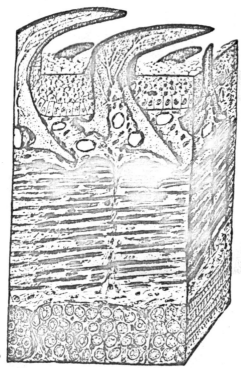

Fig. 111.—Stereodiagrammatic representation of the integument of the dogfish. Projecting spines of placoid scales are composed of dentine covered by enamel. The basal plate is buried in the stratum vasculare of the dermis which projects into it as the pulp. Septa of the vasculare project through the compactum to connect with the subcutaneous tissue adjoining the muscles.

.The basal plate is embedded in the stratum vascular which contains the chromatophores responsible for integumentary coloration. Trabeculæ of tissue extend from this region among the interlacing bundles of the stratum compactum and continue with the loosely organized fibroelastic tissue of the subcutaneous region which connects with the sheaths of skeletal muscles. (Fig. 111.)

Preparation of routine material involves decalcification for sectioning of dogfish integument and as a result the entire enamel region of the spine is lost unless the material contains developing and unerupted scales with the enamel epithelium intact. A series of stages in the development of the scale may be best observed in sections through the jaw; here the scales serving as teeth go through a process which foreshadows that in the teeth of all vertebrates.

Ctenoid Scales.—In the integument of most teleosts many overlapping scales are formed from pockets in the dermis where fibro-

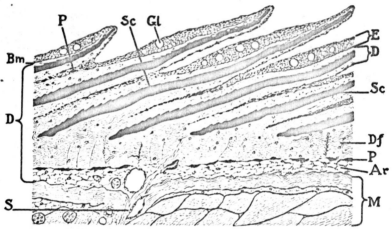

Fig. 112.—*Skin of Perch: D*, Dermis; *E*, epidermis; *Df*, dense fibrous tissue; *Ar*, subcutis; *Bm*, basement membrane; *Gl*, glandular cells; *M*, muscle; *P*, pigment cells; *S*, septum; *Sc*, scales. (Courtesy of General Biological Supply House, Inc.).

blasts, called *scleroblasts*, surround a gradually thickening and extending plate of acidophilic fibrous matrix not heavily impregnated with calcium salts. The plate so formed has a serrated border and is embedded in the fibrous stratum compactum of the dermis. A portion pushes out above the level of the early epidermis, part of which it carries along unmodified and unbroken. Scattered glandular cells of the stratified squamous epithelium forming the epidermis supply the covering protective coat of mucus.

Cycloid Scales.—These are similar to the ctenoid in development but differ in form. Chromatophores of the surrounding stratum vasculare give color to the scales and general integument while structural conditions within the scales may give rise to physical colors and iridescence. Growth of the ctenoid and cycloid scales continues by addition of material to their borders. Interruption in the accretion process gives furrows and ridges.

**Ganoid Scales.**—Among the ganoid fishes the scales are composed of adjoining but not overlapping bony plates, covered by a superficial portion of ganoin which is fibrous and uncalcified. The epithelium is not involved in this type and these scales, with their resemblance in formation to membranous bone, suggest a possible origin of the ossicles of reptiles and dermal bones arising in the skeletons of succeeding classes of vertebrates.

**Lateral Line System.**—This system arises as a linear ectodermal thickening beginning on each side of the head and extending posteriorly. First a ridge of epidermis with patches of neuro-epithelial cells is formed, then sinks to open at intervals to the surface of the epidermis. The neuro-epithelium is localized in budlike patches, called *neuromasts*, along the canal or groove so that a line of sensory structures is formed and innervated by unmyelinated sensory fibers. This lateral line system is developed among larval Amphibia but remains only as isolated neuromasts after metamorphosis. (Fig. 12.)

*Dogfish.*—A canal system is formed and located in the stratum vasculare below the epidermis with which it connects by short ducts. The wall of the canal is composed of two or three layers of cuboidal cells, those adjoining the lumen being flattened to an almost squamous condition. Surrounding the canal is a fibroelastic sheath continuing with the adjoining dermal tissue. The neuromasts are composed of two cell types. The more numerous is a slender fusiform *supporting cell* reaching from lumen to basement membrane. Among the supporting cells are several *neuro-epithelial cells.* Each of these is pyriform or fusiform with a distal pointed process reaching to the lumen of the canal and a proximal portion buried among the supporting cells. Branches of nerve fibers enter the base of the bud and associate with the proximal portion of the neuro-epithelial cells.

*Ampullæ of Lorenzini.* —In the head region are a collection of tubules derived from the embryonic epidermis. Each slants into the subcutis to end in a blind saclike enlargement or ampulla containing large neuro-epithelial cells. The ducts resemble the lateral line canal in composition and are usually filled with a mucous secretion. Both the lateral line organs and the ampullæ are associated with reception of vibrations from the surrounding water.

## INTEGUMENT OF AMPHIBIA

The skin of Amphibians is usually soft and moist, and lacks scales except in the Apoda. The epidermis is characterized by a stratified epithelium through which numerous multicellular simple alveolar glands open. Glandular cells occur scattered through the epidermis of most larval and some adult forms; a feature recalling conditions found generally among fishes. In some forms there is a gradual wearing out and replacement of epidermal cells forming the corneum, but in others there is a periodic shedding of large

patches or sheets of dead superficial cells. The corium has a thin cellular and vascular *stratum vasculare* in which chromatophores are abundant in the region immediately adjoining the epidermis. The deeper *stratum compactum* is usually composed of bundles of collagenous fibers mainly parallel to the surface with perforating and interlacing fibers extending at right angles to the stratum vasculare. Trabeculæ of loose fibroelastic tissue and scattered smooth muscle cells extend from the stratum vasculare into and through the stratum compactum to join with the subcutaneous tissue. The subcutis is composed of a thin region of loose fibroelastic tissue rich in elastic fibers and connects the dermis with underlying tissues.

In water-living forms, respiration is partially or even primarily carried on through the general integument or by modifications of it into external gills as in Necturus. In this case the stratum vasculare carries a richer capillary supply to the epidermis which it invades by papillæ. In other forms living mainly or entirely on land, as in the toad, the epidermis piles up layers of dead cornified cells into a corneum which prevents drying of underlying regions.

In the larval forms a lateral line is developed similar to conditions present among the fish but this system has only a few scattered neuromasts left following metamorphosis. These, however, are essentially the same in structure as in the fish, though located in isolated pits of the stratified epithelium of the epidermis.

### Necturus

The integument of Necturus has a stratified cuboidal epithelium forming the epidermis. Numerous club- or flask-shaped glandular cells are located among the polyhedral cells between the superficial cuboidal layer and the low columnar or cuboidal cells of the germinativum. These cells have a distal spherical cytoplasmic region filled with acidophilic granules and a tapering proximal portion extending among the surrounding cells to the germinativum. Simple alveolar glands developed from the germinativum extend down into the stratum vasculare below the network of chromatophores abundant below the epidermis. The alveolar portions of these glands may extend down to the stratum compactum and the neck or excretory duct formed by cuboidal cells reaches up to the epidermis through which it opens to the surface of the integument. Stages in activity of these glands are reflected in the size of the alveoli and the condition of the secretory cells. (Fig. 13.)

Two types of alveolar glands are differentiated. A smaller *mucous gland* is widely distributed; a larger *serous* or *poison gland* occurs dorsally. (Figs. 13 and 113.) The mucous gland is composed of columnar cells whose granular cytoplasm is basophilic if the mucus is preserved or clear if not; the nucleus is located in the proximal extremity and the cell appears to retain its integrity during secretion. A delicate reticulum of connective tissue and scattered smooth muscle cells surrounds the basement membrane of the alveolus. The poison gland extends more deeply into the corium and is surrounded by a sheath with more smooth muscle cells than the mucous type. The secretory cells are at first pyramidal or columnar in form but become filled with coarse acidophilic granules and appear to disintegrate distally in liberating the secretion. As a result the nuclei and proximal band of cytoplasm are left lining the connective tissue sheath. The function of this type of gland is presumably protective since their secretion is poisonous (acts as an emetic) and may discourage predators. The mucous glands are protective in that they produce a mucus which keeps the integument covered by a protective coating. New glands arise from the germinativum layer of the epidermis to replace old, worn-out glands.

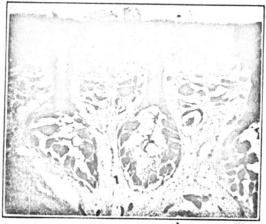

Fig. 113.—Photograph of integument of the frog with an epidermis composed of stratified squamous epithelium and associated simple alveolar mucous glands. Immediately below the epidermis there is a narrow region of loose vascular connective tissue (stratum vasculare) in which contracted chromatophores occur; below the glands the corium is composed of a dense fibrous tissue (stratum compactum). 4 mm. obj. and 5× oc.

### Frog

The integument in this form has an epidermis of stratified squamous epithelium composed of about six layers of cells, with only a single superficial layer of squamous cells which adhere to each other as a thin covering which sloughs off in sheets or patches. Glandular cells are lacking in the epidermal region except in larval stages. Pigment may occur in scattered or relatively numerous epidermal melanophores with branching processes buried among the middle layers of epithelial cells and in the dermal chromatophores of the stratum vasculare. Melanin also appears diffusely in or among the epithelial cells below the corneum. Preparations made from frozen sections of formalin fixed integument stained in hematoxylin and Sudan IV show the xanthophores (yellow pigment chromatophores) with lipoidal content. Simple alveolar glands derived from the stratum germinativum of the epidermis are buried in the stratum vasculare and are of

the same two types observed in Necturus. The poison glands are localized in the dorsal regions.

The dermis is similar in composition to conditions described for the class but the subcutis usually contains prominent lymph sacs in the dorsal regions. In frozen sections of formalin fixed material the boundary between the stratum vasculare and stratum compactum is marked by a basophilic fibrous region which continues through the compactum at intervals to join the subcutaneous tissue.

## INTEGUMENT OF REPTILES

With reptiles the land habitat is assumed, and a dry skin becomes universal. The epidermis is relatively thin, with a stratum ger-

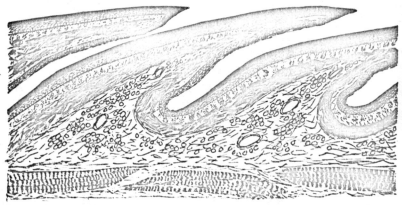

Fig. 114.—Longitudinal section through the integument of a lizard; the scales are shown in black; a layer of chromatophores occurs immediately below the epidermis under the scale but not on the under side of the fold; a dense fibrous compactum adjoins the subcutis in which groups of fat cells are abundant.

minativum of several layers and a corneum composed of a number of layers of dead, cornified squamous cells. The cornified epidermal surface covering, overlapping folds of the integument, alone forms the scales of reptiles. Some reptiles shed their skin periodically, the horny superficial corneum separates from the softer subjacent cells so that this dead upper covering of the epidermis is shed in one piece. Glands are restricted to the head and anal regions.

The claws are formed like scales by accumulations of the corneum about the ends of the digits.

The corium in reptiles varies from a very thin region, in lizards and snakes, to a relatively thick one, in alligators and turtles, composed of dense connective tissue in which bony plates or ossicles are formed. Numerous chromatophores are located immediately below the epidermal covering. When ossicles are formed they are derived from the lower corium in a manner similar to that described in intramembranous bone formation. In most turtles, both scales and bony plates are formed. Where such plates occur, the tissue of each plate is not continuous with the bony tissue of adjacent plates so that growth in size of the animal is accompanied by continued peripheral additions to the individual plates.

## INTEGUMENT OF BIRDS

The integument of birds represents an advance in development of conditions found among reptiles. The epidermis is also modified for land life with a corneum composed of accumulated cornified cells. The *scales*, prominent in reptiles, appear here primarily covering the legs while a more complicated structure of similar derivation, the *feather*, covers the body with a coat which conserves body heat and protects from environmental temperature changes, an important item among birds where a high body temperature is normal. Pigmentation occurs in the germinativum of the epidermis and chromatophores are not common in the dermis. Glands are limited to the two *uropygials* located at the base of the tail. The dermis is thin but divisible into the usual two layers, stratum vasculare and stratum compactum. The subcutis becomes prominent by the content of fat commonly accumulated in it.

### Pigeon

**Integument.**—The epidermis is composed of a stratified squamous epithelium, a layer of low columnar cells at the basement membrane and a few layers of smaller polyhedral cells form the germinativum which is covered by several layers of cornified cells forming the corneum. The thickness of the epidermis varies in different regions of the body, being thickest in the comb and mouth regions, and relatively thin over the general body surface covered by feathers. Accumulations of cornified cells of the corneum over dermal folds form the *scales of* reptilian type which occur in the leg regions.

The thin stratum vasculare forms broad papillæ causing folds in the epidermis while finer secondary papillæ carrying the germinativum inward increase the amount of capillary supply to the surface exposed. The relatively narrow stratum compactum contains interlacing bundles of collagenous fibers primarily running parallel to the surface. A network of elastic fibers extends throughout the entire dermis.

The subcutis occurs as a thick pad below the dermis and is composed of fibroelastic tissue in which there is an abundant accumulation of fat. Bundles of smooth muscle also occur in this region associated with the feather follicle which is buried here.

**Feathers.**—These epidermal derivatives have their origin, as did the scales of reptiles, in the extension of dermal connective tissue which carries along the epidermis. In the feather, the projection is a long finger-like papilla whose basal portion sinks back into the subcutis where a connective tissue

sheath surrounds an outer reflected epidermal layer. (Fig. 115 A.) This embedded portion surrounded by its connective tissue sheath is the *follicle* and into its base extends the stratum vasculare of the original papilla which has now developed as the vascular *pulp* surrounded by an epidermal collar continually giving rise to cells until the feather is formed. The smooth internal surface of epithelium covering the early pulp is broken by slender projections of the vascular pulp which continue from the collar as very slender longitudinal folds between which rods of epithelial cells are formed. These epithelial rods are covered by and continuous with the original superficial corneum which forms the *periderm* of the feather. The rods and folds are of this simple longitudinal form in the *down feather* but a more complicated development of oblique and branching rods continuing out from an undivided portion, the *rachis*, gives rise to the *barbs* and *barbules* forming the *vane* of the *contour feather*. (Figs. 115 A and B.)

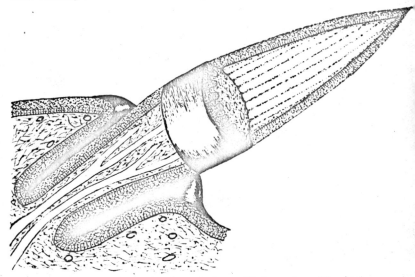

Fig. 115 A.—Developing down feather. (Redrawn from Kingsley.)

The folds and accompanying rods do not extend to the base of the feather and leave a smooth heavy or solid walled exposed *shaft* region which terminates in the buried hollow *quill* portion within the follicle. With development, the terminal portions (barbs, barbules and part of the shaft) become solid cornified epithelial structures and the vascular pulp and the germinativum layers of the shaft are slowly withdrawn down the shaft to the quill; with this removal of blood supply the epithelial mass forming the feather dries, the periderm ruptures, and the rods of epithelium come free in a puff in the case of the down feather or as interlacing barbs and barbules in contour feathers. Thus feathers represent an intricate splitting up of a corneum with the dermal pulp playing a nutritive part and then withdrawing with the germinativum to leave the dead, dry, cornified layers of epithelium. The color of a feather is, in large part, due to pigment present in the epithelial cells forming the rods but iridescence and some color is due to physical phenomena arising from structural features in the epithelial layers.

11,

After withdrawal of the pulp to the base of the quill the feather has a variable period of attachment before the pulp and germinativum withdraw from the quill and it is shed (moulted). Replacement is effected from a new papilla and follicle forming in the old site.

**Uropygial Glands.**—A pair of compound tubular glands develop at the base of the tail and the secretion product is used in dressing the feathers. Each gland originates at either side of the dorsal midline as an epidermal pocket which develops and is subdivided by connective tissue so that a resultant mass of secretory tubules forms a compound tubular gland. A main duct opens to the surface through a papilla projecting above the level

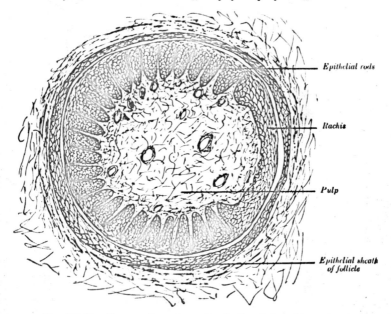

of the integument.

Epithelial rods

Rachis

Pulp

Epithelial sheath
of follicle

Fig. 115 B.—Cross section of erupting feather below skin surface.

of the integument. The extent of development of these glands varies, being greatest in aquatic forms where their oily secretion product is more freely used in dressing the feathers. In the pigeon, the two glands are poorly developed and are surrounded by a common fibroelastic capsule with only a thin septum separating them. The glandular epithelium lining the tubules has two or more layers resting upon a low cuboidal germinativum. When active new cells are derived from the germinativum, they develop an acidophilic granular cytoplasm and then fatty vacuoles differentiate as these cells are pushed toward the lumen by newly forming basal cells. The cells adjoining the lumen are cast into the lumen where they disintegrate to form the oily secretion. Inactive new cells are filled with acidophilic granules. The ducts are lined by similar vacuolated cells except in the papillæ where a stratified squamous appears.

## INTEGUMENT OF MAMMALS

In this class the integument becomes generally thicker than in the preceding classes and in contrast to the limited glandular

derivatives in reptiles and birds, the mammals possess several types of relatively wide distribution. One type in particular, the *mammary gland*, is characteristic of this class and in the female produces the milk used in nursing the young. Another epidermal derivative limited to this class is the *hair* which is present at some time in all forms and prominent in most. Associated with the hair is a branched alveolar sebaceous gland which secretes an oily substance. Other glands of coiled tubular structure, the *sweat glands*, are epidermal derivatives of less general distribution which play a part in regulation of body temperature and excretion. The scales so universal in reptiles and locally common in birds are inconspicuous except in a few aberrant forms and in the scaly tails of rodents and marsupials.

The composition of the epidermis shows variation in the thickness of its epithelial layers in different regions of the body and also differences in the type and number of derived structures such as the glands and the hairs. When the integument is colored, the pigment is located in the basal layers of the epidermis and chromatophores are of very limited occurrence.

The dermis is divisible into two blending portions, an upper, narrow subepithelial *pars papillaris* or *papillary layer*, which corresponds to the stratum vasculare of preceding classes; and a deeper, denser, and wider *reticular layer*, or *pars reticularis*, which corresponds with the stratum compactum. The papillary layer is composed of a reticular and fibroelastic network carrying a capillary supply which it projects into the epidermis by numerous *dermal papillæ*. In addition to the vascular supply, the papillary layer contains nerve endings which continue among the epithelial cells or are organized into small tactile bodies within the papillæ. The reticular layer which continues inward from the papillary layer contains a denser network of collagenous and elastic fibers which tend to parallel the skin surface in their arrangement.

The subcutis is a broad, loose fibroelastic tissue region joining the integument to underlying tissue. It usually has an abundant accumulation of fat cells and this fatty tissue, also found in birds, may function as an insulating layer aiding in the maintenance of body temperature, as well as a storage region.

**Skin of Palm or Sole.**—The epidermal covering of these regions offers an example of cellular accumulation to a marked degree and permits observation of changes leading to cornification and desquamation which progress by more rapid stages in other regions where fewer layers of cells are normally present. The epidermis here has four distinct strata, namely, *stratum germinativum*, *stratum granulosum*, *stratum lucidum*, and *stratum corneum*. All the cells formed in the germinativum become part of each of these layers before being cast from the surface or the corneum; the different strata merely represent various stages in the transformation of the epidermal cell from its origin until its death and desquamation.

*Stratum Germinativum (Malpighian Layer).*—Where this stratum adjoins the dermis, numerous dermal papillæ usually project into it, thus producing an uneven boundary region. Resting on the basement membrane is a layer of cuboidal or low columnar cells and covering it are six or more layers of polyhedral cells; the number of layers being greater between regions invaded by the dermal papillæ. Frequent cell divisions occur in several of the lower layers of cells and new cells are continuously being pushed upward. Skin color depends upon the pigment content (most commonly melanin) accumulated in and between the cells of the germinativum, but this pigment disappears as the cells are pushed upward to the corneum. Protoplasmic bridges may be demonstrated between the germinativum cells and the resultant irregular outline they produce has led to calling the

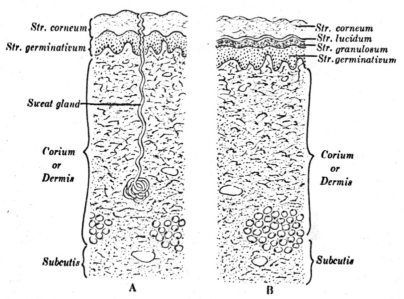

Fig. 116.—Diagram of skin structure. *A*, From back of hand; *B*, from palm of hand.

cells of this region "prickle cells." The uppermost layers of cells become more flattened as they approach the next stratum.

*Stratum Granulosum.*—This is composed of two or three layers of flattened polyhedral cells in which irregular sized and numerous basophilic granules fill the cytoplasm. These granules are composed of a substance called keratohyaline produced by chemical changes within the cells at this level. The outermost granulosum cells have nuclei undergoing degeneration and disintegration.

*Stratum Lucidum.*—This stratum appears as a clear bright band just above the stratum granulosum and consists of translucent cells so tightly packed that individual outlines are not visible. The granules, conspicuous in the granulosum, have become converted into a semifluid colloidal substance called *eleidin* Nuclei are not visible.

*Stratum Corneum.*—This superficial stratum of the epidermis is composed of many layers of dead, dry squamous cells in which the eleidin has become *keratin*. The region of these dead cells once occupied by the nucleus is a clear space. This region of cornified cells does not stain in routine preparations and appears a light yellow color. Cells at the surface are constantly being worn away, but characteristic patterns of ridges and grooves represent irregularities produced by invasions of dermal papillæ into the germinativum.

The dermis in the sole or palm presents a much heavier accumulation of fibrous elements than found in the general body integument. Numerous ducts of sweat glands spiral down from the epidermis into the lower reticular layer where the secretory portions are located. Pacinian corpuscles may also be observed buried in the connective tissue of the dermis.

Fig. 117.—A section through the footpad of the woodchuck, showing the papillary zone covered by a layer of melanin bearing germinativum cells. The granulosum is indicated below the dark stratum lucidum above which is the broad corneum. The coiled excretory ducts of two sweat glands show below the lucidum. Mallory stain. Photomicrograph. 16 mm. obj. and 5× oc.

**Sweat Glands.**—Each of these is a simple coiled tubular gland which has originated from the epidermis during embryonic development. A rod of cells develops from the early germinativum layer and extends down into the dermis where it coils several times to form a ball-like mass in the reticular layer. A lumen develops through this cord and the lower coiled portion becomes secretory. The upper part of the tubule serves as the excretory duct and runs a slightly twisted course to the epidermis. Two or three layers of cuboidal cells form the walls of this duct until it reaches the epidermis where the spiralling passage to the surface is lined by squamous cells.   The secretory portion of the gland is composed of a single layer of pyramidal or columnar cells, each with a basally located nucleus and a granular or vacuolated cytoplasm.   When active the distal end of these cells becomes filled with vacuoles of secretion and detaches from the proximal granular and nucleated part to disintegrate in the lumen as the secretion of the gland. The secretory product of the sweat glands is usually a watery and clear material but may be slightly colored from pigment present in the gland cells.   Surrounding the secretory tubule small smooth muscle cells form a thin sheath which aids in the elimination of the secretion.   These glands play a part in lubricating the epidermis, excrete salts, water and some wastes removed from the surrounding capillaries, and play an important part in regulation of body temperature.   They are restricted to limited areas in many animals; in some they occur only in the foot pads, in others they are present on the lips and snout.   (Fig. 116A.)

**Hairs.**—Unlike the development of the feather in which a dermal papilla thrusts out the epidermis and the combined tissues then sink back into the dermis, the hair originates from the epidermis by a column of cells pushed down obliquely into the dermal connective tissue.   Along the inner lateral wall of this early column a bulge of cells marks the origin of the associated sebaceous gland. The base of the column enlarges as the *hair bulb* and is invaded a short distance by a vascular dermal papilla.   A connective tissue sheath surrounds this buried epithelial portion which becomes the hair *root*.   Cells of this early root region multiply and differentiate to form root sheaths about a central rod of cornified cells forming the hair *shaft*, pushed up by cells proliferating about the papilla and over it.   The hair of the bat (Fig. 118) presents a simple hair structure but as a result of continued growth and complete differentiation of more epithelial layers, a fully formed hair follicle may contain all the following components.   (Fig. 119.)

### Human Hair

1. Connective tissue sheath:  This is derived from and continuous with the fibroelastic tissue of the dermis and is separated by a hyaline basement membrane from the adjoining epithelium of the outer root sheath.

2. Outer root sheath:  This represents an infolding of the epidermis whose stratum corneum continues to the region of the sebaceous gland. Below this the granulosum disappears, and the germinativum becomes a layer of cuboidal cells covered by squamous as the bulb region is approached.

3. Inner root sheath:  Cells from about the papilla are pushed upward in several layers which become progressively changed until they desquamate

as cornified squamous cells in the region of the sebaceous gland. An outer Henle's layer and an inner Huxley's layer of several cells are differentiated in this inner root sheath.

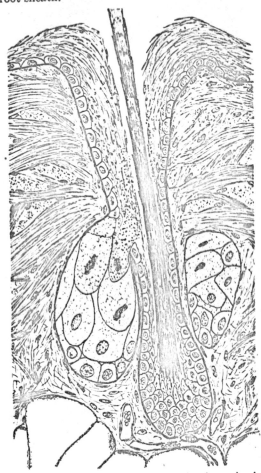

FIG. 118.—Section through the scalp of a bat, showing a simple hair and sebaceous glands.

4. **Hair shaft:** This is produced by a core of cells pushing up from the region above the papilla. The bulk of the shaft is composed of cells which rapidly become cornified after they leave the region of the bulb; this is the cortex of the hair. Some hairs present a thin column of cuboidal cells, the medulla, within the cortex and these correspond to granulosum cells in not having reached the end stages of cornification.

Immediately adjoining the inner root sheath a single layer of overlapping cornified cells forms the *cuticle*, which is the superficial layer of the exposed hair and may be readily observed in total mounts. Color of hair is due to accumulation of pigment in and between the cells forming the cortex and medulla.

Toward the region of the hair bulb all the sheaths present show a blending into the undifferentiated and proliferating cells surrounding the papilla. It is evident therefore that cross-section through a hair follicle at different levels will show variations in composition.

Some hairs, called *vibrissæ*, are modified in the follicular region for translation of tactile sensations. These hairs are normally

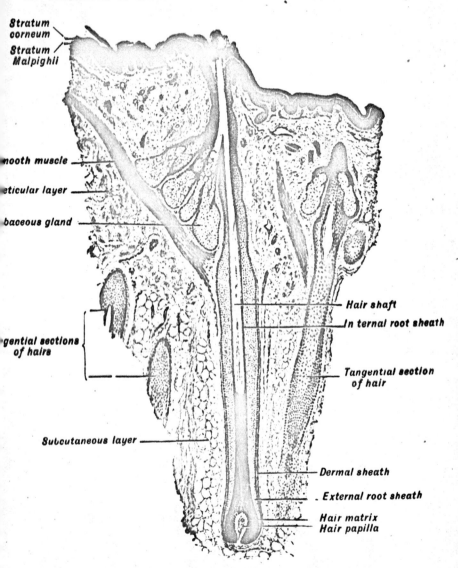

Fig. 119.—Scalp of a man. Root of a hair in longitudinal section. 32 ×. After Schaffer. (From Maximow & Bloom, courtesy of W. B. Saunders Co.).

larger than the body hairs and sensory nerve endings surround the usual connective tissue sheath, which is, in turn, surrounded by a loose vascular sheath with chromatophores and a heavier fibrous outer sheath.

Hairs are set obliquely in the skin, and on the acute angle side there is usually a small strand of smooth muscle, the *arrector pili* muscle, which extends through the dermis from the side of the follicle diagonally upward toward the epidermis. When this muscle contracts the hair may be pulled erect and a temporary ridge forms in the skin adjacent to the hair.

**Hair Replacement.**—Some hairs (angora) have an indefinite period of growth but most hairs are periodically or seasonally shed and replaced by new ones. Preliminary to shedding, the cells of the bulb region cease to form new cells giving rise to the inner root sheath and the cortex. These regions already formed then become cornified to give a thickened end commonly found on shed hairs. Following a period of inactivity the undifferentiated epithelial cells about the bulb resume activity and a new inner root sheath and hair shaft are pushed through the old outer root sheath to dislodge and replace the old hair.

**Sebaceous Glands.**—These are simple branched alveolar glands derived from the lateral proliferation of cells in the outer root sheath region of the developing hair and lie between the arrector pili muscle and the hair follicle. The excretory duct is relatively wide and has a lining of stratified squamous epithelium continuous with that of the outer root sheath of the hair whose connective tissue sheath also encloses the entire gland. The secretory alveoli are filled with stratified cells which originate from mitotically active smaller cells adjoining the basement membrane. Progressing from this basal layer there is an accumulation of fatty secretion material within the cells and an accompanying increase in their size as they approach the lumen, a process resembling conditions found in the uropygial glands. Ultimately the entire cell disintegrates and the secretion, together with the disintegrating products of the cell itself, is liberated at the side of the hair near the skin surface as an oily compound, the *sebum*. After such disintegration of the cells and the discharge of the sebum, regeneration of new epithelium of the gland takes place from the basal cells. The muscular contraction of the arrector pili muscle aids in the discharge of the secretion at the neck of the hair follicle from which it passes to form an oily covering to the skin and hair. (Figs. 118 and 119.)

**Mammary Glands.**—These are compound alveolar glands (Fig. 120) and lie in the dermis at each side of the midline in the ventral integument. They arise from invaginations of the embryonic epidermis and form in both male and female; development to functional maturity occurs in the female and regressive changes occur in the male. The excretory ducts open in the nipple, which is a conical extension of connective tissue covered with epidermis. The alveolar portions of the mammary glands are large and composed of pyramidal cells, but there is considerable variation in size, depending on the secretory state of the gland. When active, fat globules accumulate in the distal cytoplasm of the cell until this enlarged terminal

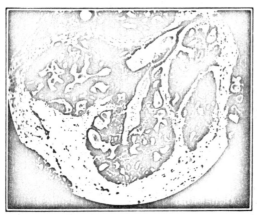

Fig. 120.—Mammary gland of human in intermediate stage of activity, showing two lobules with an interlobular duct breaking into two intralobular ducts that extend into the secreting end-pieces. A dense connective tissue surrounds the lobules and groups them into lobes. Photomicrograph. 16 mm. obj. and 5× oc.

portion is discharged into the lumen to form the secretion. The remaining nucleated basal portion of each cell soon repeats the process. Secretions accumulating in the lumen pass along small ducts which open into the larger lactiferous ducts. The number of these ducts in the nipple varies from one to many. They open to the surface at the end of the nipple where the stratified squamous epithelium of the covering skin continues inward to line their outermost portion. Before reaching the nipple, the lactiferous ducts may dilate into reservoirs for the storage of the secreted milk. In the inactive state the alveoli are collapsed and the gland is composed mainly of connective tissue.

**Nails.**—These are more readily studied microscopically than the other digital covers (*claws* and *hoofs*) of mammals. Each nail is a comparatively simple epithelial derivative from an invaginated oblique fold of the embryonic epidermis covering the dorsal surface of the tips of the fingers and toes of primates. The germinativum

region of the proximal part of the buried fold becomes the *root* of the nail and proliferates layers of cells which cornify and push out in a curved plate to cover the more distal epidermis. Laterally, the integument folds over the edge of the extending nail to form the *nail grooves* and a proximal fold covers the nail root; the stratum corneum

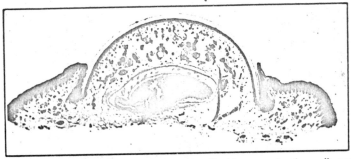

FIG. 121.—Cross-section of the finger tip and nail of human, showing nail grooves, nail and skin of the finger. Photomicrograph. × 10.

of these folds forms the *eponychium*, or cuticle, accumulating about the nail. The dermis below the nail root and the more distal epidermis, or *nail bed*, over which the nail slides outward, projects into the germinativum as longitudinal vascular folds which account for the finely ridged appearance of the nail surface. The dead, cornified layers of cells, the *hyponychium*, under the distal free end of the nail arise from the germinativum of the epidermis of this distal region.

The claws and hoofs of other mammals represent a far greater accumulation of the dead cells from the dorsal fold, *ungis*, and a development of the distal underlying epidermis into a thick pad, the *subungis*, represented only by the hyponychial region in nails.

# CHAPTER X

## THE RESPIRATORY SYSTEM

THE origin of the respiratory system in all classes is closely associated with the anterior end of the alimentary tract, the pharyngeal region. Among the fishes and Amphibia, gills are formed in pouches of the lateral pharyngeal wall to accommodate respiratory exchanges in water, but among the other classes such a direct association is only embryonic and a ventral tube, the *larynx*, opens from the pharynx into saccular structures, the *lungs*, adapted for respiration from air. The supplementary part played by the integument in respiration has already been observed in the case of the Amphibia.

### THE RESPIRATORY SYSTEM OF FISHES

In this class the lateral walls of the developing pharynx give rise to a series of paired pouches, usually five or six, which develop outward until they fuse with the ectoderm of the lateral body wall. Slits then open through the fused plates so that the pharynx cavity opens to the exterior of the body through the *gill clefts* between whose adjoining walls mesenchymal elements form a septum, the *interbranchial septum*. From both anterior and posterior surfaces, the epithelial covering of each septum is thrown into thin parallel folds by a core of vascular connective tissue and each of these folds is a *gill filament*.

A septum and the filaments on both surfaces, each surface representing a contribution from adjoining pouches, is called a *gill or holobranch*, and the contribution of each pouch is a *demibranch*. Modifications of this general development occur in different fishes and in the ascending classes of vertebrates the extent of development of this pharyngeal region is modified and reduced until it is represented by pouches appearing only in embryonic stages of mammals. Structures, other than respiratory, are also associated in their origin with the gill pouches, namely the thymus and thyroid.

A saccular structure, the *swim bladder*, derived from the anterior end of the esophagus, is present in many fishes, and may be considered under this system in view of its possible relationship to the lungs of higher forms, although it does not function as a respiratory organ in most fishes.

### Gills of the Dogfish

In the dogfish the epithelial membrane covering a demibranch is thrown into thin parallel primary filaments each with numerous finer secondary

filaments.  In the pharyngeal base of each septum a hyaline cartilage *arch* develops and smaller bars develop in the septum as *gill rays*, both serving to support the gills and keep the clefts open.  Surrounding these cartilaginous pieces, fibroelastic tissue carries branches of the afferent and efferent arteries and continues with smaller branches of these vessels into the primary filaments.  Along the base of the primary filament, bundles of smooth muscle cells occur in the connective tissue of the septum and extend into the base of the filaments.  (Fig. 122.)

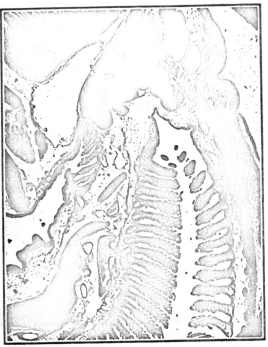

Fig. 122.—A section through the pharynx of a young dogfish, showing the first and second gill chambers, the former with only one demibranch.  A black lobulated mass of lymphoid tissue, the thymus, occurs above the gills.  The cartilage support of the septa and the gills are darkly staining.  Photomicrograph.  16 mm. obj. and 5× oc.

Each primary filament receives vascular branches supported in a core of fibroelastic tissue and scattered smooth muscle cells from the septum. The epithelium covering the septum between and beyond the primary filaments and along these to the origin of the secondary ones, is of the stratified squamous type, as is the epithelium of the pharynx.

Each secondary filament receives a capillary and delicate connective tissue supply from the primary filament; and this core is covered by a simple squamous or low cuboidal epithelium.  The blood in the capillaries of these filaments is thus separated from the water surrounding the gills by endothelium and the thin epithelial membrane covering the filament.

The tip of each primary filament is free of secondary filaments and is covered by stratified squamous epithelium below which a core of connective tissue supports an efferent vessel into which blood from the capillary net of the secondary filaments collects for return to the efferent arteries of the septum.

**The Swim Bladder.**—This structure arises as a ventral pouch from the esophagus or the pharynx behind the gill region and occurs generally distributed among higher fishes as a single chambered sac or constricted into two connecting sacs. A connecting duct, the pneumatic duct, is present during earlier developmental stages but may degenerate during development. The bladder wall is thin in the distended condition and is composed of an internal lining of simple squamous epithelium supported by fibrous and elastic elements with scattered smooth muscle cells which may form a band in the constricted region of bi-lobed sacs. The anterior part of the sac commonly has a thicker region with a secretory squamous or cuboidal epithelium associated with a rich capillary supply (the *red gland*). This region is associated with production of gas (oxygen) to inflate the sac. Where a connecting duct to the esophagus or pharyngeal region is not present to control deflation, the posterior portion of the sac has a capillary network below its simple epithelial lining which is associated with resorption of the gas to control inflation. The dipnoi retain the pneumatic duct and have a vascular bi-lobed sac shifted to a dorsal location which serves as a respiratory organ.

## THE RESPIRATORY SYSTEM OF AMPHIBIA

Gills occur in all forms during larval life and are retained in some during mature stages. The internal gills arise as simple filamentous folds from the pharynx region and represent modified septa found among the fish. These may be accompanied by external filaments derived from the integument and supplied by the same vascular branches as the internal gills. The gills present in the adult are usually the exposed integumentary derivatives as represented in Necturus.

In addition to the larval branchial system there arises a ventral pocket from the pharynx posterior to the region of the last gill pouch. (Fig. 123.) This diverticulum divides into a right and left portion extending into the body cavity to form the lungs which, with metamorphosis of many forms, have developed as the primary respiratory organ and the gills are resorbed. In many forms the lungs appear to take little or no part in respiration, which is in these cases effected by means of the integument or gills. The lungs vary from simple sacs found in Necturus to well-developed compound

alveolar structures such as are found in the frog, and to an even greater extent in the toad. The original unpaired duct with a slit-like opening (the *glottis*) into the pharynx is the forerunner of the *larynx* and *trachea,* and the two branches opening into the lungs become the *bronchi.* The glottis region shows stages in development of the larynx within this class from the simple duct surrounded by connective tissue and a small amount of muscle controlling the

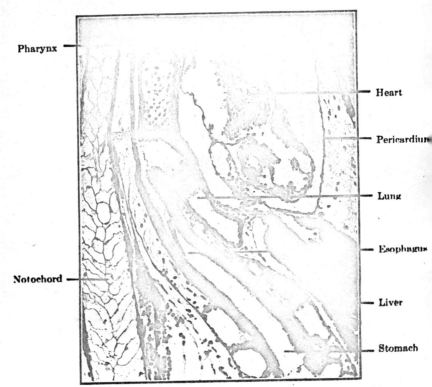

Fɪɢ. 123.—Sagittal section of Amblystoma larva showing the ventral lung diverticulum. Photomicrograph. 16 mm. obj. and 5× oc.

glottis opening (Necturus) to the more complex larynx with elements of support and movement (the frog) similar to those of succeeding classes. Accompanying the development of this system for respiration in air, there are developed, from the region where olfactory pits occur in the fish, two nasal passages opening from the integument at the *nares* and opening into the mouth through the *choanæ* or internal nares. These passage-ways are lined by epithelia continuing with the epidermis and contain neurosensory epithelial cells translating olfactory sensations.

### Necturus

In this form respiration is mainly effected through the external gills. These represent folds of the integument from which finer filamentous projections of the stratum vasculare carry a capillary supply into the covering epidermis by numerous small papillæ. The base of the gills has associated skeletal muscle by which the gills are moved. Smooth muscle cells occur as strands in the broader connective tissue septa and as isolated units in the filaments.

The slitlike glottis opens into a small tubular larynx region formed by connective tissue containing small amounts of smooth muscle and lined by columnar epithelial cells. This tubular portion divides into two parts, each immediately opening into a thin-walled, elongated sac, the lung, without subdivisions. The epithelial membrane of the lung is composed of cuboidal cells and is thrown into low narrow folds by an underlying delicate fibroelastic connective tissue carrying a capillary supply. The remainder of the wall is composed of a denser fibroelastic tissue in which are scattered smooth muscle cells; this region supports a few branches of arteries, veins, and lymphatics. A surface layer of squamous mesothelial cells covers the lung wall.

### Frog

In this and many other forms, respiration is effected mainly through the general integument but an internal respiratory system is present. Cartilage

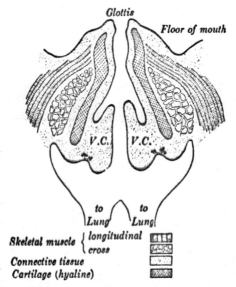

Fig. 124.—Glottis, vocal cords and entrance to lungs of frog.

parts become associated with the glottis region to form a short larynx into whose lumen a pair of dense elastic folds project as the *vocal cords*. Associated with this cartilage skeleton are skeletal muscles controlling the opening and closing of the glottis. Posterior to the larynx there is a short tracheal region also supplied with smaller cartilage bars which are lost

where it subdivides into the bronchi which immediately open into lungs. The epithelial membrane covering the glottis is usually stratified squamous and continues as such over the vocal cords, but the other portions of the larynx and the trachea have a stratified ciliated columnar epithelium with numerous goblet cells. This latter type continues along the bronchi and into the lungs over the surfaces bordering the central lumen.

In the development of the lung of the frog, and other Amphibia where respiration is partially carried on in this organ, the embryonic and primitive lung sac is modified by alveolar evagination between which the wall of the sac extends as branching septa to the central lumen. The first outpocketings, the *infundibula*, are further subdivided into alveoli about which tissues of the early septa extend and carry a vascular supply. The mature lung still maintains a saccular form with a central cavity into which the infundibula open between the network of supporting septa. (Fig. 125.)

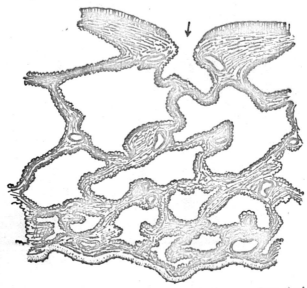

Fig. 125.—A cross-section of the frog's lung with the arrow from the lung cavity indicating an opening between septa into an infundibulum; the numerous irregular spaces are the alveoli separated by connective tissue carrying blood-vessels.

The epithelial membrane from the bronchus continues into the lung unchanged over the septa forming the broken wall for the central lumen. As the membrane extends into the infundibula, the stratified columnar condition gives way to simple ciliated columnar cells with occasional goblet cells, then to simple cuboidal cells, and finally a simple squamous membrane forms the lining of the alveolar respiratory portions. The thin wall of the lung is composed of an outer surface of squamous mesothelium below which is a narrow region of fibroelastic tissue with some smooth muscle. The tissue of the wall, except the mesothelium, continues as broader bands to form the septa into the lumen and as a delicate reticular and elastic support for the alveoli to which it carries a capillary network. Scattered smooth muscle cells and chromatophores are also present in this interalveolar tissue. (Fig. 28.) The septa have a heavier connective tissue with bundles of smooth muscle cells and support the veins to which blood returns from the alveolar capillary network supplied by arteries in the wall. With inflation, the lung wall stretches, the central lumen increases in size, and the alveoli are distended and flattened.

A greater increase in subdivisions of the infundibula and subsequent alveolar divisions increases the alveolar respiratory portion in the toad where the lung plays a greater part and resembles conditions found in the lung of relatively advanced reptiles.

## THE RESPIRATORY SYSTEM OF REPTILES

The respiratory system of this class shows great variability, ranging as it does from simple conditions similar to those of Amphibia to modifications resembling those to be found in birds. The larynx is similar to that described in the frog but the trachea may show variation from a short duct to a long tube supported by bars or rings of cartilage. The bronchi likewise may vary from a direct opening to division into two or more smaller branches which supply a similarly lobulated lung. The lung structure is similar to that of the frog in its respiratory portion but a saccular region without alveolar modifications may foreshadow the more elaborate extension of air sacs in birds. The bronchi also show stages in degree of their incorporation into the lung until a definite intralobular bronchus is surrounded by the alveolar respiratory portions.

### Lizard

In this form, the glottis and larynx are very similar to those of the frog. There is developed a fold of pharyngeal tissue, the *epiglottis*, covered by stratified ciliated columnar epithelium supported by fibroelastic tissue in which skeletal muscle fibers are located that control the movement of the fold. The trachea is similar to that of the frog but is longer; its cartilage rings extend into two short bronchial subdivisions.

The lung of the lizard has a respiratory portion in which infundibula and alveolar sacs supported by septa are structurally similar to conditions found in the frog. Another portion of the lung has the structural features of a simple saccular lung such as in Necturus and is thought to act here in a mechanical capacity as a reservoir for air. Thus the saccular form with a central lumen is still a prominent feature among the reptiles although in some a more compact respiratory mass of alveoli is developed about the bronchi.

## THE RESPIRATORY SYSTEM OF BIRDS

With this class the respiratory system shows a marked and peculiar development of the lung, which has the appearance of a spongy mass, over conditions in preceding classes, where the saccular structure remained apparent in most, even though alveolar development produced a spongy wall. The long trachea is held

open by a series of cartilage rings which continue into the bronchi. Each bronchus enters the lung in a medial ventral region, where it enlarges as the antrum or vestibule, then continues as a main duct or *mesobronchus* through to the distal end of the lung, giving off *secondary bronchi* named according to their position in the lung. Each of the secondary bronchi from either the vestibule or mesobronchus divides into smaller bronchi of uniform diameter, the *parabronchi* or *air pipes*, which usually connect at their distal ends with other parabronchi, thus forming a network of these structures without any ending blindly. Infundibula and respiratory alveoli are derived from the walls of the parabronchi to form the bulk of the lung. The distal end of the mesobronchus and several secondary bronchi continue from the lung as extensive thin-walled air sacs or reservoirs which extend into various parts of the body and into the bones. Air enters these directly and returns through parabronchi and alveoli; thus they may play a part in buoyancy, act as reservoirs and play some part in temperature regulation.

The vocal center of birds is not in the larynx but a similar structural arrangement, the *syrinx*, located in the trachea at its division into the bronchi. Cartilage rings are modified in this region and membranes projecting into the tracheal lumen vibrate as air is forced past them. The connective tissue wall is thickened in this region and a mass of skeletal muscle associated with the wall changes the lumen diameter and governs the pitch of sounds produced.

### Pigeon

The structure of the larynx resembles conditions observed in the frog and reptile with the addition of a more conspicuous cartilaginous skeleton. The stratified squamous epithelial membrane of the pharynx continues past the glottis a short distance before a transition to a stratified ciliated columnar membrane takes place. This stratified columnar epithelium is composed of only two or three layers of cells but gives an appearance of greater thickness due to the numerous closely packed, short, tubular mucous glands. A thin region of subepithelial connective tissue, the *tunica propria*, connects the membrane with the surrounding cartilage pieces or groups of skeletal muscle fibers. Isolated lymphoid nodules occur in the tunica propria. A similar epithelial and connective tissue composition forms the lining of the trachea to the region of the syrinx with the addition of numerous goblet cells among the superficial columnar cells. At the syrinx, the epithelium is composed of two layers of low cuboidal cells without cilia and without associated glands. The connective tissue is greatly increased and a mass of skeletal muscle fibers occurs outside the cartilage rings. As the trachea breaks into the bronchi below the syrinx, the epithelial membrane is composed of a layer of cuboidal cells supporting a layer of ciliated columnar cells among which goblet cells are very numerous. Short tubular glands occur in this membrane in the region between the cartilage rings.

Sections of the lung present a number of various sized, relatively large ducts and a multitude of small uniform ones surrounded by the respiratory tissue. The single largest smooth walled opening represents the vestibule, the several next largest are the secondary bronchi, the smallest smooth walled ducts are the bronchial branches of these secondaries. The numerous small uniform openings immediately surrounded by the respiratory tissue are the parabronchi.

Each parabronchus has opening from it numerous radially arranged diverticula called *atria* separated by septa. Each atrium is subdivided into several *infundibula* from which a number of *alveoli* arise. The atrium

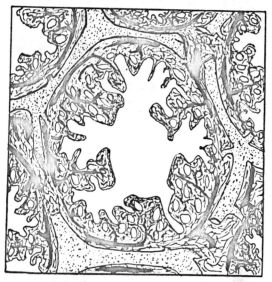

Fig. 126.—A cross-section of a parabronchus, showing atria opening into infundibula which divide into the alveoli. The arterial supply is in black, the veins are stippled.

and its subdivisions compose a lobule which is separated from adjoining lobules by interlobular septa of connective tissue carrying the vascular capillary supply to the alveoli and infundibula. Branches of the prominent pulmonary vein and less conspicuous artery lie in the thin connective tissue wall between the bases of the lobules of adjoining parabronchi. A simple squamous or very low cuboidal membrane lines the broken wall of the parabronchus and rests upon a region of fibroelastic tissue and smooth muscle. A simple squamous membrane extends into the atrium and its subdivisions where it rests upon a delicate reticulum supporting the capillary supply. Special preparations indicate the probability of a continuous layer of epithelium over the respiratory surfaces although this is difficult to demonstrate.

## THE RESPIRATORY SYSTEM OF MAMMALS

The respiratory system in this class presents essentially similar structures in most forms, contrary to the variability among forms

of the preceding classes. When the mouth of a mammal is closed, air is taken in through the nasal passages into the larynx and on to the trachea which divides into a bronchus for each lung. Air passes from the bronchus through smaller branches to bronchioles and eventually reaches the microscopic end-pieces, the respiratory alveoli, where gaseous exchange takes place.

The nose is an organ composed of bone, cartilage, muscle, skin, and epithelial membranes, so constructed as to provide open ways for the passage of air. The integumentary composition continues some distance inward from the nares but stratified squamous epithelium, hairs and sebaceous glands are then lost and replaced by a ciliated pseudostratified columnar epithelium with numerous goblet cells which continues to line later branchings until the bronchiolar divisions are reached. The olfactory area of the passage has epithelium composed of three types of cells. There are small basal cells and long, thin supporting cells between which are scattered fusiform neuro-epithelial cells associated with olfactory reception.

The nasal cavity opens into many irregular spaces, or *sinuses*, lined with a thin columnar membrane with goblet cells which is closely joined by its underlying connective tissue to the periosteum of the bony depressions forming the sinuses. The nasal passage continues posteriorly into the pharynx, where the epithelium consists of pseudostratified ciliated epithelium. Many of the long superficial cells are goblet cells, and the surface of the membrane is generally well moistened with mucus. Under the epithelium is fibroelastic connective tissue carrying lymphatics, blood-vessels, nerves, and small mixed mucoserous glands.

**The Larynx.**—The larynx has a skeleton of a number of cartilaginous pieces, some of them single units, others occurring in pairs. In general, these cartilages are of the hyaline variety and are covered with perichondrium which merges with the fibroelastic connective tissue forming the external covering of the larynx. Many small muscles of the voluntary striated type are associated with the cartilages. Toward the lumen, from the cartilages, is a fibroelastic connective tissue which may be called a *submucosa*. Immediately underlying the epithelium is a looser vascular fibroelastic tissue called the *tunica propria*, which may contain many lymphocytes and isolated lymphoid nodules. The epithelium of the mucosa is of the pseudostratified ciliated variety, except over the vocal cords and under the epiglottis where it is stratified squamous.

The *vocal cords* are a pair of shelf-like tissue masses. extending from the lateral walls of the larynx into the laryngeal cavity. Each vocal cord has an external skeletal muscle mass. Internal to this toward the lumen, is dense elastic tissue with a stratified squamous epithelial covering.

**The Trachea.**—The trachea is a dilated tube extending from the larynx to the bronchi. It is just below the skin of the neck in the mid-ventral line and dorsal to it is the esophagus. Laterally the muscles and blood-vessels of the neck are associated with fibroelastic connective tissue which also forms the outer covering of the trachea. The thyroid gland lies against its ventral surface just posterior to the larynx. As it enters the thorax, the trachea divides into two branches, the bronchi, one of which enters each lung.

Embedded in the tracheal connective tissue are crescents of hyaline cartilage which keep this air passage dilated. In old animals they

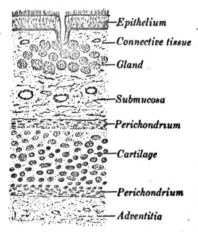

FIG. 127.—Mammalian trachea cross-section.

may become fibrous or undergo partial ossification. The opening of each cartilage crescent is adjacent to the esophagus and is occupied by branching and anastomosing bands of circular smooth muscle. The cartilages are enclosed in perichondrium and the superficial portions of the perichondrium merge with the adventitial connective tissues and with similar fibroelastic connective tissue lying between adjacent cartilages. The internal connective tissue may be called a submucosa and is rich in elastic fibers. (Fig. 127.) In it are many small compound mucous and mixed mucoserous glands. The submucosa also contains many scattered lymphocytes and occasional lymph nodules.

The mucosa is composed of ciliated pseudostratified epithelium containing numerous goblet cells which add mucus to that from the submucosal glands, thus keeping the internal surface of the trachea moistened.

**The Lungs.**—Since the respiratory system of mammals arises embryologically as a diverticulum from the embryonic foregut and develops as a compound alveolar gland, the trachea represents the principal excretory duct which divides posteriorly into two bronchi and many smaller bronchioles. The lung is thus divided into many lobules which are conical or pyramidal in shape and composed of a number of terminal bronchioles and their subdivisions; adjacent lobules are separated from each other by interlobular connective tissue carrying arterial and venous vessels. The lungs are invested with a thin double membrane, the *parietal* and *visceral pleura* similar in structure to the peritoneum, with a potential space between the

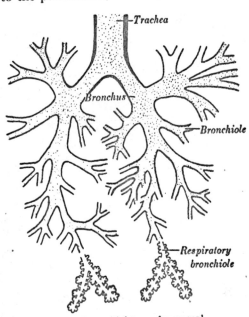

FIG. 128.—Bronchial tree of mammal.

two membranes. The visceral pleural membrane adjacent to the lung contains smooth muscle in its connective tissue and dips down into the spaces between adjacent lung lobes to continue with the connective tissue between the lobules.

*Bronchi and Branches.*—Each bronchus has about the same structure as the trachea but as it subdivides into bronchioles the size of the tubes decreases as the branching progresses. (Fig. 128.) Histological changes also appear. Cartilage crescents change to flat cartilage plates which become smaller and smaller in the branchings until finally no cartilage supports the smallest bronchioles. Patches of smooth muscle arranged concentrically around the tube appear just within the cartilage plates in the tunica propria. As the branches decrease in size the muscle increases proportionately until in the very small or terminal bronchioles there is no cartilage but a distinct circular sheet of smooth muscle is present outside the tunica propria. The epithelium changes gradually from a pseudo-stratified variety with goblet cells until in the small bronchioles there is but one layer of ciliated columnar epithelium and the goblet cells have disappeared. The glands in the tunica propria, which in the larger bronchi were so numerous, have decreased so that there are none in the smallest branches. The mucosa and tunica propria in smaller branches form longitudinal folds, nearly filling the lumen when the lung is not dilated.

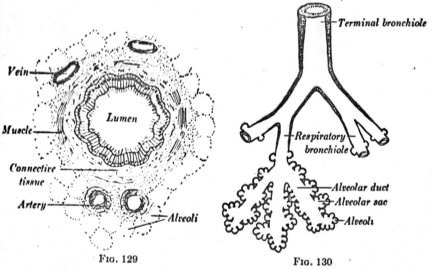

FIG. 129                    FIG. 130

FIG. 129.—Diagram of section of a terminal bronchiole, the lumen lined with ciliated columnar epithelium.

FIG. 130.—Terminal bronchiole of mammal and its branches.

*Terminal bronchioles* (Fig. 129) are separated from the respiratory tissue by their adventitia, a thin layer of fibroelastic connective tissue. The tunica propria of connective tissue is rich in elastic fibers arranged lengthwise of the tube and supports the mucosa of ciliated columnar epithelium lining the lumen.

Each terminal bronchiole divides into two or more *respiratory bronchioles.* (Fig. 130.) Near its origin, the mucosa of this subdivision has ciliated columnar epithelium; distally the cilia are lacking and the cells are cuboidal. Outside the mucosa the wall is very thin, consisting of fibrous tissue containing numerous elastic fibers and scattered smooth muscle cells. It has a few small saccular

diverticula, the *respiratory* or *pulmonary alveoli*, whose lining consists of squamous epithelium invested with a rich capillary network.

At its distal end the respiratory bronchiole divides into two or more short, thin-walled, irregular *alveolar ducts*. The simple squamous epithelium of the thin wall is supported by a very small amount of fibrous tissue with elastic fibers and a few scattered smooth muscle cells. The wall is broken along its length by many saccular diverticula, either *alveolar sacs* or single pulmonary alveoli. (Fig. 131.) The fibrous tissue, elastic fibers, and smooth muscle

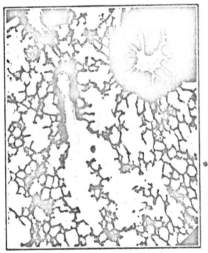

Fig. 131.—Photograph of the lung of a rabbit, showing a small bronchiole in upper right. In the center a respiratory bronchiole is shown breaking into two alveolar ducts and their alveoli. 16 mm. obj. and 5× oc.

cells are chiefly in the wall of the alveolar duct, around the openings to the alveolar sacs and pulmonary alveoli. The alveolar sacs are not single bladder-like enlargements, but each consists of a cluster of respiratory or pulmonary alveoli which are analogous with the secretory end-pieces of a gland like the parotid. Alveolar sacs and respiratory alveoli have walls composed of a squamous epithelial membrane, reticular cells, argyrophil and elastic fibers. The lining of the alveolar surface is still a controversial subject; evidence now supports the concept of a continuous epithelial covering in most forms; in others, sections show breaks where capillary endothelium forms the surface lining. Whatever its composition this membrane is constantly bathed by watery fluid and there is a constant loss of water from the lungs. The alveolar wall usually contains large cells called *dust cells*, which are macrophages that have phagocytosed particles of carbon or other foreign material reaching the alveolar surface. Their origin is debatable though probably from the histocyte or reticular cell. They may migrate into the bronchioles to be carried out with the mucous sheet or enter the vessels for removal.

Each pulmonary unit, therefore, consists of a respiratory bronchiole and its alveolar sacs and pulmonary alveoli. The alveolar sacs and alveoli are invested with a fine, close-meshed network of large capillaries, so thick-set that the spaces between adjacent capillaries is less than the width of the capillaries. Between adjacent alveoli there is also a rich meshwork of reticular and elastic fibers, and scattered smooth muscle cells. Routine sections show the structure of alveolar walls poorly and special preparations are necessary to demonstrate their composition.

*Vascular Supply.*—The lungs are supplied by two sets of blood-vessels, namely, (*a*) the bronchial arteries and veins, and (*b*) pulmonary arteries and veins. The bronchial vessels arise from the systemic system and their branches extend through connective tissue down into the interlobular connective tissues. The pulmonary artery arises from the right ventricle and has a branch to each lung, where its branches follow those of the bronchi. Alongside a terminal bronchiole is a very small branch of a pulmonary artery. This branches as the respiratory bronchioles are formed, so that near the alveolar ducts and sacs the pulmonary arterioles break into capillaries which invest the alveoli. At the lateral borders of the alveoli of a pulmonary unit, the small venules originate which unite to form small veins of the pulmonary venous system. In a section of a lung, the branches of the pulmonary vein are somewhat distant from a bronchiole. The pulmonary venous system carries blood partially depleted of carbon dioxide and enriched with oxygen to the left auricle to be distributed to all organs and tissues.

The lungs are innervated by branches of the sympathetic system and vagus (tenth cranial) nerve. The abundant supply of smooth muscle and elastic tissue present play an important part in the recurring movements of inspiration and expiration. In addition to these, there are the muscular diaphragm and the intercostal muscles which play a rôle in respiratory movements.

Before birth the lung resembles a compound tubulo-alveolar gland, the terminal pieces being lined with cuboidal epithelium. At birth, the contact of the air with the body usually acts as a stimulus to start up the series of inspirations and expirations that continue until death. Usually, before birth and inspiration of air the alveoli become partially distended and have a fluid content, but this distention is accentuated in a few hours after birth so that the lining cuboidal cells of the terminal pieces are flattened to squamous form.

# CHAPTER XI

## THE DIGESTIVE SYSTEM

ARISING from the simple embryonic invaginations which form the fore and hind gut, there develops in all vertebrates a system for service in digestion and absorption of food, and elimination of the unused residues of these processes. This system is composed of a canal of varying lengths which extends from the lips at the anterior or oral opening to the posterior cloacal or anal opening.

Food is taken in at the mouth, where it is usually subject to the mechanical process of mastication by the tongue and the teeth. The secretions of the glands of this region pass into the oral cavity to aid in lubricating the food for passage. Food thus crushed and lubricated passes into the esophagus which conducts it to the stomach where digestive juices are poured upon it from the glands of the stomach walls. Very little, if any, absorption occurs in the stomach where the food is stored temporarily and is actively worked upon by digestive enzymes. It is passed from the lower end of the stomach by peristaltic waves into the small intestine, whose surface is greatly increased by folds. Secretions from small glands and cells of the epithelial membrane in the intestinal wall, together with the secretions from the pancreas and the liver, which are introduced here by ducts from these two organs, are all mixed with the food mass in the lumen. Under combined chemical activities of the secretions added to it, the food is broken into products which are capable of being absorbed through the epithelial wall of the intestine. Passing through the small intestine the unabsorbed portion of the food enters the large intestine where absorption of water takes place. The glands lining the walls of the large intestine are mainly active in coating the lumen with a protective mucus which may also lubricate unusuable materials and waste by-products of digestion for passage and elimination.

### ORAL CAVITY

**Lips.**—The transition from the integument over either jaw into the oral cavity is commonly marked by a slight or well-defined fold, the lips, at which point there is a change in histological structure from that typical of the integument to conditions characteristic of the oral cavity.

**Teeth.**—These are projections above the oral surface over the jaws used for holding prey and reducing it or other food into form suitable for swallowing. The true tooth which is typical of most vertebrates is very similar to the placoid scale in its origin and is a product of both epithelium and connective tissue. Another less common type among vertebrates is a *cuticular tooth* derived entirely from accumulation of cornified epithelial cells.

**Tongue.**—Although a fleshy projection from the floor of mouth into the oral cavity forms a tongue in nearly all vertebrates, it varies widely in the extent of development, degree of motility, and histological composition. It occurs as a fleshy immotile fold supported by a cartilaginous skeleton among fish; as a muscular motile flap in some Amphibia; as a slender, very motile, muscular, tubular projection in some reptiles with the incorporation of part of the hyoid apparatus; as a horny non-muscular structure in birds, motile through action of associated hyoid skeletal parts; and as a primarily muscular and very motile organ among the mammals.

**Oral Glands.**—Among the fishes, glandular modifications are limited to the scattered glandular cells of the lining epithelium, but in the other classes there are an increasing number of glandular derivatives of the cavity which increase in the complexity of their organization until the peak of development is represented by the compound *salivary glands*.

### ALIMENTARY TRACT

The portion of the digestive system between the oral cavity and cloacal or anal opening is in the form of a tube which shows great variation in length and complexity of development in various forms. However, the wall of the tube has a histological organization that is fundamentally similar in all forms; it is composed of four coats or tunics of tissues, namely, *mucosa, submucosa, muscularis,* and *adventitia* or *serosa*.

**Mucosa.**—This innermost coat of the tube is composed of an epithelial membrane and the thin region of supporting reticular and fibroelastic tissue called the *tunica propria* or *lamina propria*. An additional thin inner circular and outer longitudinal layer of smooth muscle, the *muscularis mucosæ*, when present, marks the external boundary of the mucosa and the inner boundary of the submucosa. In the absence of the muscularis mucosæ, the tunica propria is more densely organized where it continues directly with the broader region of loose fibroelastic tissue forming the submucosa. The mucosa presents the greatest variability of all the coats through the different modifications of the lining epithelium and the glandular derivatives of it in the various divisions of the alimentary tract.

**Submucosa.**—This is a region of loose fibroelastic tissue carrying the branches of vessels supplying the capillary network to the mucosa. A plexus of sympathetic neurons, *Meissner's plexus* or the *submucosal plexus*, occurs in this region and fibers from it extend into the mucosa. In some regions glands derived from the mucosa extend down into the submucosa.

**Muscularis.**—An internal circular and an external longitudinal layer of muscle, usually smooth in type but striated in the regions at either extremity of the tube, form the muscular tunic. In the fibroelastic connective tissue separating the two muscle layers there is a sympathetic plexus. *Auerbach's plexus* or the *myenteric plexus*, whose fibers innervate the muscle tissue.

**Adventitia or Serosa.**—The outermost coat of the wall is composed of fibroelastic tissue which continues with adjoining tissues as the adventitia or *fibrosa* where the tube is not within the body cavity. Within the body cavity, or cœlome, this adventitial layer is supplied by the peritoneum surfaced by mesothelium, and is called the *tunica serosa*.

Such a general structural plan is true for the gut wall throughout the classes, but variations in the component elements and their arrangement occur even between closely related forms or in the same form at different periods of development. A description of all the variations within a class is impractical, but conditions in a common representative of each class will be considered. Such consideration will deal primarily with mucosal conditions where variations are most marked and characteristic for the various regions; consideration of the other coats will be omitted unless they vary from the conditions described as generally characteristic.

**Liver.**—This is the largest and most universal gland among the vertebrates and is derived as a compound tubular structure from the embryonic gut. It lies outside the gut wall, filling a large part of the body cavity, and connects with the gut through a duct representing the original diverticulum from which it developed. The cellular composition is remarkably uniform in view of the variety of functions associated with this gland and the vascular supply is extremely abundant about the secretory tubules. The liver functions involve storage of fats and glycogen, secretion of bile salts which are contributed to the intestine, excretion of bile pigments and other wastes removed from the blood, formation of urea, and others. Experiments have demonstrated marked regenerative powers on the part of the liver; the undestroyed cells multiply rapidly to replace large amounts of hepatic tissue.

**Pancreas.**—This is much smaller than the liver but also originates as a diverticulum of the embryonic gut. It develops as a tubulo-alveolar gland with secreting acini composed of serous cells whose secretions are carried to the duodenum near which it lies. In addition to this exocrine structure, there is present in most vertebrates an associated endocrine tissue localized as the *Islands of Langerhans* whose secretion, *insulin,* enters the blood steam and governs sugar metabolism. This island tissue is derived from the small pancreatic ducts and then usually loses direct connection with them. Pancreatic tissue is also capable of limited regeneration following injury but atrophies if the excretory ducts are obstructed or ligated. Island tissue is not destroyed by such interference with the excretory ducts and can regenerate from duct epithelia.

**Pyloric Ceca.**—These structures are present among the teleosts where they occur as several or many finger-like diverticula of the duodenum at the pyloric junction. Their composition is similar to that of the intestine into which their small lumens open and their secretory products are added to the duodenal content.

### The Digestive System of the Dogfish

**Oral Cavity and Pharynx.**—A single large cavity is differentiated into an anterior mouth or oral portion and a posterior pharynx, both lined by a continuation of the stratified squamous epithelium and supporting connective tissue found in the integument. The mucosa of the mouth is broken through over the cartilages of the upper and lower jaws by rows of large p'acoid scales which here constitute the teeth. The origin of these structures is identical with that of the scales of the integument where they have already been described. In other parts of the mouth and in regions of the pharynx about the gill clefts scales are also present. The tongue is represented by a thickened pad of connective tissue in the floor of the mouth. Toward the back of the mouth longitudinal folds of underlying connective tissue are formed and become larger through the pharynx region from which they extend into the esophagus.

**Esophagus.**—The transition from mouth through the pharynx to the esophagus is marked by an increase in cell layers composing the epithelial membrane and the appearance of numerous mucous cells. The submucosal tissue, which is scanty in the mouth, becomes better developed as the esophagus is approached and forms high papillæ and prominent longitudinal folds which together with secondary mucosal ones fill the lumen of the esophagus. Large areas of myeloid tissue may be found in the submucosal tissue at the junction of the esophagus and stomach. (Fig. 132, *A*.)

**Stomach.**—The submucosal papillæ disappear as the esophagus approaches the cardiac stomach where shorter longitudinal submucosal folds form the *rugæ*. Smooth muscle bundles appear in the muscularis of the lower esophagus and finally replace the skeletal type when the stomach is reached; and the external coat is a serosa surfaced by cuboidal mesothelium. (Fig. 133.)

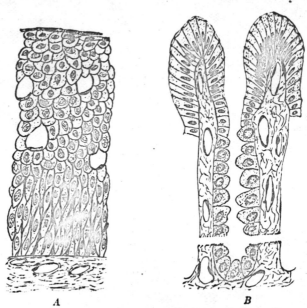

A                              B

Fɪɢ. 132.—Mucosa of the esophagus (*A*) and mucosa of the fundic stomach (*B*) of the dogfish. The break in the fundic gland represents a length of gland equal to that from the neck of the gland to the break.

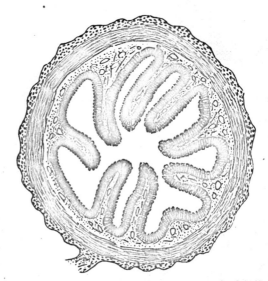

Fɪɢ. 133.—Diagram of a cross-section of the stomach of a dogfish (Squalus acanthias). This shows ruga-like folds of submucosa extending in toward the lumen. The mucosa contains closely arranged simple tubular glands. A muscularis mucosæ separates these glands from the submucosa. The muscularis coat is represented by a circular smooth muscle sheath and a thin longitudinal sheath. The serosa is relatively thick.

The mucosa of the stomach is composed of a superficial membrane of long tapering columnar cells and numerous associated tubular glands. The distal portion of the superficial cells has a characteristic clear border which usually appears unstained in routine sections. Special methods demonstrate this to be an alkaline mucus which forms a continuous coat of relatively uniform thickness over the surface, possibly preventing autolytic action on the stomach tissue by the enzymes in its lumen. The superficial cells secreting this border have oval, darkly staining nuclei located in the proximal half of the cell. The cytoplasm is composed of finely granular and fibrillar acidophilic material sharply differentiated from the distal mucous border.

Folds of the superficial membrane form *gastric crypts* or *pits* lined by the same type of epithelium. From these crypts, tubular *gastric glands* develop and are surrounded by a delicate reticulum of the propria supporting a capillary supply. Two types of glands may be differentiated and are named for the cardiac and pyloric regions of the stomach.

In the *cardiac glands* a short neck portion of the gland immediately adjoins the crypt and is lined by low columnar or cuboidal cells whose darkly staining nuclei nearly fill the cell. The cells of this region are usually associated with the production of new cells for the superficial membrane or for the deeper glandular region. The secretory part of the tubule is composed of columnar cells; their nuclei are spherical, lightly staining and located at the proximal portion; the cytoplasm is filled with small strongly acidophilic granules. A denser fibroelastic tissue composes the propria at the base of the glands and a very thin muscularis mucosæ separate it from the submucosa. (Fig. 132, *B*.)

The pyloric region of the stomach has fewer and shorter glands than the cardiac region. The *pyloric glands* are also more twisted and the cuboidal or low columnar cells forming their walls lack the strongly acidophilic granules found in the preceding glands. At the junction of the pyloric region with the intestine the muscularis has a band of circular muscle forming the pyloric sphincter.

**Duodenum.**—The transition from the pylorus to the intestine is marked by an increased number of longitudinal mucosal and submucosal folds, a loss of the pyloric glands, and a change in the nature of the superficial epithelium.

The superficial epithelium is still columnar in form but most of the cells are goblet cells actively secreting an accumulation of mucus in the distal half of the cell and having a granular acidophilic proximal portion of cytoplasm containing the nucleus. This superficial membrane folds to form short tubular pockets lined by the same type of cells but with less prominent mucous secretions, and the tunica propria projects the mucosa into the lumen as thin folds. A number of large spherical cells filled with coarse acidophilic granules (eosinophils) may appear among the bases of the columnar cells. Lymphocytes occur abundantly in the tunica propria and myeloid nodules may be organized here and in the submucosal tissue throughout the duodenum and following valvular intestine. Areas of granulocytes, especially eosinophils, occur in the submucosa of these two regions and the granular cells noted in the mucosa may represent invasions of these granulocytes. (Fig. 134.)

**Spiral Valve (Ileum).**—The posterior end of the duodenum broadens and contains the beginning of the submucosal fold which extends across the broad

lumen as it spirals to form the conspicuous valvular part of the intestine. This submucosal fold, which forms the spiral valve, carries along the mucosa which is thrown into numerous small folds by the tunica propria. Short tubular pockets occur between the base of the mucosal folds and are lined by the same type cells as the superficial mucosa. The mucosa of the spiralling folds and also the wall between the spirals has an epithelial membrane composed of long slender cells with a brush or striated border and an acidophilic granular cytoplasm in which mucus or vacuoles may

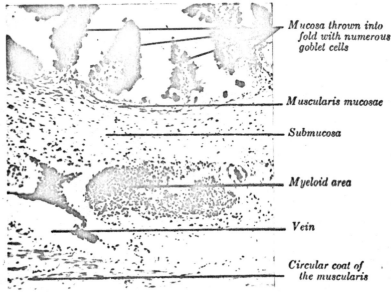

*Mucosa thrown into fold with numerous goblet cells*

*Muscularis mucosae*

*Submucosa*

*Myeloid area*

*Vein*

*Circular coat of the muscularis*

Fig. 134.—A transverse section of the duodenum of the dogfish. Photograph. 16 mm. obj. and 5× oc.

occur distally. An oval nucleus is located in the middle or proximal region of each cell. Goblet cells occur scattered more abundantly among the absorptive cells over the folds than in the pockets. The tunica propria is commonly invaded by numerous lymphocytes and eosinophils which may migrate among the columnar cells and into the intestinal lumen. The wall of this valvular intestine is similar to that of the duodenum except that the muscularis has a very thin longitudinal layer of smooth muscle.

**Colon and Rectum.**—The valvular intestine abruptly narrows to a tube of much smaller caliber and the prominent submucosal fold is lost. The mucosa still has low longitudinal folds and these continue to the cloaca. Goblet cells and eosinophils increase in numbers. The colon, which is the region adjoining the spiral valve, almost immediately continues into the rectum, the junction of the two being marked by the origin of the rectal gland. The epithelium of the colon is composed of slender columnar cells, many of which are goblet cells, glandular pockets are absent and a muscularis mucosæ is usually absent. The muscularis has the inner and outer layers of equal but not prominent development. In the rectum the epithelium has two or three layers with the superficial one of low columnar and goblet cells.

13

**Cloaca.**—The junction of the rectum with the wide cloaca is marked by a transition to stratified squamous epithelium similar to the epidermis. The tunica propria and submucosa of this region become continuous with the dermis of the integument. The smooth muscle continues over the cloaca to the region of the external opening where it is replaced by skeletal muscle.

**Rectal Gland.**—A short main collecting duct extends from the rectal lumen to a central space in the gland from which collecting ducts radiate to end in a number of twisted tubular secretory end-pieces. The lining of the main duct is similar to the epithelium of the rectum, the wall about the duct and the sheath about the gland represent continuations of the peritoneum or serosa of the rectum. The central space of the gland is lined by two or three layers of low cuboidal cells, the radiating ducts have two and then a single layer of cuboidal cells. Spherical cells filled with mucus occur commonly in the duct epithelium. The secretory cells of the tubules have a denser proximal cytoplasm with a striated appearance, the distal cytoplasm varies from a relatively clear area to a content of coarse acidophilic granules. Sections of these tubules resemble the convoluted tubules to be studied in the kidneys. The function of this gland is not known.

**Liver.**—This gland is divided into large right and left lobes and a small median lobe containing a gall-bladder representing an enlargement of the common bile duct which continues into the duodenum. No lobules are separated and the glandular tissue is compactly organized. The development of venous capillaries between the secretory tubules is accompanied by reduction of the tubule lumen to a minute canal. The duct lining varies from the very tall columnar cells in the gall-bladder, the main duct and its branches, to the shorter cells in subsequent divisions until the smallest ducts have a low cuboidal lining. The distal third of the duct cells contains an acidophilic mucus. The gall-bladder, the main duct and its branches have a definite muscularis of smooth muscle but the smaller ducts have a gradually diminishing wall until only a delicate connective tissue sheath surrounds them. A fibroelastic sheath with some smooth muscle surrounds the liver and is surfaced by cuboidal mesothelium.

The hepatic cells are pyramidal in form with the apex facing the very small lumen and the broader proximal portion resting on the reticular tissue adjoining the capillary network. In routine sections the cytoplasm has numerous small or a few large clear vacuoles, which can be demonstrated to contain fats by special techniques, and a small amount of scattered finely granular acidophilic material. There are also scattered cells distended to spherical form with dark pigment. The vascular network separating the liver cords is in the form of sinusoids with walls of endothelium and reticular tissue. The reticular cells here are the *Kupffer* cells which act as macrophages and phagocytose débris from the sinusoids.

**Pancreas.**—Like the liver this gland arises as a diverticulum of the intestine and develops as a tubulo-alveolar gland. The original diverticulum forms the main excretory duct which subdivides into interlobular ducts that in turn break up into intralobular ones whose small branches form secretory ducts opening into the acini. The entire gland is enclosed in a very thin connective tissue sheath whose elements continue into the gland to form the supporting fibroelastic and reticular tissue about the ducts and end-pieces. The mesothelium covering the sheath is composed mainly of cuboidal cells but an area of ciliated columnar cells commonly occurs along

the ventral surface. The main duct and its branches have a mucosa composed of an epithelial membrane of very tall closely packed columnar cells with oval nuclei located in the proximal region of a finely granular acidophilic cytoplasm; the tunica propria is surrounded by a muscularis of circular and longitudinally arranged smooth muscle. The interlobular ducts also have tall columnar cells but no muscularis. The intralobular ducts have a cuboidal epithelial lining and a thin tunica propria only. The secretory ducts have a very low cuboidal membrane supported by a very thin tunica propria.

The secretory cells of the end-piece or acinus may reflect back over the secretory duct and as a result of this arrangement sections often show the end cells of the duct in the lumen over the secretory cells, a condition leading to naming them *centro-acinar* cells. The secretory cells are tall

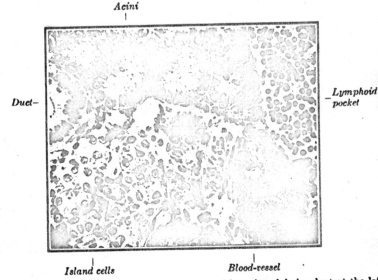

*Acini*

*Duct—*

*Lymphoid pocket*

*Island cells*          *Blood-vessel*

Fig. 135.—A section of the dogfish pancreas with an interlobular duct at the left and a lymphoid pocket at the right. The pancreatic acini have coarsely granular cells and centro-acinar cells are present. An island composed of lightly staining acidophilic cells separated by capillaries adjoins the interlobular duct. Photomicrograph. 4 mm. obj. and 5× cc.

pyramids in form when active, but are shorter during inactive stages. A spherical nucleus with a prominent nucleolus lies in the proximal portion and the cytoplasm of this region is filled with small basophilic granules. The distal half of actively secreting cells is filled with coarse acidophilic zymogen granules. (Fig. 135.)

Prominent and numerous pockets or channels lined by endothelial or reticular cells and filled with lymphocytes similar to those found in the lymphoid tissue of the spleen occur among the pancreatic acini. No red blood cells or granulocytes are present in these pockets; blood-vessels may be closely adjoining and appear to drain them.

**Islands of Langerhans.**—These occur as small groups of cells separated by capillaries and commonly associated with the smaller intralobular ducts.

Such islands are apparently derived from the ducts but lose the connection, contain no lumen, and function as endocrine glands. The cells contain a spherical vesicular nucleus usually without a nucleolus and the cytoplasm is lightly acidophilic or relatively clear. Special preparations may demonstrate several types of cells present.

## The Digestive System of the Frog

**Oral Cavity.**—The lips are represented by a fold of dermis along the outside edge of the jaws and at this point there is a loss of the alveolar glands of the epidermis. The stratified squamous epithelium of the epidermis continues past the ridge of the jaws into the oral cavity where stratified ciliated columnar epithelium with numerous goblet cells forms the lining of the mouth (except about the teeth) and pharynx to the beginning of the esophagus. The dermis is replaced by the tunica propria and submucosa in the oral cavity; the chromatophores so abundant in the integument occur as scattered elements in the tunica propria. Numerous papillæ of tunica propria extend into the epithelial membrane. Scattered sensory bodies composed of neuro-epithelia form the taste-buds of this region.

**Teeth.**—At points along the jaw and over the prevomers, patches of epithelial cells form an enamel organ covering a conical papilla of connective tissue. From this association teeth develop and project an enamel covered portion slightly above the surrounding stratified squamous epithelium. The development of the enamel, dentine and pulp follows a sequence similar to that described in placoid scale formation. However, instead of having a basal plate buried in underlying connective tissue like the placoid scales, the base of each of the conical teeth is intimately associated with a shallow pit or alveolus in the underlying bone. The connective tissue adjoining the basal region of dentine of the tooth gives rise to osteoblasts which deposit a bony *cementum* layer with embedded osteocytes fusing the tooth with the bone of the jaw.

*Epidermal teeth* form in the larval stages through accumulations of cornified epithelial cells over connective tissue papillæ in the lip region but are lost with metamorphosis and the development of the true teeth.

**Tongue.**—The tongue of some Amphibia may be merely a connective tissue pad in the floor of the mouth as in the case of many fish, but in the frog this early pad corresponds with the basal portion to which a larger glandular and muscular part is added. The tongue so formed is attached to the anterior floor of the mouth near the jaw with a broad, flat, free motile portion folding back along the floor of the mouth when at rest. The lower surface of the resting tongue is covered by an epithelial membrane like that of the oral cavity, namely, stratified ciliated columnar epithelium with numerous goblet cells. Over the free end this changes to a simple columnar epithelium and invaginations form numerous simple or branched tubular mucous glands. Between the openings of these glands the tunica propria pushes out the epithelial membrane in numerous slender finger-like projections, the *filiform papillæ*, and fewer broader topped papillæ, the *fungiform papillæ*. At the bases of these papillæ there is a transition from the superficial tapering columnar cells of the papillæ with their finely granular acidophilic cytoplasm to the broad columnar mucous cells filled with coarse cytoplasmic granules. At the peak of mucous secretion the cells nearly fill the lumen of the glands, but following liberation of the secretion to the

surface the cells are shorter, have a finely granular cytoplasm, and the lumen appears very wide. The vascular tunica propria which fills in among the glands continues inward as a fibroelastic tissue and joins the similar tissue composing the sheaths of the skeletal muscle bundles that form the bulk of the tongue. Occasional isolated lymphoid nodules occur in the tunica propria of the glandular region. (Fig. 136.)

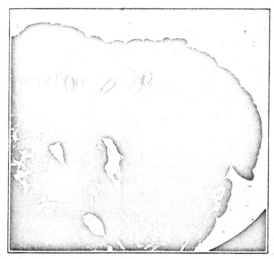

Fig. 136.—Photograph of the tongue of the frog. The upper portion shows the glandular surface, papillæ, and a lymphoid nodule. 32 mm. obj. and 5× oc.

**Oral Glands.**—A number of simple tubular glands are arranged into two groups, one called the *intermaxillary* gland and the other the *palatal gland.* Each is located in the region indicated by the name and the individual tubules open into the oral cavity by excretory ducts lined with columnar epithelium. The secretory end-pieces are composed of columnar cells with basal nuclei and a distal cytoplasm filled with the acidophilic granules. The secretion may supplement that of the tongue glands in forming a sticky covering to the tongue.

**Esophagus.**—The mucosa of the pharynx is thrown into numerous low longitudinal folds which extend into the esophagus where they become more prominent. The epithelial membrane is the same as in the pharynx and oral cavity. Invaginations along the esophagus give rise to compound tubulo-alveolar mucoserous glands located in the submucosa and tunica propria. The excretory duct shows a transition from the stratified ciliated columnar of the esophagus to low columnar near the secretory end-piece. The secretory cells are of mucous and serous types, some alveoli are composed entirely of one type while other alveoli have both mucous and serous cells combined.

The muscularis is composed of skeletal muscle in the pharynx region, but nearer the stomach this is replaced by a broad circular and a narrow longitudinal layer of smooth muscle.

**Stomach.**—When the esophagus opens into the stomach the epithelial membrane changes to a simple columnar type characterized by a clear unstained distal region and an acidophilic granular proximal cytoplasm containing the nucleus, a type of cell already encountered in the dogfish stomach. A muscularis mucosæ makes its appearance in the stomach region and the submucosa forms several longitudinal folds, the rugæ. The cardiac portion of the stomach which immediately adjoins the esophagus is extremely short and contains few or no tubular mucosal glands, but its submucosa may contain a carry-over of some of the submucosal glands of the esophagus. Two major divisions of the stomach are readily distinguished in histological sections, the *fundus* or major portion, and the *pylorus* which adjoins the duodenum. In both these regions the superficial epithelium folds to form gastric pits from which simple or branched tubular gastric glands extend into the tunica propria. (Fig. 137.)

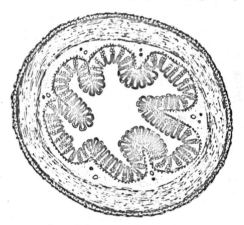

Fig. 137.—A cross-section of the stomach of a frog. The mucosa consists of simple or branched tubular glands whose basal secretory cells are serous in character and acidophilic and the cells at the mouth of the gland appear to be mucous and basophilic. There is a well-defined muscularis mucosæ. The submucosa is thickest in the region of the rugæ. The muscularis coat is represented by a thick circular and a thin longitudinal sheath of smooth muscle. A thin serosa is present.

*Fundic Glands.*—The columnar cells of the pits become shorter and lose the distal clear mucous border of the superficial cells. The neck region opening into the gastric pit is composed of short columnar mucous cells with distal clear cytoplasm, in routine sections, and with nuclei at the proximal extremity. The remainder of the tubule is composed of cuboidal or pyramidal cells with centrally located nuclei in a cytoplasm filled with acidophilic granules. The gastric glands of Necturus (Fig. 138) are like those in the frog.

*Pyloric Glands.*—These glands have shorter gastric pits and shorter more twisted secretory tubules. The mucous cells of the neck region are lacking and cuboidal cells with less granular acidophilic cytoplasm extend from the gastric pits to the base of the glands.

**Small Intestine.**—The transition from the pylorus to the small intestine is marked by the loss of gastric glands and the formation of numerous long slender branching mucosal folds. The epithelial membrane thus intricately folded is composed of columnar cells with a striated border and finely granular acidophilic cytoplasm. Scattered among these cells are goblet cells which become more numerous progressing down the tube toward the

cloaca. A muscularis mucosæ is poorly represented or absent. Eosinophils occur frequently among the bases of the epithelial cells and lymphocytes appear scattered in the tunica propria or as nodules in this region.

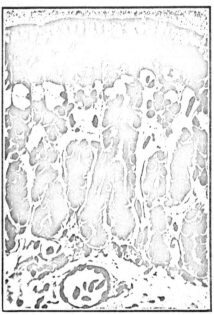

Fig. 138.—A section of the stomach of Necturus, showing the superficial cells with a clear distal mucous content, the few mucous cells in the neck of the glands, and the more granular darkly staining secretory cells in the fundus of the simple or branched tubular glands. Photomicrograph. 4 mm. obj. and 5× oc.

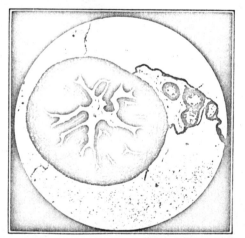

Fig. 139.—Photograph of a cross-section of the small intestine of the frog, showing branching longitudinal folds. Blood-vessels are shown in the supporting mesentery. 32 mm. obj. and 5× oc.

**Large Intestine.**—The portion of this region adjoining the small intestine (the *colon*) is a short broad-lumened region in which the long intricate mucosal folds are absent. In their place is a network of mucosal folds so low that the lumen may appear smooth under low magnifications. The lining epithelial membrane is composed primarily of goblet cells. A muscularis mucosæ is poorly represented or absent and the muscularis has two thin layers. A narrower posterior region (the *rectum*) has a number of longitudinal submucosal folds which fill the lumen in the empty tube. The epithelial membrane is composed of goblet cells. The muscularis is much better developed than in the anterior region.

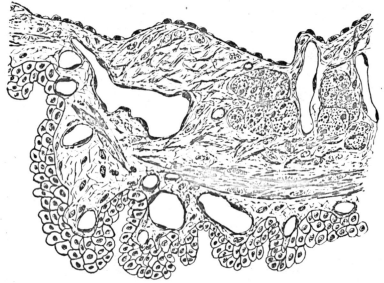

Fig. 140.—Cloaca of the frog. The mucosa is folded and composed of from two to three layers of cuboidal cells over a vascular tunica propria-submucosa. The muscularis has a broken coat of smooth muscle with skeletal muscle occurring towards the anus. Mesothelial cells cover the external surface.

**Cloaca.**—The rectum opens into the broader posterior cloacal region where low longitudinal mucosal folds are covered by an epithelial membrane composed of two or three layers of cuboidal cells among which are scattered spherical mucus-filled cells. Towards the opening of the cloaca this type of epithelium is replaced by stratified squamous. The muscularis is not continuous but is composed of bundles of smooth muscle cells except at the posterior end where skeletal muscle fibers appear.

**Liver.**—The structure of the liver is more readily studied here than in the dogfish where the heavy content of fatty material leaves clear vacuolated cells resembling fat cells in routine sections. The early tubules fuse so that none end blindly and the cords of large polyhedral hepatic cells are clearly separated by broad sinusoidal capillaries. The lumens of the tubules are reduced to networks of narrow channels joined by grooves, called *bile canaliculi*, formed between adjoining faces of hepatic cells. The bile canaliculi empty into the smallest ducts lined by low cuboidal

epithelium at the point of origin of the early tubule. The larger collecting bile ducts have a columnar epithelial lining and a muscularis. Special preparations demonstrate glycogen and small amounts of fat in the hepatic cells but the loss of these in routine preparations leaves clear areas among which a small amount of granular acidophilic cytoplasm forms a network. Pigment commonly occurs in the hepatic cells and has been reported to be

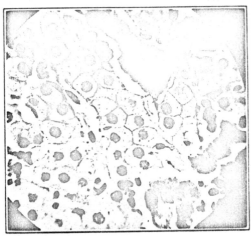

Fig. 141.—Section of liver of Amphiuma, showing rows of large polyhedra hepatic cells separated by sinusoids. Cells filled with pigment are also shown Photomicrograph. 4 mm. obj. and 5× oc.

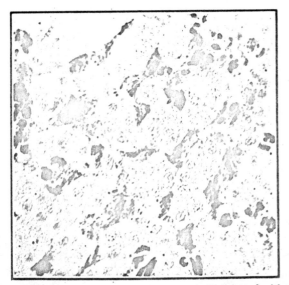

Fig. 142.—A section from the liver of a frog repeatedly injected with trypan blue to show the Kupffer cells which have ingested the dark particles of dye and nearly fill the sinusoids. Photomicrograph. 4 mm. obj. and 5× oc.

more abundant during the winter. A peculiar feature of the liver is the action of the sinusoidal cells which pick up foreign particles and cellular débris and may be filled with pigment derived from phagocytosed old red cells. These sinusoidal cells, called *Kupffer cells*, may be demonstrated along the sinusoids by injections of colloidal dye particles. Under these conditions they become macrophages, which suggests that they are reticular cells either closely associating with the endothelium of the sinusoids or forming part of the wall of these spaces.

**Gall-bladder.**—This represents a saccular diverticulum of the main bile duct with similar tall columnar cells with clear acidophilic cytoplasm and a distal mucous border. The tunica propria rests on interlacing bundles of smooth muscle covered by a serosa. Its walls continue with those of the duct where the muscularis is arranged into an inner circular and an outer longitudinal layer.

**Pancreas.**—In origin and structure similar to conditions in the dogfish but it is much smaller. The secretory tubules and alveoli are separated by capillaries and very little supporting tissue. The secretory pyramidal cells have a proximal basophilic cytoplasm in which the nucleus is located and a distal more prominent region of cytoplasm filled with coarse acidophilic zymogen granules. Centro-acinar cells with smaller and darker nuclei and more homogeneous acidophilic cytoplasm occur frequently in the lumen of sections across the junction with the secretory duct.

**Islands of Langerhans.**—As in the dogfish, these occur as cords of cells associated with the small pancreatic ducts but have no lumen and secrete into the blood. Their cytoplasm is clear or contains fine acidophilic granules in routine sections, but special techniques may demonstrate characteristic eosinophilic and basophilic granular content indicating several cell types.

## The Digestive System of a Lizard

**Oral Cavity.**—The stratified squamous epithelium and underlying dermis of the integument continue over the jaws with only a slightly thickened fold, at which point scales are no longer present but a layer of cornified cells covers the surface. Within the oral cavity the epithelial membrane becomes thicker and the tunica propria projects numerous small papillæ into it. Modified epithelial cells become the neuro-epithelia forming the taste-buds of this region. In the posterior part of the oral cavity and through the pharynx the epithelial membrane has a superficial layer of ciliated columnar cells and numerous goblet cells. Below these are two or three tightly packed layers of small cells with very little cytoplasm. Chromatophores occur in the tunica propria of the oral cavity and through the pharynx.

**Teeth.**—Associated with the jaws, are more prominent conical teeth derived in a manner similar to those of the frog. However, they are attached to a ledge of the underlying jaw by a lateral and basal cementum region. Closely adjoining the erupted tooth, another infolding of the epithelium has a small developing tooth associated with it. The poison fangs of some snakes are specialized teeth which form a groove or tube connecting with a basally located *poison gland*. (Fig. 143.)

**Tongue.**—The tongue contains the parts present in the frog plus an added median contribution with a broad muscular basal attachment posteriorly. The under surface of the tongue and around the tip to the upper surface is covered by a smooth membrane of stratified squamous epithe-

lium; the upper surface behind the tip has numerous broad papillæ. Between the papillæ of the middle and posterior regions the epithelium is commonly of stratified columnar type with numerous goblet cells and a similar membrane covers the sides of the tongue where it attaches to the floor of the mouth. The hyoid apparatus extends anteriorly into the tongue as an unpaired os entoglossum and a posteriorly located hyoid and first branchial cartilage to which the skeletal muscle bundles of the retractor muscle of the tongue are attached.

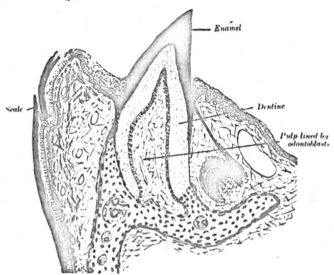

FIG. 143.—Section through the jaw of a lizard showing mature tooth attached to jaw and small developing tooth on the right.

**Oral Glands.**—These resemble those of the frog in being associations of simple branched tubular mucous glands opening to the oral surface by short excretory duct portions lined with columnar cells. The *labial gland* is such a group whose tubules open at the base of the teeth on the inner lip surface. The secretory cells are columnar in form with basal nuclei and finely granular acidophilic cytoplasm. The *sublingual* is composed of a similar group of tubular glands, one located at either side between the base of the tongue and the teeth.

**Esophagus.**—At the junction of the pharynx with the esophagus the mucosa is thrown into a number of longitudinal folds by the submucosa from which secondary smaller mucosal folds may project. The epithelial membrane is a pseudostratified ciliated columnar type in which goblet cells are common. Chromatophores occur in the tunica propria of the upper esophagus.

**Stomach.**—Upon entering the stomach the mucosa is composed of a membrane of simple tall tapering columnar cells and associated tubular gastric glands. The submucosa forms a few broad longitudinal folds or *rugæ*. The greater part of the stomach has *fundic glands* in which the superficial columnar cells line the gastric pits but the neck of the gland has a region of shorter columnar or cuboidal cells filled with acidophilic granules.

The body of the gland and the branching terminal portions have larger cells of columnar form with the nucleus located in a granular proximal cytoplasm; the distal part of the cell contains a mucus secretion which may appear quite clear in routine preparations. The *pyloric glands* differ from the fundic type in having shorter twisted glands composed of mucous cells and lacking the acidophilic neck cells.

**Small Intestine.**—The mucosa of this region is thrown into numerous high thin folds covered by tall columnar cells with striated border and numerous goblet cells, the latter increasing in numbers posteriorly. Glands are not present. Elements of the muscularis mucosæ extend into the mucosal folds which broaden basally and include the submucosa. The circular muscularis is particularly well developed.

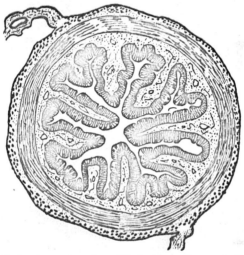

Fig. 144.—Diagram of a cross-section of the lower esophagus of a lizard. Note the extensions of the submucosa into the lumen covered by pseudostratified columnar epithelium with many goblet cells. The submucosa supports blood-vessels. The muscularis coat is represented by a well-defined circular sheath. The longitudinal coat is represented by relatively few muscle cells.

**Large Intestine.**—The elaborate folds of the small intestine are lost in passing to the large intestine where folds are shorter, fewer, and unbranched in the anterior portion and practically disappear in the posterior region. The epithelial membrane is composed mainly of goblet cells and the muscularis mucosæ is better represented than in the preceding division. The muscularis has a relatively thin circular layer and a more prominent longitudinal layer.

**Cloaca.**—As the large intestine continues into the broader cloacal region the muscularis mucosæ is lost but the epithelial membrane is similarly composed of goblet cells for a distance before joining a stratified squamous type. The muscularis of the intestine likewise continues over a distance but gradually decreases in amount and skeletal muscle appears posteriorly.

**Liver and Gall-bladder.**—These present conditions similar to those in the frog.

**Pancreas.**—Likewise similar to pancreas of the frog, but islands are not conspicuous in the lizard although they may be in other forms. (Fig. 145.)

## The Digestive System of the Pigeon

**Oral Cavity.**—The mouth of birds opens from the bill or beak which represents a great accumulation of cornified cells where the epidermis folds over the jaws, a condition also found among some reptiles. From the internal margins of the bill, a stratified squamous epithelium continues to line the oral cavity but many more layers of living cells are present than in the epidermis and only a few layers of superficial cells are cornified. Such an epithelial membrane resting upon a vascular tunica propria, which extends papillæ into it, continues through the pharynx and into the esophagus.

Fɪɢ. 145.—Section of pancreas of the water snake (Natrix). It is similar to the pancreas of a mammal but relatively less connective tissue makes it more compactly glandular. The light gray areas are sections of islands of Langerhans. Photograph. 32 mm. obj. and 5× oc.

**Teeth.**—These structures are absent though a dental ridge or lamina is reported during development in some instances; and true teeth occur in fossil birds.

**Tongue.**—The intrinsic musculature of preceding tongue types is lost and the tongue is reduced to a slender rigid structure motile through movement of skeletal parts similar, though reduced, to those of the reptile. The anterior free part of the tongue is composed of a covering epithelial membrane of stratified squamous type with a heavy accumulation of cornified cells supported by the centrally located os entoglossum surrounded by fibroelastic tissue. Over the posterior attached part the epithelium loses the horny surface layer of cells; taste-buds occur in the stratified squamous epithelium and along the lateral walls small groups of tubular mucous glands open by short crypts to the surface.

**Oral Glands.**—There are small simple mucous glands, similar to those in the tongue, scattered about the oral cavity, especially in the roof of the mouth. A compound tubular sublingual gland occurs at each side of the tongue and the mucous secreting tubules open through an excretory duct in the midline beneath the tongue. An *angle gland*, similarly composed of mucous secreting tubules, lies below the integument in the corner of the mouth on each side.

**Esophagus.**—The pharynx opens into a tubular esophagus with a similar stratified squamous membrane thrown into longitudinal folds with numerous glands at the bases and along the sides. In these glands a thin neck region opens from the surface to a wider lumen from which a number of tubular branches extend. The secretory columnar cells are of mucous type with a relatively clear distal cytoplasm containing strands of basophilic material, in routine sections, and a proximal granular cytoplasm containing the nuclei. This tubular esophagus extends only a short distance before dilating into a thin-walled saclike region, the *crop*, where the longitudinal folds diverge and flatten, then converge posteriorly to larger folds as the crop continues with the posterior tubular esophagus. There is no muscularis mucosæ and the muscularis has an inner longitudinal and an outer circular layer. (Fig. 146.)

**Crop.**—The mucosa has the same type of epithelial lining as the tubular esophagus but glands are lacking and the tunica propria is rich in elastic fibers. As in the preceding region no muscularis mucosæ is present. It differs in having lymphoid nodules occurring frequently in the tunica propria and submucosal tissue. The muscularis has an inner longitudinal layer and an outer network of circular smooth muscle. During the breeding season the crop contains a milky secretion used in feeding the young. This is associated with increased thickness of the epithelial membrane and fatty accumulation in the cells which are shed into the lumen to disintegrate. Some contribution to the secretion may be made by the mucous glands of the esophagus.

**Stomach.**—The esophagus opens into a narrow glandular division, the *proventriculus* or glandular stomach, which posteriorly dilates into the muscular stomach or *gizzard* with the peculiar dorsal and ventral accumulation of muscular wall.

*Proventriculus.*—The mucosal development of this region is very characteristic. The superficial epithelial membrane is composed of columnar cells, as in other stomachs, and gastric crypts occur from which tubular glands extend, but this glandular mucosa is then folded into pockets. As a result each pocket has the appearance of a large compound gland with a central broad duct from which the secretory tubules radiate. The mucosa lining the stomach lumen between pockets has columnar cells with distal mucous border thrown into folds by the tunica propria so that crypts are formed but very short tubular glands, or no glands, project from them. Within the pockets, however, long tubular glands extend from the crypts adjoining the pocket lumen. Here the superficial and crypt lining is composed of tall mucous columnar cells and the secretory portions contain cuboidal cells with marked acidophilic homogeneous cytoplasm surrounding a wide lumen. The tunica propria extends a delicate supporting tissue about the glands and joins the submucosa as a thin region adjoining the longitudinal muscle layer of the muscularis. (Fig. 147.)

*Gizzard.*—The junction of the proventriculus with this region is accompanied by the loss of the submucosal folds and the associated pockets of glands. The mucosa forms a smooth lining to the gizzard lumen and from

it closely packed straight tubular glands project into a compact and vascular tunica propria. The secretory cells are cuboidal or low columnar in form with an acidophilic finely granular cytoplasm which is more conspicuously acidophilic in the distal region. A prominent nucleus occupies the central region of the cell and mitotic figures are common in the cells of the lower half of the tubules. The secretion fills the lumens and as it reaches the surface joins with that of adjoining glands to form a hard continuous layer which presents striations representing the contribution of

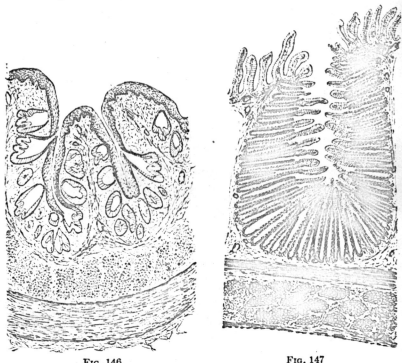

FIG. 146                                FIG. 147

FIG. 146.—Cross-section of the esophagus of the pigeon, showing the peculiar branched alveolar glands.

FIG. 147.—A section through part of the proventriculus, showing the glandular pocket with walls composed of tubular glands.

each glandular lumen. This horny covering layer of the gizzard is of nearly uniform thickness throughout except at the junction with the intestine and proventriculus where it tapers down and disappears. It is maintained by constant additions from the underlying glands to replace material worn away at the surface. (Fig. 148.)

The longitudinal inner layer of muscularis continues for a short distance in the gizzard but disappears in the thicker submucosal connective tissue formed here. The circular muscle coat becomes thickened to a remarkable degree dorsally and ventrally. Sections show numerous large interlocking bundles of large smooth muscle cells enclosed in fibroelastic tissue sheaths. Laterally, a circular muscle coat, not so exceptionally developed, joins the two heavy masses. The muscle cells composing the gizzard wall are rich in cytoplasm which is acidophilic and macroscopically this muscle has a dark color.

**Small Intestine.**—The transition from the gizzard to the small intestine is marked by the loss of the horny layer covering the mucosa, loss of the gastric glands, presence of a longitudinal muscularis mucosæ, and presence of a muscularis composed of inner circular and outer longitudinal layers. The mucosa is characteristically modified. The superficial epithelium, composed of columnar cells with striated border, distal clear mucous or slightly acidophilic granular cytoplasm and proximal nucleated portion, is thrown into numerous long slender finger-like folds by the tunica propria. These

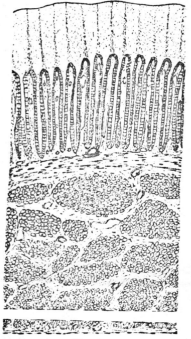
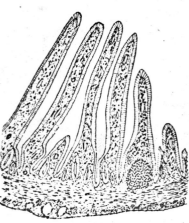

FIG. 148                    FIG. 149

FIG. 148.—A section through part of the gizzard of the pigeon, showing the tubular glands and their accumulated secretion product lining the lumen of this region. The break in the muscular region represents an omission of twice as much similarly composed muscular tissue.

FIG. 149.—A cross-section of the duodenum of the pigeon, showing the villi, the short tubular glands, and a single lymphoid nodule.

are called *villi* and are found in this class and also in mammals. Each villus contains a core of tunica propria tissue supporting a blindly ending lymph capillary and a blood capillary network. A few scattered smooth muscle cells from the muscularis mucosæ also extend into the villi. At the base of these structures there are short single or branched tubular glands, the glands of Lieberkühn, lined by similar columnar cells with lightly acidophilic granular cytoplasm. Mitotic figures are frequent in the cells of these glands. Goblet cells appear scattered among the columnar cells lining the

duodenum but increase in numbers towards the end of the small intestine. The villi likewise become broader and shorter in the lower small intestine. Lymphocytes occur in the tunica propria of the villi and lymphoid nodules occur at their base over the entire intestinal region but are more numerous posteriorly.

**Ceca.**—The junction of the small and large intestine is marked by two blind pockets or ceca extending out from the intestine. The narrow lumen in each is continuous with that of the intestine and the mucosal lining has a similar structure but the villi are broad. Lymph nodules are common and distend the bases of the villi. The muscularis is thinner than in the intestine.

**Large Intestine.**—Similar in structure to the small intestine but with shorter and less numerous villi, very short Lieberkühn's glands, and abundant goblet cells.

**Cloaca.**—The opening of the large intestine into the cloaca is marked by a loss of villi but the epithelial membrane is still composed of columnar cells and numerous goblet cells until the cloacal opening is approached and stratified squamous epithelium forms the surface layer. Glands are absent in the cloacal wall except for a few simple mucous ones at the external opening. Skeletal muscle replaces the smooth musculature which continues from the large intestine about midway into the cloaca.

**Liver.**—Fusion of the early tubules gives a network of hepatic cords whose cells pass their secretions by canaliculi to the capillary lumen of the tubule to collect in the small bile duct composed of low cuboidal cells. The small polygonal hepatic cells are filled with an acidophilic, finely granular cytoplasm and have a central spherical nucleus. The intertubular capillary network is prominent and the phagocytic Kupffer cells can be demonstrated. The cells lining the capillaries or sinusoids are represented in routine sections by elongated darkly staining nuclei. Small lymphoid nodules occur in the connective tissue supporting the hepatic ducts and larger blood-vessels.

**Pancreas.**—The organization is similar to that in the reptile, with little supporting connective tissue about the end-pieces, so that a compact mass of secretory cells appears. The secretory tubules contain the characteristic serous cells with a proximal more homogeneous cytoplasm containing the nucleus and a distal cytoplasm containing coarse acidophilic granules. The cytoplasm may lack the distal granulation and be uniform throughout following or preceding a period of secretory activity. Sections across the tubules commonly show centro-acinar cells represented by small darkly staining nuclei.

**Islands of Langerhans.**—These occur as readily observed areas of closely packed cords of cells with pale or lightly staining acidophilic cytoplasm. The centrally located spherical nucleus usually has a nucelolus present.

## THE DIGESTIVE SYSTEM OF MAMMALS

**Oral Cavity.**—The opening of the mouth is bordered by muscular folds, or true lips, surfaced outside by integument and over the end and internally by a mucosa composed of a thick stratified squamous epithelium with few layers of cornified cells. Numerous papillæ project into this membrane from the vascular tunica propria; and

14

integumentary features are lost usually over the free ends of the lips. The oral cavity is lined by a similar mucosa and a looser fibroelastic submucosa attaching to underlying tissues. Consideration of glands in this class will be limited to those of the tongue and the prominent salivary glands.

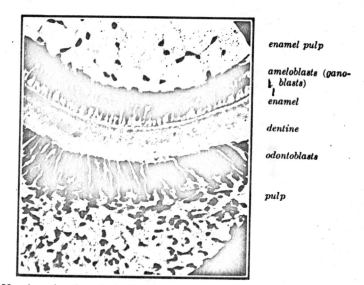

*enamel pulp*

*ameloblasts (gano-*
*blasts)*

*enamel*

*dentine*

*odontoblasts*

*pulp*

Fig. 150.—A section through the developing tooth of a pig, showing the columnar enamel cells above a light area of beginning enamel deposit which adjoins the broader and darker dentine deposit. The layer of elongate odontoblasts outlines the pulp region which extends to the bottom of the picture. Photomicrograph. 4 mm. obj. and 5× oc.

**Teeth.**—The teeth of mammals are more conspicuous structures than in preceding classes, although the course of their development is very similar to that outlined in the development of the placoid scale. An exposed enamel-covered crown region has one or more conical dentine roots extending into sockets or alveoli of the jaw. A thin cementum layer forms a collar about the dentine from the cessation of the enamel below the *gum*, a heavy mucosal and submucosal fold over the jaw and about the teeth, to the region of the basal root canal through which the pulp enters the tooth. A connective tissue membrane (periodontal membrane) surrounds the cementum and lines the socket so that these teeth are not normally ankylosed, though held firmly in place.

An epithelial thickening forms over the developing jaw and projects into the underlying connective tissue as the *dental lamina.* Papillæ of connective tissue extend into the epithelial layer and the cap-like covering of epithelium becomes the *enamel organ.* The

epithelial cells adjoining the surface of the connective tissue papillæ become slender columnar *ameloblasts* or *ganoblasts* which elaborate the enamel as a basal cuticle. The more distal cells of the epithelial cap, or enamel organ, acquire a reticular appearance due to accumulation of fluid between the cells. At the same time, connective tissue cells of the papilla form a layer adjoining the ameloblasts and assume a columnar form. These connective tissue cells, the *odontoblasts*, are associated with elaboration of the dentine in a manner very similar to bone formation except the cell bodies recede toward the core of the papilla, the *pulp*, as dentine is deposited adjoining the enamel. Processes of the odontoblasts extend through the dentine as *dentinal tubules*.

**Tongue.**—The mammalian tongue is an active organ composed, in greater part, of voluntary muscle sheathed by a mucous membrane continuous with that of the mouth and pharynx. Extrinsic muscles entering the tongue posteriorly connect it with the cartilages of the pharynx and effect extension and retraction of the tongue. The body of the tongue is composed of the intrinsic muscle which is directly concerned with the flexing movements of the tongue.

A vertical partition, the median or lingual septum, of dense fibro-elastic tissue extends from the lower to the upper surfaces and from the base to the tip dividing the tongue into two equal lateral portions. Small bundles of muscle fibers of the skeletal type are arranged longitudinally, vertically, and transversely, and cross each other at right angles. The muscle fibers and bundles are separated from each other by thin sheets of fibroelastic and adipose connective tissues in varying amounts.

Between the muscular portion of the tongue and the epithelial sheath there is a narrow region of subepithelial connective tissue from the surface of which numerous papillæ extend into the overlying epithelium. This connective tissue is continuous with that separating the muscles of the tongue.

The epithelium of the mucosa of the tongue is of the stratified squamous type throughout and the surface is smooth along the sides and on the ventral surface, but the dorsal anterior two-thirds is roughened by papillæ of varying sizes and shapes (Fig. 151) and is called the papillary portion. The posterior third of the tongue may lack papillæ of any kind, but may have lymphoid tissue forming nodules, called the lingual tonsil, beneath the superficial mucous membrane. In the papillary region, four types of papillæ may be found, namely, *filiform, fungiform, foliate,* and *circumvallate.*

*Filiform papillæ* are the most numerous and occur in rows throughout the papillary zone. Each is formed by a conical core of connective tissue that projects well out beyond the general surface of the tongue and is covered by the stratified squamous epithelium. The superficial cells of the epithelium of these papillæ in some animals become heavily cornified and present a rough, filelike surface, as in rodents, that is useful in masticating food.

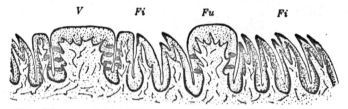

FIG. 151.—Diagram of three different types of tongue papillæ. *V*, Vallate; *Fi*, filiform; *Fu*, fungiform.

*Fungiform papillæ* are much fewer in number than the filiform and are scattered irregularly over the papillary region among the filiform papillæ. They are formed by extensions of the connective tissue that broaden out as they rise above the general level of the tongue. The epithelial covering is thin, so that these papillæ appear red, due to the blood of the underlying connective tissue showing through. Taste-buds may appear in the side walls of the fungiform papillæ.

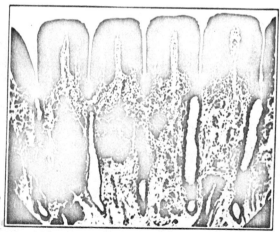

FIG. 152.—Section through foliate papillæ of a rabbit, showing von Ebner's gland. in the underlying tissues with ducts opening between papillæ. Photomicrograph. 16 mm. obj. and 5× oc.

*Foliate papillæ* (Fig. 152), as the name implies, are leaflike and occur along each lateral margin of the tongue toward the rear of the papillary zone. They occur in varying numbers as narrow,

parallel, consecutive, vertical ridges separated by furrows. They are poorly defined in man but well represented in such animals as the rabbit and opossum. Here they may be seen as an oblong patch on each side of the tongue. The primary papilla of connective tissue has three definite secondary projections over which the epithelial coat forms a smooth surface. Numerous taste-buds occur in the lateral epithelial walls of these papillæ. (Fig. 153.)

The *circumvallate* or *vallate papillæ* occur just in front of the *foramen cecum*, which is a shallow depression posterior to the papillary region. They are arranged in a V-shaped pattern, with the apex of the "V" toward the foramen cecum, are few in number, and are the largest type of papillæ. Each has a knob-shaped form with a flat top and is surrounded by a deep furrow or fossa, so that the papilla does not project above the general level of the tongue. The primary connective tissue papilla is divided into a number of smaller secondary papillæ covered with stratified squamous epithelium. Numerous taste-buds occur in the epithelium of the side walls and in the epithelium of the opposite wall of the fossa.

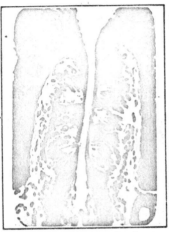

Fig. 153.—Photograph of taste-buds in the walls of the foliate papillæ of the rabbit. 4 mm. obj. and 5× oc.

The blood-vessels and nerves for all types of papillæ are supported in the connective tissue core. Fibers of the gustatory nerve pass to the sensory cells of the taste-buds located in the various papillæ. Each *taste-bud* is somewhat cask-shaped; the epithelial wall is formed by flat fusiform epithelial cells that are arranged like the staves of a cask. One end of this casklike bud is open and faces the fossa (furrow) about the papilla. The space within the wall of flat epithelial cells is occupied by two kinds of specialized epithelial cells derived from embryonic ectoderm. There are long spindle-shaped cells, called supporting cells, and among these are long, tapering, sensory cells with hairlike external tips that project into the opening to the fossa. Each of the sensory cells is connected basally with a fiber of the gustatory nerve. Substances entering the mouth in solution come into contact with the hairlike tips of the sensory cells, which when stimulated give the sense of taste.

Many serous and mucous glands are present in the tongue.

Serous glands, known as *von Ebner's glands*, are numerous in the neighborhood of the foliate papillæ and among the muscle masses. The ducts from these glands open to the exterior through the bottom of the fossa between the adjacent papillæ. (Fig. 152.) Mucous as well as serous glands are present in the region of the circumvallate papillæ in many mammals.

**Salivary Glands.**—In addition to the numerous small glands scattered in the mucosa and underlying connective tissue of the oral

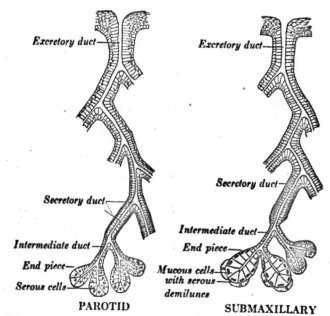

Fig. 154.—Diagram showing structure of the parotid and submaxillary glands.

cavity, there are in mammals three pairs of salivary glands which arise from the walls of the embryonic oral cavity as epithelial buds. These three pairs of glands, the *parotid, submaxillary,* and *sublingual,* display marked histological variation even in closely related species. Their secretions are poured into the mouth as saliva in response to various stimuli, and serve to keep the oral surface moist and to lubricate the food.

*Parotid Glands.*—Near the base of each external ear is the largest of the salivary glands, the parotid, whose main excretory duct opens into the oral cavity. (Fig. 154.) The lobes and lobules into which the gland is divided are supported by a relatively dense interlobular fibroelastic connective tissue in which a branching system of excretory ducts is located. The largest ducts are lined with a

stratified columnar epithelium, but their main branches have a single layer of columnar cells. Adjoining the smallest excretory ducts there are the so-called secretory ducts which occur within the lobules. The secretory portions are composed of columnar epithelial cells with striated basal portions. The secretory ducts divide into intercalated or intermediate ducts, which are very small and formed of cuboidal cells. These terminate in the secreting end-pieces where there are relatively large pyramidal cells of the serous type with rounded nuclei more or less centrally located. The lumens in these secreting end-pieces are very small. The whole field presents a uniform appearance as regards the secreting cells, a condition which is usually not apparent in either of the other salivary glands.

Fig. 155.—Intermediate duct breaking into secretory end-pieces of the submaxillary gland of the cat, showing mucous cells surrounded by crescents of serous cells. Photomicrograph. 4 mm. obj. and 5× oc.

*Submaxillary Glands.*—Each gland is located below the angle of the lower jaw and adjoins the ventral part of the parotid; the secretion is carried into the oral cavity by an excretory duct which opens on the side of the tongue well forward. The division into lobes and lobules and the arrangement of ducts is similar to that found in the parotid. (Fig. 154.) There are two types of cells in the alveoli or secreting end-pieces. A serous type of cell similar to that found in the parotid may be found forming many of the alveoli. Another type of cell is present also, the mucous cell, with lighter, clearer cytoplasm, which takes a basic stain and has basally located nuclei. (Fig. 155.) Outside of some of these mucous cells are crescents or demilunes of serous cells. The secretory ducts are more extensive in the submaxillary than in the parotid gland. In man, serous cells predominate, but in many other animals, as in the cat, the mucous cells predominate.

*Sublingual Glands.*—The sublingual glands are located at the base of the tongue and, like the parotid and submaxillary are divided into lobes and lobules, but the intercalated ducts are lacking as may also be a large proportion of the secretory ducts. Most of the glandular end-pieces in the cat are composed of cells of the mucous type, with more numerous crescents of serous cells than in the submaxillary; in other forms serous cells may be more numerous.

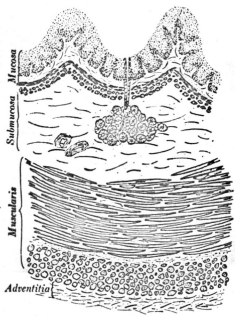

Fig. 156.—Diagram of a cross-section of a mammalian esophagus.

**Esophagus.**—Connecting the pharynx with the stomach is a tube with the characteristic four coats of the digestive canal already outlined. (Fig. 156.) In the region of the neck the adventitia consists of loose fibroelastic tissue connecting the esophagus with neighboring structures in the neck. As it passes through the thorax this outer coat becomes a serosa (visceral peritoneum), which is composed of an outer thin mesothelial membrane and an underlying thin layer of connective tissue. The muscularis may have striated voluntary muscle fibers in the upper region of the esophagus, a mixture with smooth muscle in the middle region, and finally a lower portion composed entirely of smooth involuntary muscle. Its

composition is variable, however, for in some animals striated muscle may be found reaching to the stomach. The very loose fibro-elastic tissue of the submucosa contains large blood-vessels and numerous compound tubular mucous glands whose ducts open through the mucosa. A muscularis mucosæ marks the beginning of the mucosa, except in the upper portions of the esophagus where it may be missing. Within the muscularis mucosæ is the fibroelastic tissue of the tunica propria, which projects as papillæ into the stratified squamous epithelium resting upon it. In addition to the deep mucous glands found in the submucosa there may also be simple branched tubular glands lying in the tunica propria of the posterior end adjoining the stomach and resembling those to be found in the cardiac portion of the stomach. When the esophagus is contracted, the mucosa is disposed in longitudinal folds and the lumen is closed.

**Stomach.**—The mucosa at the lower end of the esophagus is marked by an abrupt transition from a relatively smooth surface and stratified squamous epithelium to the folded and glandular mucosa of the stomach lined by simple columnar epithelium. Below the mucosa the transition is more gradual and the deep mucous glands of the esophagus often extend over into the stomach. Folds in the stomach wall involving submucosa and mucosa form ridges, or *rugæ*, observed best in the empty stomach. (Fig. 157.) Small pits ,or *gastric crypts*, are easily visible with slight magnification of the internal mucosa surface. The mucosa is quite thick, due to the presence of simple tubular gastric glands which are roughly divisible into three types: the cardiac, fundic, and pyloric glands.

*Cardiac glands*, found where the esophagus and the stomach join, are relatively few in number. In these glands the cells are chiefly of the mucous type. Cardiac glands are small, simple branched tubular in form, with a short excretory duct lined by columnar cells. The twisted secretory tubules are formed from cuboidal or columnar cells. There is great variation in the number of cardiac glands, and in some cases they are absent.

*Fundic glands* are most numerous and produce the essential elements of gastric juice; the cardiac and pyloric glands may function mainly as mucous glands. The fundic glands are branched tubular in form, with a relatively short excretory portion extending into the gastric pit, and glandular portions that are generally very much longer. (Fig. 158.) The cells of the gastric pit walls are columnar in type. A constricted portion of the gland near the gastric pit is called the *neck*, and from it each secretory tubule leads to a dilated end. Two types of cells, the *chief* or *zymogen cells* and the *parietal cells* make up the secreting tubules. The *chief cells* are roughly pyramidal, their cytoplasm shows secretion granules distally and nuclei are located in the proximal half. The secretory activity of these cells is associated with the production of zymogen

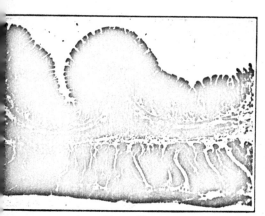

Fᴵɢ. 157.                    Fᴵɢ. 158.

Fᴵɢ. 157.—Photograph through a ruga of the fundus of the dog's stomach. Note the broad extension of the submucosa surmounted by the glandular mucosa. The muscularis has a thick circular and thinner longitudinal coat. A muscularis mucosæ follows the outline of the glandular mucosa. 32 mm. obj. and 5× oc.

Fᴵɢ. 158.—Diagram of tissues in the fundus of the stomach. *A*, Mucosa with simple branched tubular glands. The black dots represent parietal cells. Note muscularis mucosæ below the glands. *B*, Submucosa with artery and vein. *C*, Muscularis. This being a longitudinal section, the inner circular muscle is cut across and the outer longitudinal muscle is cut lengthwise. *D*, The serosa with an external limiting membrane of mesothelium.

granules, which give rise to the pepsin of the gastric juice. Scattered along the secreting tubule, between the chief cells and the basement membrane, and more numerous toward the neck, are the *parietal cells* which are larger than the chief cells. These cells are oval or polygonal, their finely granular cytoplasm has an affinity for acid dyes, and the large spherical nucleus is centrally located. Parietal cells are associated with the production of the hydrochloric acid present in the gastric juice, and are often called *oxyntic* or *acid cells* for this reason. (Fig. 159.) Another type of cell, the *argentaffin* or *enterochromaffin cell*, is found scattered in the connective tissue immediately adjoining the chief cells and also in the small intestine. These cells contain acidophilic granules which also react with chrome salts in a manner similar to those found in the adrenal

medulla. They can also be demonstrated by silver impregnations. The origin and function of this cell type is uncertain.

The *pyloric glands* intermingle with the fundic type in that portion of the stomach near the small intestine. The transition is gradual; parietal cells become less and less numerous and finally no longer appear in the more typical pyloric glands. The gastric pits become longer, and the secreting tubules are more twisted than in the fundic region. The cells of the pyloric glands are distinctly mucous in appearance.

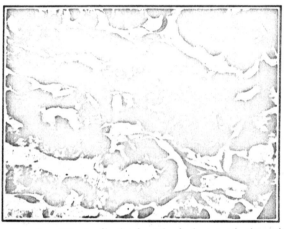

Fig. 159.—A section of the fundic glands of the dog's stomach, the parietal cells are larger and darker, the chief cells have smaller nuclei and a granular cytoplasm. Photomicrograph. 1.9 mm. obj. and 5× oc.

The tunica propria of the stomach extends in between and around the secreting tubules of the gastric glands, and the muscularis mucosæ lies just below the deepest ends of the secreting tubules. Scattered diffusely throughout the tunica propria are lymphocytes, but in some regions solitary lymph nodules occur. The submucosa is typical, being composed of loose fibroelastic connective tissue whose longitudinal ridgelike extensions form rugæ. The muscularis may have three layers in some regions, an inner oblique, a middle circular, and an outer longitudinal layer. In the pyloric region the two inner layers are thickened to form a sphincter muscle. The serosa is composed of a coat of loose fibroelastic connective tissue enclosed by a single layer of mesothelium.

Although the stomach functions mainly as a temporary place for storing food, some digestion occurs as a result of glandular action. Proteins may be converted into proteoses and peptones by the action of pepsin, while another enzyme, rennin, if present in the gastric juice, plays a rôle in the digestion of milk.

**Small Intestine.**—The same four coats noted in the stomach form the wall of the small intestine, but here the muscularis is quite regular, with an outer longitudinal and an inner circular layer. (Fig. 160.) The mucosa possesses characteristic features that

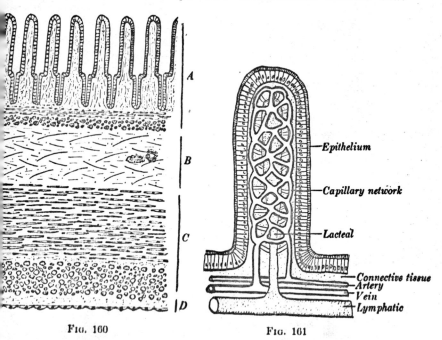

FIG. 160             FIG. 161

FIG. 160.—Diagram of tissues in the wall of the small intestine of a mammal. *A*, Mucosa showing villi with the glands of Lieberkühn extending basally between them. At the base of these glands is the muscularis mucosæ. *B*, Submucosa with an artery and vein. *C*, Muscularis coat with an inner circular and an external longitudinal muscle coat. *D*, Serosa with its external limiting membrane of mesothelium.

FIG. 161.—Diagram of a villus.

deserve closer attention. The inner surface of the canal generally shows circular and oblique folds involving the mucosa and part of the submucosa. These folds, paralleling each other and extending part way around the lumen at irregular intervals, are called *valvulæ conniventes*, or *plicæ circulares*. The mucosa is nodified by extension into the lumen of papilla-like projections which may be leaf-like, finger-like, or broadly club-shaped. These structures are known as *villi* and are diagnostic features of the small intestine of mammals and birds. They serve to increase the surface and function in the process of absorption.

The villi in a relaxed condition of the tract nearly fill the lumen. When the intestine is distended the villi are shortened along with stretching of all the other layers of the wall. Each villus has a core of the loose fibroelastic tissue from the tunica propria and scattered smooth muscle cells from the muscularis mucosæ. Simple columnar epithelium with a striated border, a distal mucous region, and a proximally located nucleus cover the villi. Scattered among the absorptive columnar cells are goblet cells  These appear in varying

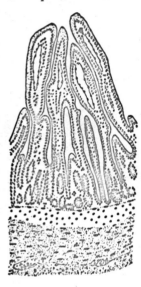

numbers and become more markedly abundant in the ileum. Within the epithelium of each villus there is loose connective tissue, a basket-work of blood capillaries, a nerve net, and some diffuse lymphoid tissue. A dilated blind lymph capillary, a *lacteal*, occupies the central portion. The villi vary in shape, size, and number in various mam-

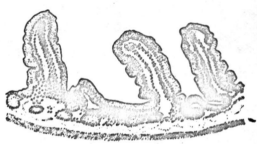

*Contracted*             *Distended*

Fig. 162.—Shows how different the structure of the small intestine is when strongly contracted and normally distended with food material.  × 80.  (Cowdry's Histology, redrawn from Johnson, courtesy of Am. J. Anat.)

mals. From the bases of the villi extend simple tubular glands which formed as invaginations of the embryo gut epithelium. These are called Lieberkühn glands and extend down to the muscularis mucosæ. The epithelium lining them is continuous with that covering the villus, but the cells are shorter and have no striated border. Near the base of these glands occur coarsely granular, basally striated cells, the *cells of Paneth*, with coarse acidophilic granules which secrete a serous fluid containing an enzyme. These cells are widely distributed throughout the epithelium of the digestive canal of higher vertebrates. The argentaffin or enterochromaffin cells, referred to in the stomach, also occur as scattered units in the connective tissue adjoining the epithelial cells of the glands. Lymphocytes infiltrate among the epithelial cells of villi and glands.

The tunica propria packs in between the Lieberkühn glands, as well as forming the core of the villi. Its light, loose reticular network and denser fibroelastic tissue supports a diffuse lymphoid tissue, and solitary lymphoid nodules are relatively common. In the ileum, lymphoid nodules form a number of groups, called Peyer's patches, which may extend from the tunica propria into the submucosa. No villi cover such areas. The muscularis mucosæ may be of varying distinctness with an outer longitudinal and inner circular layer of smooth muscle.

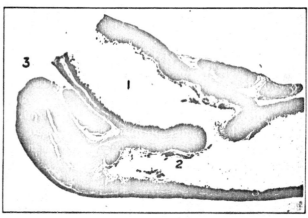

Fig 163.—Photograph of the ileocecal junction of the cat, showing the valve separating the *1*, ileum; and *2*, cecum. (10 ×) Colon extends to the right. End of cecum at *3* is location of appendix, when present.

The submucosa of loose fibroelastic tissue carries the larger blood and lymph vessels, Meissner's nerve plexus and, except in the region of the duodenum, has no glands. Branched tubular glands, *Brunner's glands*, appear in the submucosa of the upper region of the duodenum and often extend over into the adjoining region of the pyloric stomach. The secretory portion of these glands is composed of pyramidal or columnar epithelium. The secretion contains a proteolytic enzyme similar to pepsin in its action. Ducts from these glands lead up through the mucosa and open either between the villi or into the crypts of Lieberkühn glands. The cells lining the excretory ducts are similar to those of the epithelium lining the duodenum.

**Large Intestine.**—The ileum is separated from the large intestine by the ileocecal valve over which there is a transition to a mucosa characteristic of the large intestine. The same four coats make up the wall here as observed in the case of the small intestine, but

there are no villi and the mucosa has many tubular glands extending to the muscularis mucosæ. These glands are homologous with the glands of Lieberkühn of the small intestine, but are longer and Paneth cells are absent. The cells lining the surface of the lumen are tall columnar with numerous goblet cells. Passing down into the glands, the cells become shorter and goblet cells become more numerous. Goblet cells are most numerous in the mid-region of the glands. The basal cells are less differentiated and give rise to cells replacing worn-out superficial cells. The goblet cells of glands secrete mucus into the intestinal lumen, and thus aid in the passage of the fecal material which becomes more solid due to absorption of water through the intestinal wall.

The wall of the *cecum* usually has lymph nodules in the submucosa. In some forms, as in the rabbit, these nodules may encircle the lumen and form the greater part of the wall with a reduction in amount of connective tissue and muscularis.

The *vermiform appendix* is a blind pouch extending from the end of the cecum at its junction with the small intestine. (Fig. 163.) The wall has a mucosa with Lieberkühn glands but the characteristic feature is the abundance of lymphoid tissue which is present, not only as nodules in the mucosa and submucosa, but also as diffuse tissue throughout the tunica propria. The circular coat of the muscularis is well represented, but the outer longitudinal coat is thin. In some cases the glands may be obliterated by lymphoid tissue and the lumen filled with lymphocytes that penetrate through the mucosa.

**Rectum and Anus.**—The rectum has long and large tubular glands and solitary lymph nodules are common in its mucosa and submucosa. Longitudinal folds of the mucosa appear in the lower part of the rectum, and with them occurs a change in the character of the mucosa. The columnar epithelium and simple tubular glands of the rectum change abruptly to stratified squamous epithelium of the anus, and this epithelium is continuous with the skin. The muscularis of the rectum has two complete layers, but near the anus striated muscle replaces the smooth muscle and forms a sphincter.

**Pancreas.**—The pancreas has been called the salivary gland of the abdomen, and at first glance resembles the parotid in the serous appearance of its secretory cells. It is a compound tubulo-alveolar gland lying behind the stomach and attaching to the duodenal wall. No distinct capsule covers it, and its lobules are separated by a loose fibroelastic tissue. The secreting end-pieces, which may be tubular or short and roughly spherical, are formed of pyramidal cells.

The cytoplasm of these cells is lighter staining toward the lumen and more deeply staining with striated appearance in the proximal region. (Fig. 165.) The lighter portion contains coarse zymogen granules, which are presumably forerunners of the enzymatic secretions. In the proximal half of the cell there is a nucleus with a chromatin network and one or more nucleoli. In sections, centro-acinar

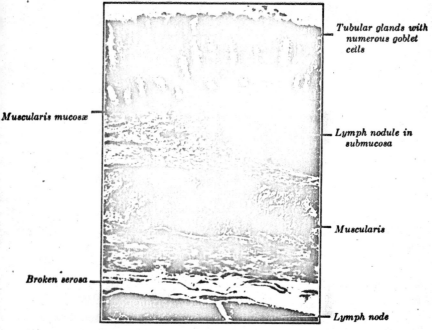

*Tubular glands with numerous goblet cells*

*Muscularis mucosæ*

*Lymph nodule in submucosa*

*Muscularis*

*Broken serosa*

*Lymph node*

FIG. 164.—Photograph of a longitudinal section through the dog's rectum, contraction bands may be observed in the longitudinal coat of the muscularis. Photomicrograph 16 mm. obj. and 5× oc.

cells may occupy the lumen of many acini along the inner ends of the secreting cells. These cells represent a continuation of the intercalated ducts which project a short way into the acinar lumen. Such cells have no secretory granules and possess a small deeply staining nucleus. Intercalated ducts lined with first cuboidal then low columnar pass to small excretory ducts lined with a tall columnar epithelium. The large excretory ducts are lined with a stratified columnar epithelium and pass into the main duct (duct of Wirsung), which opens into the intestinal lumen. Enzymes (trypsin, amylase, and lipase) present in the pancreatic secretion break down the proteins, starches, and fats into simpler compounds.

Though at first glance it resembles the parotid of mammals, the pancreas differs in the nature of its secretory cells, in the looser arrangement of the interlobular connective tissue, in the absence of secretory ducts, and finally in the presence of certain groups of

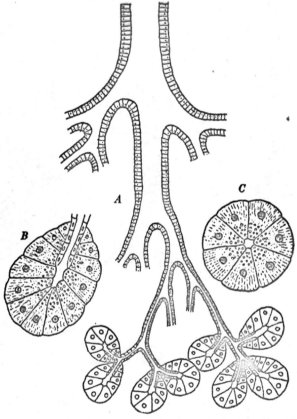

Fig. 165.—Diagrams showing structure of pancreas. *A*, A small excretory duct with its branches terminating in secretory end-pieces. The intercalated ducts extend part way into the end-piece. *B*, Longitudinal section of an end-piece, showing centro-acinar cells (involuted intercalated duct) and the secretory cells which have basal striations and secretory granules toward the lumen. The secretory cells are serous in type. *C*, Cross-section of a secretory end-piece distal to centro-acinar cells.

very distinct lightly staining cells forming pancreatic islets or the islands of Langerhans.

The *islands of Langerhans* are composed of spherical groups of from few to hundreds of lightly staining cells irregularly scattered among the acini and along the ducts as already observed in lower forms. (Figs. 135 and 145.) These cells are arranged in cords

15

forming a network with numerous wide capillaries passing between the cords. (Fig. 166.) By a special technique two types of cells are demonstrated on the basis of secretory granules which are not in either case like those of the acinar cells of the pancreas. One, the *alpha* or A cell, with fine cytoplasmic granules insoluble in

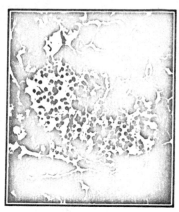

FIG. 166.—Section of a rat's pancreas, showing an island of Langerhans. Photomicrograph. 4 mm. obj. and 5× oc.

alcohol and a large oval nucleus with little chromatin apparent, is found most frequently in the center of the island. The second type, the *beta* or B cell, is smaller and more numerous, with a nucleus richer in chromatin, and cytoplasmic granules soluble in alcohol, as is insulin. The C, or indifferent cells contain no cytoplasmic granules and are thought to be the source of new A and B cells. The secretion of these island cells, insulin, passes into the blood and governs the metabolism of carbohydrates.

**Liver.**—The liver arises as a diverticulum of the mid-gut and develops into a compound tubular gland. Among fishes it may retain this simple glandular condition with blindly ending secretory tubules. With the amphibia and reptiles the tubules fuse to form a network and the liver cells surround a small central lumen into which secretions are poured from bile canaliculi which form as a network of grooves between the adjacent faces of the cells. The connective tissue is not abundant, and no lobulation occurs. In mammals there is an increase in amount of connective tissue and lobulations are indicated where connective tissue accompanies the larger blood-vessels; the lumens of the embryonic end-pieces of the gland do not develop, so that only cords of cells are apparent and an increasing amount of connective tissue results in a division of the gland into lobules, and groups of these form lobes.

A fibroelastic connective sheath completely surrounds the liver and at the hilum, where the blood-vessels enter, the connective tissue of the capsule continues inward, accompanying the vessels, and divides the liver into several lobes, which in turn are subdivided into numerous lobules. (Fig. 167.) The liver lobule is the unit of

FIG. 167.—Photograph of several lobules in the liver of the pig.  3.2 mm. obj. and 5× oc.

hepatic structure in mammals, each lobule being roughly a five- or six-sided polyhedral prism in form and is composed of anastomosing cords of liver cells that radiate outward from the center which is occupied by a central vein.  In sections the individual cords have two rows of cells whose boundaries are normally clearly defined. The individual cells are polyhedral in form, with a central nucleus, or sometimes two or more nuclei, with one or more nucleoli.  Granules of glycogen may be demonstrated in the cytoplasm.  Fat droplets appear to be normally present and vary inversely in amount with the glycogen.  Pigment granules may also be present.  Considering the variety of functions in which the hepatic cells participate, it is surprising that there is only one type of cell.  Instead of the cells pouring their secretions into a lumen at the distal border of the cells, as is the case in other exocrine glands, the hepatic cords have a network of small canaliculi, the *bile canaliculi*, running between adjacent faces of cells forming the cords.

To understand the composition of the liver it is important to understand the distribution of the blood-vessels to a lobule.  Blood enters the liver from two sources, the *hepatic artery* and the *portal vein*, and leaves through the *hepatic veins* which empty into the *vena cava*.  The afferent vessels, the hepatic artery and portal vein, enter at the hilum and divide into large branches following the septa separating the lobes.   Smaller branches form the *interlobular arteries* and *veins* which follow the septa between the lobules.   The interlobular branches of the portal veins give off short branches passing to the surface of the lobules where they break up into an intralobular capillary network.   (Fig. 168.)   The hepatic artery

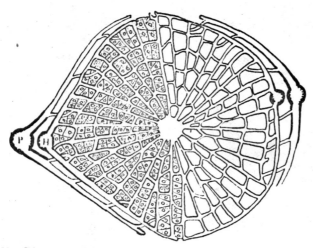

Fig. 168.—Diagram of a cross-section of a lobule of the liver of a mammal with the hepatic cells converging toward a common center.  *P*, Section of a branch of the portal vein in the interlobular connective tissue; *H*, branches of the hepatic artery near the branch of the portal vein; branches of this portal component extend to form the capillary system of the lobule.  Some branches of the hepatic artery make connection with the portal vein.  The diagram shows the capillaries forming a meshwork among the cords of liver cells.  The capillaries converge toward the intralobular vein (*IL*) in the center of the lobule.

follows the portal vein in its branching to the interlobular septa, where its finer branches break up into capillary networks, some of which supply the septa and then join the finer branches of the hepatic vein, while others enter the lobules to join with the intralobular capillary system.

The intralobular capillary network is composed of wide-lumened, *hepatic sinusoids.*  These anastomose irregularly along the outer surfaces of the cords of hepatic cells and everywhere separate the cords from each other, so that each cell may have two or more sinusoids in contact with it, a disposition not found in the case of other gland cells.  The sinusoids carry the blood toward the center of each lobule, where they empty it into the central vein which emerges at the base of the lobule.  Each central vein joins a sublobular vein which eventually unites with the hepatic veins, the efferent blood-vessels of the liver.  In addition to the endothelial cell proper, which is small and flat with a darkly staining nucleus,

there are present along the walls of the sinusoids other larger cells, the *Kupffer cells,* with a number of cytoplasmic processes and a larger vesicular nucleus. By intravenous injection the Kupffer cells can be shown to be active in ingesting foreign particles from the blood passing through the sinusoids, *i. e.,* they become macrophages and are part of the reticulo-endothelial or macrophage system. Some believe they are derived from the cells of the delicate reticular tissue enveloping the sinusoids; others consider them derived from endothelial cells. (Figs. 141 and 142.)

Between the adjacent faces of the hepatic cells the *bile canaliculi* appear as grooves between the adjoining cell walls. By silver impregnation and injection the bile canaliculi (Fig. 169) appear to

Fig. 169.—Photograph of injected bile canaliculi in the liver of a rabbit. These are indicated by the network in black. Nuclei of liver cells are faintly stained. 4 mm. obj. and 5× oc.

be bounded by a delicate non-cellular membrane formed by the adjoining hepatic cell walls. These canaliculi are functionally comparable to the lumens of other glands, and into them is collected the bile secreted by the hepatic cells. Each hepatic cell may have more than one bile canaliculus into which it discharges bile, but they occur only between adjoining surfaces of cells and not along the free surfaces which adjoin the blood sinusoids. These canaliculi form a branching network and join those of adjoining hepatic cords to carry the bile outward toward the periphery of the lobule. At the periphery of the lobule they collect into small *bile ducts* in the interlobular septa. These interlobular bile ducts have walls formed of flat or cuboidal epithelium and coalesce to form larger ducts following the course of the portal vein and hepatic artery through

the septa. With increasing size of the bile vessels, the epithelium
of their wall changes to tall columnar which is surrounded by a
coat of connective tissue and scattered longitudinal smooth muscle
cells. The larger bile ducts from each lobe empty into a larger
hepatic duct that in turn joins the common bile duct leading into
the duodenum.

The three vessels coursing close together through the connective
tissue septa of the liver, i. e., a branch of the hepatic artery, a
branch of the portal vein, and a bile duct, form the so-called *portal
canal* peculiar to the liver. The vein is the largest, the bile duct
is second in size, and the artery is the smallest vessel of the three.

As a gland the liver is peculiar in passing its secretions peripherally to the collecting ducts and, although the hepatic cells are only
of one type, they are presumably equally capable of many different
functions. Moreover, the blood courses not outward from a center,
but in toward the center of each lobule where it is collected into
efferent veins that follow at first a course different from the small
afferent vessels and ducts of the gland. The amount of connective
tissue varies in different animals, being particularly well represented
in the pig liver, where the interlobular connective tissue clearly
marks the boundaries of the lobules. The arrangement of the
hepatic cells is unique as regards their relation to sinusoids, and
the bile canaliculi are mere troughs between the adjacent faces of
two cells.

The liver is associated with the production of bile which is carried
to the duodenum, where it is mixed with food and pancreatic
enzymes. Part of the bile consists of secretion products from the
liver cells, and in part it consists of excretions which the liver cells
have removed from the blood. Apparently liver cells are able to
excrete foreign substances that have entered the blood. Bile acids
produced by the liver cells take part in the absorption of fats from
the intestine. The liver also has important endocrine functions.
It forms urea from ammonium carbonate and later on the urea is
removed from the blood by the kidney and excreted. The most
important endocrine function of liver cells involves taking such
a simple carbohydrate compound as glucose from the blood and
changing it to temporarily insoluble glycogen. Then, as tissues,
especially the muscles, need this fuel the liver reconverts glycogen
back into simple sugar (glucose) in which form it is distributed by
the blood-vascular system. The presence of insulin derived from
islands of Langerhans in the pancreas is essential to the carrying
out of this function. Tests show that liver cells, depending on the
diet, in some cases show a preponderance of protein products, at

other times of glycogen, and at still other times of fats. An extract, called heparin, obtained from liver tissue prevents the clotting of blood. Another substance obtained from liver tissue stimulates the production of erythrocytes. Liver tissue possesses great power of regeneration, but the removal of the entire organ results in the death of the organism in a short time.

**Gall-bladder.**—The largest bile ducts from the lobes of the mammalian liver usually connect with a pouch, the gall-bladder, which lies along the posterior under surface of the liver. The cystic duct continues outward to join the common bile duct. The wall of the gall-bladder consists of three coats, a mucosa, muscularis, and an adventitia similar to the duct wall. However, the mucosa is much folded and has a covering layer of tall columnar epithelial cells with basal nuclei. The tunica propria carries blood-vessels, and toward the neck region of the pouch there occur small tubulo-alveolar glands. The muscularis possesses interwoven bundles of smooth muscles arranged as an inner longitudinal layer and an outer thicker circular and oblique layer. The outer part of the adventitia is not so dense as the inner and supports blood and lymph vessels and nerves.

# CHAPTER XII

## THE EXCRETORY SYSTEM

THE oxidation phenomena grouped under metabolism, and involving both synthesis and destruction of cell materials, are accompanied by the production of waste products. Such waste products include carbon dioxide, mineral salts, water, and numerous simple nitrogenous compounds. These are mainly removed from the organism in aqueous solutions. We have already observed that in vertebrates carbon dioxide and some water are removed from the blood through the respiratory system, and that the integument plays a part in the elimination of small amounts of waste. However, among most animals a distinct excretory system has been evolved to deal with nitrogenous wastes.

In the primitive chordates and during embryonic development of higher forms there is a segmental arrangement of tubules composing the excretory system. These tubules open from the cœlome by ciliated funnels, the *nephrostomes*, and empty into a collecting duct with an outlet to the cloacal region. With the cephalochords such tubules have nephrostomes in the cœlomic cavity and are also associated with coils of blood-vessels, so that metabolic products are removed from both the cœlomic fluid and the blood. With the vertebrates there is an increasing efficiency in the development of tubules for the removal of wastes from the blood, and they become organized into one of three types of excretory organs called *kidneys*. These arise segmentally in the embryo along the mid-dorsal region, one on each side, at different levels. The three types have a common source of origin in the mesoderm of the intermediate cell mass, the *nephrotome*, which lies lateral to the mesodermal segments and connects them with the somatic and splanchnic layers of mesoderm enclosing the cœlome. Tubules formed from this mesodermal region become grouped along the mid-dorsal region to form each type of kidney.

In the cyclostomes, young fish, and larval amphibians, the *pronephros*, or head kidney, is functional; in adult fishes and amphibians, the *mesonephros*, or middle kidney, is functional; in reptiles, birds, and mammals, the *metanephros*, or posterior kidney, becomes the functional organ. During the embryology of those forms having the metanephros, the other two types are formed successively and

( 232 )

may function temporarily until the metanephros takes over the excretory function.

## THE PRONEPHRIC SYSTEM

A urinary system of this type is functional in myxinoid cyclostomes (hagfishes); in other cyclostomes it persists but yields its place as a functional system to the mesonephros appearing caudad to it. In the embryological development of higher forms the pronephros is formed but may never function, degenerates, and excretion is effected temporarily, or permanently, by the mesonephros.

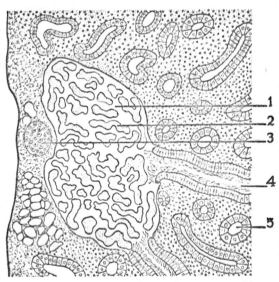

Fig. 170.—Drawing of a portion of the kidney of Lamprey. *1*, Glomus; *2*, **blood-vessels of glomus**; *3*, artery; *4*, ciliated tubule leading from nephrostome; *5*, tubules. (Courtesy of the General Biological Supply House, Chicago, Illinois.)

The *segmental ducts* or *pronephric ducts*, however, become associated with the mesonephric system. The structure of the pronephric system may be studied in cross-sections of young lamprey larvæ (or early embryos of all forms) posterior to the pharynx region. A series of several tubules forms the pronephros, below the peritoneum at both sides of the dorsal midline extending to the lateral body wall and along it ventrally a short distance. The segmental or pronephric duct lies at the ventral tip of the pronephros.

**Pronephros.**—The pronephric tubules are relatively few in number and arranged in a series connecting with the common segmental duct. Each tubule may be considered as beginning with a ciliated opening or *nephrostome*, the lips of which continue with the mesothelium of the cœlomic lining. A capillary network from branches of the dorsal aorta pushes its covering cœlomic lining outward toward the nephrostomes and forms a *glomus*. The capillary network of the glomus is supported by a scanty amount of connective tissue and collects into small veins which pass among the tubules to empty into the postcardinal veins. Thus material leaving the capillaries passes through their endothelial wall and the mesothelial membrane into the cœlomic space about the glomus before entering the nephrostomes. At the junction of the nephrostome with the squamous mesothelium, which may fold to partially encircle the glomus, a few cuboidal cells occur but columnar cells with long cilia are characteristic of the wall of the short segment of tubule immediately adjoining the nephrostome. The cilia are directed away from the nephrostome and fill the lumen of the tubule. The following segment is slightly coiled, and forms the major part of the short pronephric tubule. Its walls are composed of broad columnar or cuboidal cells and it coils to a join a straight tubule whose cells are smaller cuboidal in form.

**Segmental (Pronephric) Duct.**—The straight portion of the pronephric tubule joins the segmental duct which is lined by columnar epithelium and surrounded by a sheath of fibroelastic tissue. A few smooth muscle cells occur in the connective tissue sheath which continues with similar tissue supporting the tubules in the region of the pronephros. Posteriorly, a more distinct coat of encircling smooth muscle cells occurs and a serosa is found when the duct lies in the cœlome.

## THE MESONEPHRIC SYSTEM

The mesonephros, or Wolffian body, forms caudad to the site of the pronephros and is composed of more numerous tubules developing metamerically in pairs. Additional similar ones are derived by budding of the earlier tubules. These tubules fuse mesially with the segmental duct which now becomes the mesonephric or Wolffian duct. In elasmobranchs the segmental duct is assumed to split and give rise to another duct, the Mullerian duct, but in most forms this duct is considered to arise separately from the urogenital fold. With development, the mesonephric tubules become gathered into a more or less compact mass, the kidney. In fishes, each kidney is usually an elongated segmented body up under the peritoneum, close to the backbone. In the urodeles the kidneys are also elongated, but in frogs and toads they are shorter and broader. In these latter forms, the kidney becomes free in the body above

the viscera but is retroperitoneal and connected with the body wall by sheets of periotoneal tissue.

The mesonephric tubule is more complex than the preceding pronephric tubule. In the embryonic tubules the proximal end may have a distinct nephrostome, as in the case of the pronephric tubule, but differs in that a *glomerulus* projects into each uriniferous tubule below the region near the nephrostome. The arterial tuft is thus surrounded by a double capsule of reflected tubular tissue, *Bowman's capsule,* an inner *visceral* and an outer *parietal layer* of squamous epithelium, and the whole is called a *renal corpuscle.*

Fig. 171.—Photograph of a section through the kidney of a frog. Simple squamous epithelial cells of the parietal layer are shown lining the space, separating the visceral layer and glomerulus. The arterial vessels are shown entering the glomerulus at the top. 4 mm. obj. and 5× oc.

In such an arrangement the fluid from the blood is filtered through the inner visceral layer of the capsule and passes directly into the lumen of the mesonephric tubule without first passing into the cœlomic fluid, as in the case of the pronephros. With development the nephrostomes may close or lose their attachment with the mesonephric tubules and open by short tubules into veins. In urodeles they persist through life but many of them degenerate in anuran kidneys. Continuing from the glomerulus there is a proximal secreting portion of tubule that in turn connects with the mesonephric duct. (Figs. 171 and 172.)

The mesonephros is the functional kidney of most adult cyclostomes, elasmobranchs, teleosts, and Amphibia. It is functional for a short time in certain young lizards and for a short time after birth in the monotreme, Echidna, and in the marsupial, Didelphys. The kidney of the frog may be taken as an example of the functional mesonephros, although wide variations in structure and function may be found in the mesonephros of different representatives. A glomerulus is absent in some fishes, but a proximal convoluted portion, an intermediate segment, and a distal convolution are generally present in all forms.

## Frog

**Mesonephros.**—The kidney of the frog is a flattened, relatively broad, elongated body lying within the body cavity dorsal to the viscera. It is composed of an aggregate of mesonephric tubules, called *nephrons*, whose distal ends unite with the main collecting duct, the mesonephric duct, which runs along the outer lateral edge and continues posteriorly to join the cloaca.

Each *nephron* has several different regions. At the proximal end of each is the renal corpuscle (Figs. 171 and 172), formed by a glomerulus of arterial capillaries encapsulated by the double layer of thin, flat, epithelial cells forming *Bowman's capsule*. As the tubule continues distally the cells become cuboidal, or low columnar, and are more distinctly outlined. The region of the tubule just distal to the capsule, the *neck*, has a narrow lumen surrounded by small ciliated cuboidal cells with small central nuclei. From the *renal corpuscle*, as Bowman's capsule and the glomerulus are called, the mesonephric tubule extends dorsally where it coils, as the *proximal convoluted* portion, then returns as the *intermediate duct* to the ventral region to coil again, as the *distal convoluted* portion, in the vicinity of the renal corpuscle before continuing back dorsally to join one of the collecting ducts that runs along the dorsal region from the medial to lateral edge of the mesonephros. In physiologically active tubules the proximal convolution is composed of large cuboidal or low columnar cells with brush border and acidophilic granular cytoplasm. The end of the proximal convolution composition is marked by the constricted intermediate portion lined by low ciliated cuboidal cells. The distal convolution of the tubule is composed of cuboidal cells, usually smaller than those of the proximal convolution and bordering a larger lumen; these cells lack the brush border but their acidophilic cytoplasm is denser proximally and has a striated appearance. The terminal straight portion which joins the collecting dorsal duct is composed of cuboidal cells with clear cytoplasm and no striations. A number of nephrons empty into the collecting dorsal ducts which are composed of cuboidal or low columnar cells with clear cytoplasm, surrounded by a fibroelastic sheath. The dorsal ducts, in turn, empty into the mesonephric duct running along the lateral edge of the mesonephros. Nephrostomes are commonly present on the ventral surface and can be observed occasionally in sections. The best method of demonstrating them is to place an excised kidney in toluidine blue which quickly colors the cells of the nephrostome and its adjoining tubule. Injections of carbon or carmine into the peritoneal cavity may also be used to demonstrate the location and connection of the nephrostomes and the tubules leading from them. The ciliated cuboidal cells of the nephrostome continue into an associated ciliated duct which ends blindly or opens into a vein. In the

latter case, the nephrostome and its associated duct are called peritoneal funnels and effect an immediate entry of cœlomic fluids into the vascular system.

In the male frogs a number of the tubules of the kidney are joined in the neck region by vasa efferentia from the testis and thus effect passage of sperm into the mesonephric duct during the breeding season. Sperm may be found filling many of the tubules at this season.

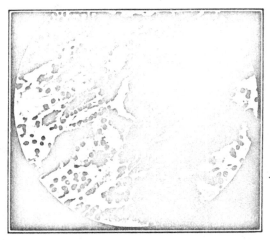

**Fig. 172.**—Photograph of a section of the frog's kidney, showing a glomerulus surrounded by Bowman's capsule, the parietal layer of which continues into the neck of the uriniferous tubule. Sections of distal convoluted and straight collecting regions and adjoining capillaries surround the renal corpuscle. 4 mm. obj. and 5 × oc.

The adrenal gland appears macroscopically as a wavy golden line at either side of the mid-ventral surface and in sections its glandular cells are incorporated in the connective tissue and vascular supply of the kidney.

The mesonephros is covered by the peritoneum and a thin capsule of connective tissue. Myeloid tissue is common in the sheath and also about the larger vessels and even about the capillaries within the mesonephros.

Amphibian kidneys have a peculiar blood supply. Branches of the dorsal aorta, called renal arteries, carry arterial blood to them, and venous branches from the kidneys unite to form the postcaval veins which return blood to the heart. In addition to these, renal-portal veins arising from veins in the legs also pass to the kidneys. The renal arteries are connected with the glomeruli of the renal corpuscles. The capillary network around the tubules is derived from the renal-portal veins. All the blood returns to the heart *via* the postcava.

Despite many physiological experiments with the frog's kidney, the manner of its functioning is not thoroughly understood. Some observations of the living kidney have shown an intermittent flow of blood through the glomeruli, with some glomeruli thus being retired from or recalled to active functioning as conditions demand. The neck region and the narrow ciliated portion at the lower end of the proximal convoluted tubule have been observed to contract, and presumably regulate urinary flow. The flow of urine from the distal convoluted tubule to the collecting duct is rapid. Experiments indicate that the glomerular filtrate in living frogs has the same composition as blood plasma except for fats and large protein molecules. Glucose has been found reabsorbed from proximal convoluted portion while chlorides and water are reabsorbed in the distal convoluted portion with a resultant concentration of the urine. The constricted or intermediate portion and distal convolution are primarily involved in absorption from the lumen. The constricted ciliated portions before and behind the proximal convolution may act as valves and constitute the pressure regulating portion of the nephron.

**Mesonephric Duct.**—This duct runs along the dorso-lateral region of the mesonephros and during its passage is enclosed in fibroelastic tissue of the mesonephros. Posterior to the kidney the duct lies free in the cœlome associated with the Müllerian duct and surrounded by a serosa. The mucosa of the mesonephric duct is composed of a single layer of low columnar cells in the anterior region but posteriorly the epithelial lining becomes pseudostratified (Fig. 173). Some of the columnar cells are ciliated, others

Fig. 173.—Photograph of a cross-section of the mesonephric duct of Necturus in the region of the kidney. 4 mm. obj. and 5× oc.

are goblet cells. A thin tunica propria lies below a distinct basement membrane and projects the mucosa into longitudinal folds. A thin circular band of smooth muscle cells and scattered longitudinal ones form a muscularis surrounded by fibroelastic tissue of the adventitia or serosa.

**Cloacal Bladder.**—Posterior to the openings of the mesonephric ducts into the cloaca there is a ventral diverticulum which forms the cloacal bladder. In a relaxed state this sac is much shrunken and folded but may be distended to considerable size with fluid from the cloaca. The mucosa is similar to that of the cloaca (Fig. 140), two or three layers of cuboidal cells thrown into folds by a tunica propria with a rich capillary supply and scattered chromatophores. The muscularis is limited to bundles of inner circular and outer longitudinal and oblique smooth muscle surrounded by a serosa. The urine is temporarily stored in this bladder and some water

may be resorbed from it by the mucosa. Body movements play a part in the evacuation of the cloacal bladder.

## THE METANEPHRIC SYSTEM

The metanephros develops from the caudad nephrogenic tissue near the cloaca at the base of the mesonephric duct, and is composed of a compact mass of tubules. The Bowman's capsule and secreting portions of the tubules are formed from the caudad nephrogenic tissue, but the collecting portions arise as outgrowths of the mesonephric duct, which was formed at the time of appearance of the pronephros and is retained after the degeneration of the tubules of that kidney. The glandular portion of the entire tubule, *i. e.*, that part developing from nephrogenic tissue, is called a *nephron*. At about the time when nephrogenic tissue begins developing metanephric tubules, a bud evaginates from the bend of the mesonephric duct where it joins the cloaca. This bud pushes forward to the anterior lumbar region of the body cavity, where it expands and becomes associated with the nephrogenic tissue. The duct portion of this prolonged evagination becomes the *ureter*, or main excretory duct of the metanephros. The expanded anterior portion is the primitive pelvis and gives off anterior buds that form the calyces from which branching evaginations give rise to systems of branched collecting tubules. The latter fuse with the uriniferous tubules that have been developing during this same period. This collecting system forms a conical mass of treelike branched collecting tubules that constitute the major portion of the medulla of the kidney and extend radially into the cortical portion occupied mainly by the secretory tubules with which they fuse.

The nephrons of the metanephros are more complex and more numerous than those of the mesonephros and do not at any time have a nephrostome associated with them. Bowman's capsule closely surrounds the glomerulus and continues distally to the neck of the tubule. Continuing from the neck, the tubule becomes convoluted for some distance, then constricts and straightens to descend and loop back to form a wider distal convoluted portion. The distal convoluted portion finally joins with a collecting tubule by a junctional tubule or in some cases by a short arched portion.

This type is the permanent kidney of reptiles, birds, and mammals, but before its appearance the other two types successively precede it in embryological development. The caudad portion of the pronephric duct remains as the mesonephric duct, and this in turn by evagination from its caudad portion gives rise to the ureter of the metanephros, and the original main portion of it becomes converted into the male genital duct, the vas deferens, for these forms.

The mammalian kidney may be used as an example of this type, since details of its structure are well known and give all the structural characters. The kidneys of birds and reptiles have similarly composed nephrons but their organization is less compact and the kidneys have a more elongated and lobulated form.

### Mammal

**Metanephros.**—Mammalian kidneys are bean-shaped organs located in the lumbar region against the dorsal body wall. (Fig. 174.) They appear to be free in the body cavity, but are held in place by the sturdy trunks of

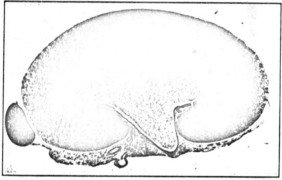

Fig. 174.—Photograph of a longitudinal section of a rat's kidney, showing a single papilla extending into the calyx at the hilus. The darker striated region surrounding the papilla (medulla) is the cortex. The adrenal is shown closely attached to the kidney on the left. × 20.

the renal arteries, renal veins, and by the ureters. The peritoneum, which splits into connective tissue sheets or fascia at the outside border of each kidney, also aids in support. The posterior fascia unites with the front of the spinal column, and the anterior fascia covers the front of the kidney and its vessels, passing over the aorta to meet the corresponding fascia from the other kidney. There is usually considerable fatty tissue between the kidney and its fascia. The outer margin of each kidney is convex, but the mesial border presents an indentation, called the hilus. (Fig. 174.) Here the renal artery, renal vein, and ureter connect with the kidney. The entire kidney is covered with a loose capsule of connective tissue which is similar to the peritoneum in composition. There is little connective tissue within the substance of the kidneys, although the capillaries are accompanied by a rich reticular network.

If the entire kidney is divided lengthwise into two halves in a plane parallel with the adjacent body wall, additional features can be seen macroscopically. At the hilus can be seen the expanded funnel-like continuation of the ureter, called the *pelvis*, the internal end of which is further subdivided into small funnel-like divisions, called the *primary calyces*, each

of which divides into *secondary calyces*. The main collecting tubules open into the secondary calyces. (Fig. 175.)

The body of the gland is divided into two zones, an external zone just within the capsule, called the *cortex*, and an inner zone, the *medulla*, toward the pelvis. Toward the hilus of the human kidney the medulla is divided into a number of triangular masses, with the base of each directed toward the cortex and the apex of each fitting into a minor calyx of the pelvis as a papilla. These triangular appearing masses are known as renal pyramids and are in reality conical masses of tubules which are more markedly separated as lobular masses in birds and reptiles. The human kidney

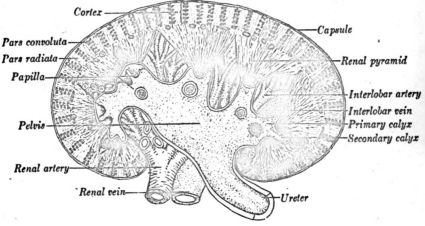

FIG. 175.—Diagram of a longitudinal section of a human kidney.

may have twenty renal pyramids, but usually they are not so numerous. The kidneys of marsupials, insectivors, rodents, and carnivors have usually only a single renal pyramid. In the medullary zone between the renal pyramids are branches of the renal artery and vein embedded in connective tissue; cortical components separating the pyramids are known as the *columns of Bertini*. An examination of the cortex with the aid of a hand lens or low-power objective, reveals alternating light and dark radial striations. The lighter striations, called *medullary rays*, are composed of collecting tubules, extend into the medulla but not to the capsule. (Fig. 175.) The darker regions are called *pars convoluta* and show a series of small dotlike structures, *renal corpuscles*, together with convoluted portions of the nephron accompanied by a capillary network. Before progressing further it is essential to understand in detail the structure and distribution of the nephron which is the structural unit of the kidney. Each kidney possesses thousands of these tubules.

*The Nephron.*—Attention has already been called to the dotlike structures, the renal or Malpighian corpuscles, visible in the pars convoluta striations. Each tubule begins with one of these structures, as in the case of the mesonephric tubule. Each renal corpuscle consists of a capillary complex, known as a glomerulus, which is surrounded by Bowman's capsule, a double-walled structure of squamous epithelium. An afferent arteriole

16

carries blood into the glomerulus and an efferent arteriole carries blood
away, the two arterioles being adjacent where they continue into the
capillary tuft. The capillary tuft is itself closely invested with the visceral
wall of Bowman's capsule, which fits in close around the arterioles as they
join the capillaries of the glomerulus. This same inner, or visceral wall, of
Bowman's capsule is reflected back as the outer, or parietal, wall. The
parietal wall continues down around the inner wall and forms a narrow
neck at the end of the renal corpuscle opposite the entrance of the arterioles.
(Figs. 171, 172, and 176.)

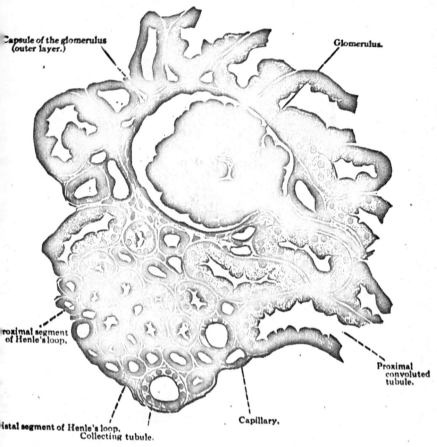

Capsule of the glomerulus
  (outer layer.)

Glomerulus.

roximal segment
  of Henle's loop.

Proximal
convoluted
tubule.

distal segment of Henle's loop.
  Collecting tubule.

Capillary.

Fig. 176.—Section from the cortex of the kidney. (Bremer—Weatherford's
Textbook of Histology, courtesy of the Blakiston Co.)

The neck continues into a portion of the uriniferous tubule known as
the proximal convoluted tubule. The wall of the neck portion consists first
of small low cuboidal cells. The proximal convoluted portion, composed of
several cells with brush border in cross-sections, is very much contorted,
extending somewhat toward the surface at first, then turning toward the
medulla and finally continuing into the medulla as a very much narrower

portion, known as the descending limb. This portion has a few flattened cells about an irregular lumen in sections and extends radially in the medulla for some distance, then forms a loop, known as Henle's loop, and turns back as the ascending limb running alongside the descending limb. The ascending limb is somewhat thicker than the descending limb and has three or four flattened low cuboidal cells about an irregular lumen in sections. As it passes into the cortex, the tubule becomes the much thicker and contorted distal convoluted tubule situated near the proximal convoluted portion. The distal convoluted portion has cuboidal cells without a brush border but with proximally striated cytoplasm and a larger lumen than the proximal convoluted region. Toward the cortical surface it joins a collecting tubule by a short junctional tubule. The collecting tubules have sharply outlined cuboidal cells with darkly staining nuclei and clear cytoplasm. These collecting tubules join the others which in turn join larger tubules, until the largest collecting ducts, *papillary ducts*, in the papillæ

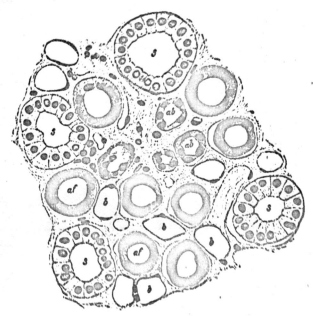

Fig. 177.—Section across the middle of Malpighian (renal) pyramid. *ab,* Thin segment of medullary loop; *af,* thick segment of medullary loop; *b,* capillaries; *s,* collecting tubules. (Schafer, after Kölliker, Schafer's Histology.)

open into the calyces. (Fig. 178.) The functions of the various regions is presumed to be similar to those observed in experiments with the mesonephros, *i. e.,* glomerular filtration of plasma except for fats and large protein molecules; glucose reabsorption in proximal segment; chloride and water reabsorption in the distal segment with resultant concentration of the urine.

A consideration of the cortex shows that a pars convoluta consists chiefly of renal corpuscles, together with proximal and distal convoluted portions of the uriniferous tubules. A pars radiata is formed mainly by collecting tubules. The medulla consists chiefly of collecting tubules, together with the descending and ascending limbs, and Henle's loop. Little has been said about the blood-vessels involved in all these regions, for the vascular supply will be considered separately later.

As indicated, a number of branchings, about seven, occur between a given papillary duct and the smallest collecting tubules draining into it. Each papillary duct is like a tree with many branches, the collecting tubules of different grades originating from the single trunk. All of these branches constitute parts of the collecting system and have the same origin as the

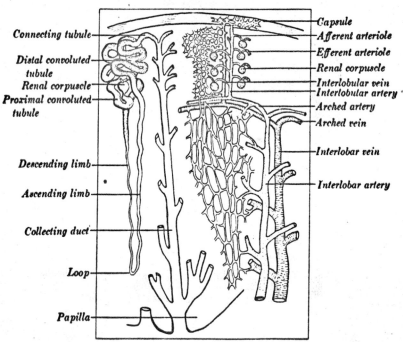

Connecting tubule
Distal convoluted tubule
Renal corpuscle
Proximal convoluted tubule
Descending limb
Ascending limb
Collecting duct
Loop
Papilla

Capsule
Afferent arteriole
Efferent arteriole
Renal corpuscle
Interlobular vein
Interlobular artery
Arched artery
Arched vein
Interlobar vein
Interlobar artery

Fig. 178.—Diagram of the uriniferous and vascular system of a mammalian kidney.

calyces, pelvis, and ureter in the evagination of the mesonephric duct. The nephron, which develops from nephrogenic tissue and takes part in the elaboration of urine, consists of those parts from Bowman's capsule through the distal convoluted portion. The main function of the excretory tubule is to conduct urine from the secretory tubule, or nephron, to the pelvis. (Fig. 178.)

*Blood Supply of the Kidney.*—The renal artery and renal vein divide into trunks, of which the greater number pass over the front of the pelvis in man but ventrally in quadruped mammals. Branches of these, known as *interlobar arteries* and *veins*, extend between adjacent pyramids to the boundary between cortex and medulla where, as *arcuate arteries* and *veins*, they curve at right angles to lie between the cortex and medulla. From the arcuate arteries, small vessels (*interlobular arteries*) extend radially toward the cortex. From each interlobular artery a number of

*afferent glomerular arterioles* originate, one to each renal corpuscle. Each *efferent glomerular arteriole* forms a capillary network in the cortex surrounding the convoluted tubule of that nephron, and extends alongside the collecting tubules of the cortex. This capillary network connects with the interlobular veins running alongside the interlobular arteries, and then these join the arcuate veins. The capillary system of the cortex joins with the capillary supply of the medulla. Here the capillary network surrounds the systems of collecting tubules and those portions of the nephrons which are located in the medulla. The capillary network of the medulla connects with radially directed *venulæ rectæ*, which are small veins connecting with the arciform veins. The latter branches join to form interlobar veins, which occur alongside interlobar arteries and eventually join with the renal vein. Not only is the kidney well supplied with arteries, veins, and capillaries, but there is also a rich lymphatic system. The nerves supplying the kidney are branches of the sympathetic plexus.

*Regeneration.*—Limited regeneration is possible from multiplication of differentiated cells of the nephron but not from cells of the collecting tubules. Destruction of all the cells of the convoluted region results in collapse of that nephron.

*Abnormalities.*—Concretions of crystalline material may form small *stones* which lie in the pelvis or pass painfully down the ureter. Obstruction of a ureter may occur and in this case the kidney affected undergoes atrophy and the other kidney hypertrophies. Under abnormal conditions leading to death of renal cells the affected areas may be a center for calcium deposits and calcified regions result. Fat accumulation commonly occurs in the cells of the convoluted portions and glomerulus and then in the conducting tubules, when extensive degeneration may follow. Such accumulation in renal cells occurs first in the proximal cytoplasm, then throughout. Lipoids are reported as common in the proximal and distal convoluted cells even after starvation.

**Ureter.**—In reptiles, birds, and mammals where the metanephros is the functional kidney, the ureter occurs as a new structure developing from the basal portion of the old mesonephric duct, as already noted.

In all cases, the ureter has three distinct coats. In mammals the lining is composed of transitional epithelium like that of the kidney pelvis with which it is continuous. This, with an underlying tunica propria of loose fibroelastic connective tissue, constitutes the mucosa. (Fig. 179.) It forms longitudinal folds, so that in cross-section the lumen appears to be star-shaped. Outside the mucosa there is a muscularis coat which usually exhibits an inner layer of scattered longitudinally arranged strands of smooth muscle cells and an outer, thicker zone of circularly disposed smooth muscle cells. These two sets of muscle cells produce the peristaltic motion which continuously carries drops of urine away from the kidney. Covering the muscularis coat is the serosa. Among birds and reptiles the ureter lining is commonly of columnar epithelium with distal mucous secretion. Nearer the cloaca a basal layer of smaller cells is interspersed among the tapering ends of the columnar cells. The muscularis in the lizard is composed of scattered bundles of circular smooth muscle cells; in the pigeon a definite muscularis is formed.

**Bladder.**—The bladder occurring among the amniotes has been called an allantoic bladder, but embryological studies have shown that the allantois is not involved in the formation of the bladder of these forms. Ophidia, Crocodilia, many Lacertilia, and Aves have no bladder. Turtles, some lizards, and all mammals have one.

An idea of the development of the mammalian bladder may be gained from a study of its development in man. In embryos, the posterior end of the embryonic gut is somewhat expanded and lies ventrally against the ectodermal body wall. Later, in this region, an endodermal diverticulum from the cloaca will meet an ectodermal invagination to form the anal opening. From the bend where each mesonephric duct joins the cloaca a bud will form, and from this will develop the ureter of the metanephric kidneys already described. Somewhat later the cloaca in this region subdivides into two passages entirely separated from each other. The more

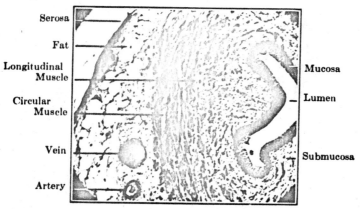

Serosa

Fat

Longitudinal Muscle

Circular Muscle

Vein

Artery

Mucosa

Lumen

Submucosa

Fig. 179.—Section across the dog's ureter. Photomicrograph 16 mm. obj. and 5× oc.

dorsal of the two forms the rectum, and the ventral forms a urogenital sinus. This occurs when the embryo is about eight weeks old in humans, and while it is taking place the urogenital sinus itself is subdividing into a dorsal and ventral portion. The allantois and mesonephric ducts connect with the dorsal portion of the urogenital sinus. The ventral, so-called phallic, portion is later involved in the development of the urethra region of the genital ducts of both sexes, especially with the penis of the male, and continues to expand to become a wide, muscular-walled sac, the bladder. At the anterior ventral end of this enlargement is a stalk of tissue, the urachus of the embryo, but in the adult this is the middle umbilical ligament tying the bladder to the body wall. The ureters shift their position so as to join the wall of the developing bladder, and as the latter grows forward it carries the ureters with it, separating them from the mesonephric ducts which are retained to become functional in connection with the reproductive system of the male.

The mammalian bladder has four coats of tissue making up its wall, namely, the mucosa, submucosa, muscularis, and adventitia. (Fig. 180.) The mucosa, like the ureters, is lined with transitional epithelium. The behavior of this type of epithelium in the distended and empty bladder has already been described in the consideration of epithelia. In the empty bladder the mucosa is wrinkled by folding of the underlying submucosa.

In some bladders there are simple glandlike pockets in the epithelial wall. There being no muscularis mucosæ, the submucosa of fibroelastic connective tissue unites with the tunica propria underlying the epithelial lining. A study of a cross-section of relaxed bladder wall shows a broad muscularis divided into a thick middle coat with circularly arranged cells, an innermost

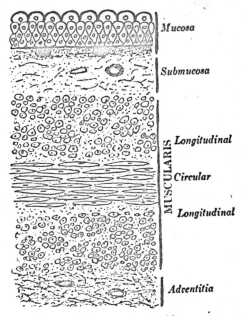

*Mucosa*

*Submucosa*

*Longitudinal*

*Circular*

*Longitudinal*

MUSCULARIS

*Adventitia*

Fig. 180.—Diagram of mammalian bladder.

Fig. 181.—Photograph of the urethra of a female mouse.. The lumen is lined by a thin stratified epithelium. In the submucosa are mixed serous and mucous glands which extend into the underlying skeletal muscle. 16 mm. obj. and 5× oc.

region with a thin layer of longitudinally arranged cells, and an outside region also with longitudinal layers of cells. The muscle tissue, although loosely arranged, is very strong. The adventitia consists of fibroelastic connective tissue and merges with a peritoneal coating. At the junction of the bladder with the urethra the circularly disposed smooth muscle forms the internal sphincter of the bladder.

**The Urethra.**—The urethra is limited to mammals and differs in the male and female. In the male it forms the duct of the penis, and an account of its structure will be considered with the male system of reproduction. The female urethra is short (Fig. 181) and extends from the bladder to the vestibule where it opens into the vestibule along with the vaginal part of the female reproductive system. Internally it presents longitudinal folding of the mucosa. The epithelium of the mucosa is commonly transitional near the bladder and stratified squamous as it enters the vestibule. Glandular pockets with mucous cells or deeper sinuses with associated mucoserous glands may occur in the urethral walls. A muscularis coat with an inner longitudinal coat and an outer circular coat is surrounded by a fibrosa. Near the junction of the urethra with the vestibule there is an external sphincter muscle of the skeletal variety outside the smooth muscle.

# CHAPTER XIII

## THE FEMALE REPRODUCTIVE SYSTEM

AMONG the vertebrates, the sexual systems are generally separated, different individuals developing into either male or female, but for a time during the early embryology the male and female sexual systems follow the same developmental plan and are indistinguishable either anatomically or histologically. Elements of both systems are developed at this time, though ultimately only one differentiates to a functional level. In early vertebrate embryos the urogenital fold develops on either side of the dorsal midline. From the greater part of this fold the urinary system develops, as already described; but from the mesial ventral surface a longitudinal thickening arises to form the genital ridge. This ridge is covered with a cuboidal epithelium and separated from the developing kidney by mesenchyme. The simple epithelium of the genital ridge proliferates into a stratified zone of polyhedral cells in which two types of cells soon make their appearance. Larger spherical cells, the primordial sex cells, are scattered among the cuboidal or polyhedral indifferent cells, and the underlying mesenchyme forms stringlike masses projecting into the epithelial mass. This mass represents the early indifferent stage in development of the sex glands, or gonads. The excretory ducts of the genital system are also closely associated with the urinary system. Two longitudinal ducts are developed on each side from the mesoderm lining the cœlome, and these open caudally into the cloaca. One duct is the Wolffian duct, already described in considering the excretory system, the other is the Müllerian duct, which becomes the oviduct of the female. With development, sexual differentiation occurs, and the system associated with the sex so determined progressively differentiates while the elements of the other system degenerate.

**The Ovaries.**—The female organs of reproduction consist of the ovaries in which the ova are produced, and a pair of ducts, the oviducts, by which the ova are conducted away. The ovaries of vertebrates are usually paired organs, but occasionally, as in the skate and birds, one ovary degenerates, or, as in certain teleosts, the two ovaries fuse. In the embryonic gonad, stringlike continuations of the underlying mesenchyme divide the epithelial cells into cords and carry along developing blood-vessels. Thus, each gland is composed of spherical cells supported by connective tissue, and the whole covered by an epithelial membrane continuous with the peritoneal lining. The first indication of ovarian differentiation

( 249 )

appears in the development of a layer of the cuboidal or polyhedral cells to form follicle or nurse cells about larger primordial sex cells. Generally a single layer of cuboidal or columnar cells surrounds each maturing ovum and assists in the elaboration of the nutrition for its development. By the activity of these cells, yolk is added in the case of yolk-bearing eggs so that adequate nutrition is stored for future developmental demands to be met after fertilization.

Not all the ova and their follicle cells complete development. A number appear to reach various stages of differentiation and then disintegrate and are resorbed with an accompanying invasion of the surrounding connective tissue, a process called *atresia*.

The condition of the ovary shows considerable variation in the different groups of vertebrates and the development of the ovum likewise varies. Among the oviparous forms the fertilized egg develops outside the body and must depend upon its stored nutrition. In some viviparous forms it may likewise have to depend entirely or in part upon stored nutrition. In placental mammals, no yolk storage occurs and nutrition is furnished the embryo throughout its development directly from the mother.

**The Oviducts.**—There are many variations in the egg-conducting apparatus. In some forms, such as the cyclostomes, and some teleosts, no oviducts are present and the eggs liberated into the body cavity pass to the outside through pores in the cloacal region. In other teleosts, folds of the peritoneum form funnel-like sacs connecting the ovary with the cloaca. They are composed of fibro-elastic connective tissue with some smooth muscle and surfaced by a simple epithelial membrane.

In some of the lower vertebrates it appears that the Wolffian and Müllerian ducts may arise from a longitudinal splitting of the embryonic segmental or pronephric duct, but usually the oviducts or Müllerian ducts arise in both the male and female as a fold in the ventral lateral surface of the mesonephric cell mass near its anterior end. The anterior end forms a groove that remains open while posteriorly the fold forms a tube or cord of cells that develops a lumen. The posterior portion grows caudally to fuse with the cloaca or urogenital sinus, but the anterior end remains open into the body cavity and is called the *ostium abdominalis*. In elasmobranchs, amphibians, birds, and monotremes, the eggs pass into the abdominal cavity and from there procede anteriorly through the body cavity into the ostium abdominalis of the oviduct to be conducted to the cloaca. In mammals the ostium closely adjoins the ovary so that passage of the egg in the body cavity is normally very limited.

In vertebrates below the mammals, as a rule, the two oviducts open separately into the cloaca. In mammals, a longitudinal septum, the *perineum*, divides the embryonic cloacal region into a dorsal rectum and a ventral urogenital vestibule before birth. In these forms the Müllerian ducts fuse into a single passageway whose posterior portion forms the *vagina*, which opens into the vestibule separately from the urethra.

The oviducts show modifications depending upon the type of egg and its future development. In the case of the large, shelled eggs of birds and reptiles, there are specialized portions of the ducts which secrete the additional material. In the placentals, the egg is fertilized in the upper portion of the oviduct and then conducted to a lower portion, the uterus, which is modified for implantation and internal development of the embryo.

In general, the oviducts have ciliated columnar epithelium lining the lumen. Simple tubular glands of varying prominence, depending on the season, extend into the subepithelial fibroelastic connective tissue and loose fibroelastic connective tissue of the submucosa forms folds projecting the mucosa into the lumen. Below the submucosa there is usually a broad coat of circular smooth muscle separated from a less prominent outer longitudinal coat by a region of vascular fibroelastic connective tissue.

**Estrus.**—A consideration of the ovary and the development of ova from the primitive germ cells to the time of their liberation indicates that such ovarian activity varies considerably in different forms. Usually there is a regular cyclical appearance of ovulation; in some forms it occurs annually, but in others it occurs at shorter intervals.

Among the fishes, the mature eggs are commonly discharged into the water during a spawning season, at which time males and females congregate. Copulation does not occur, but sperm are discharged into the water in the vicinity of the eggs so that fertilization and further development are external. In some forms, as in the dogfish, fertilization is internal and development of the embryo occurs in the modified posterior portion of the oviducts, the *uterus*. In these cases the male clasps the female and the ventral fins are modified to conduct sperm to the cloacal opening of the female, from which region they move up into the oviducts to fertilize the ova.

In the Amphibia, as in the frog, fertilization is also external, but is aided by a close proximity of the male and female in an embrace called amplexus, a pseudocopulation. When the females become turgid with mature eggs, the male clasps a female tightly and as the eggs are discharged sperm are poured over them. In ther forms, as in the newt, sperm may be deposited in packets which are picked up by the swollen wall of the cloacal opening of the female.

Among the reptiles, birds, and mammals, sperm are introduced into the female cloaca or vagina by a hempipenis or penis, and fertilization later occurs in the oviducts.

Most vertebrates, including the lower animals, show mating interest at the time of ovulation, and their outward behavior is generally influenced by this internal condition. There are some accompanying changes in the oviducts and uterine regions. In the lower forms these changes involve an activity of the glands adding albumen and shells to the eggs, but in those forms where development is internal there are additional preparatory changes in the uterus.

In most mammals, ovulation occurs during or shortly following the period known as heat, rut, or estrus. In the rat, cycles of heat, or estrus, occur every four days, in the guinea-pig every sixteen days, in the pig every twenty-one days unless fertilization occurs. In each of these periods there are characteristic uterine changes before ovulation and also changes in the vaginal condition. The estrual cycles in these forms can be followed by changes in the vaginal cells to the period just preceding, or at ovulation, when the animal is said to be in heat. A desire for mating is manifested at this time, and at the time of or following copulation, ovulation occurs. Many follicles also nearly mature at this time undergo atresia and follicles of the next cycle arise from small or primary follicles. Should copulation not be effected, ovulation usually occurs, the egg degenerates, and the cycle is begun anew with the maturing of other follicles.

In man and the primates the main evidence of a regular estrual cycle is the phenomenon known as menstruation, which occurs with the failure of fertilization. In these forms the uterine changes are much more extensive and involve a remarkable thickening of the mucosa of the body of the uterus. In case the egg is not fertilized before it reaches the uterus there follows a loss of the major portion of the uterine mucosa together with considerable blood. Menstruation represents a failure of the reproductive process and is followed by regeneration and proliferation accompanying follicle development in the ovary. Maturation of follicles usually ceases with fertilization and is renewed after birth of the young.

## FEMALE REPRODUCTIVE SYSTEM OF FISHES

**Ovaries.**—In myxinoid cyclostomes, an unpaired, elongate gonad held by a median dorsal mesentery. No genital ducts are present,

and the ova and sperm are liberated into the body cavity from which they pass to the urogenital sinus by two pores. The anterior portion of this gonad produces ova and the posterior portion produces sperm, but both are not functional at the same time. In this case an individual functions first as a male and then as a female. In some cyclostomes only one portion may be functional, though the other is present.

Most elasmobranchs have a pair of ovaries but in some, such as the skate, the female has a single ovary; the right ovary degenerates. In the functional ovary, ova mature periodically and are liberated to be picked up by a pair of oviducts opening behind the peri-cardium. The eggs of this group are the largest among the fishes and usually only a small number mature each season; this is particularly true of forms like the dogfish where development is internal.

The teleost fishes generally produce the smallest eggs and also the most numerous; sometimes millions may be formed each season. The ovary here arises as an evagination of the embryonic wall of the body cavity on each side of the midline, and becomes surrounded by a fold of the peritoneum which encloses it like a sac and continues caudally to form a duct connecting the ovary with the cloaca. In this case the eggs do not pass into the general body cavity when mature, but continue down this duct to the cloaca.

In general, the ovaries vary from an inactive stage, in which few oögenic cells occur in the connective tissue of an elongate membranous fold, to the active stage, in which the ovary becomes filled with developing ova. In the active stage the connective tissue covering of the ovary is extremely thin, and the mass of maturing ova is visible through it. The oögenic epithelial cells covering the ovary become active before each breeding season, and oöcytes and follicle cells are proliferated. Each ovum becomes surrounded by a single layer of flattened epithelial nurse cells and a delicate sheath, or *theca*, of connective tissue supporting a capillary network. As the ova mature, a storage of yolk occurs in the cytoplasm and they distend the connective tissue until, at the time of ovulation, they break through the follicular sheath and ovary wall into the body cavity. Cells derived from the nurse cells fill in the cavity left by the ovum and form a corpus luteum in ovoviviparous and viviparous forms.

**Shell Gland.**—Derived from and closely associated with the lower part of the oviduct there may be a compound tubular gland, the shell gland. The secretory cells of the tubules contain an acidophilic granular cytoplasm and their secretion forms the shell about the descending fertilized egg. In skates the shell glands are large but in the dogfish they are small and non-functional.

### Dogfish

**Ovary.**—In this form a pair of ovaries occurs; each arises as a medial dorsal fold into the body cavity covered by peritoneum. The fold is attached to the connective tissue of the dorsal body wall where blood-vessels enter it; the remainder becomes free in the anterior body cavity and is covered by a cuboidal or low columnar germinal epithelium continuous with the cuboidal mesothelium of the peritoneum and mesentery. The vascular connective tissue forming the body or stroma of the ovary contains many developing blood cells, making it a myeloid center in this form. (Fig. 182.)

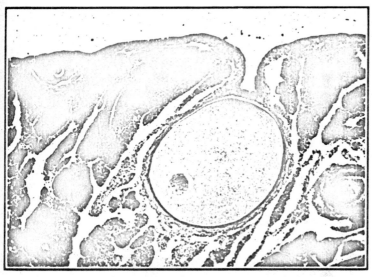

Fig. 182.—A section through the ovary of a young dogfish, showing a maturing follicle below a pocket in the germinal epithelium. A smaller atretic follicle is located near the surface at the left. The stroma of the ovary is packed with myeloid cells. Photomicrograph. 32 mm. obj. and 5× oc.

In the developing young form, or an old one approaching the breeding season, the germinal epithelium dips into the ovarian stroma and forms a cord or ball of cells. One of these enlarges as an oöcyte and others form a sheath of flattened nurse or follicle cells about it, thus composing a primary follicle. As development progresses the follicle separates from the germinal epithelial membrane and lies in the connective tissue which adds a sheath about the nurse cells. Maturation of the follicle is accompanied by increases of cytoplasm in the ovum; at first this is finely granular but then coarse yolk granules appear and accumulate. The cell membrane of the ovum is surrounded by a thick bright area, the *vitelline membrane*, and the peripheral cytoplasm adjoining it shows fine striations. Accompanying the growth of the ovum in size, the nurse cells increase in numbers and form a single layer of closely packed tapered short columnar cells with a coarsely granular acidophilic cytoplasm; their nuclei have a coarse chromatin network and a nucleolus. The mature ovum is a relatively large yolk-filled

sphere surrounded by nurse cells. The follicle finally ruptures the connective tissue sheath and the covering ovarian tissue to enter the body cavity
and the opening, or ostium, of the oviduct.

In the active ovary a number of atretic, or degenerating and resorbing
ovarian follicles occur and only a few follicles progress to maturity. The
mature yolk-laden ovum is surrounded by an inner narrow basophilic membrane and a thicker outer clear vitelline membrane. Following extrusion
of the ovum the follicle collapses and the nurse cells form a corpus luteum
that is resorbed following birth of the developing pups located in the uterine
portion of the oviduct.

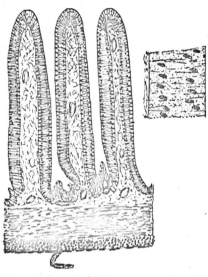

Fig. 183.—Drawing of a cross-section of the upper portion of the dogfish oviduct
showing the folds covered by columnar epithelium. The inset to the right shows
the peculiar alternation of epithelial cells with distal and proximal nuclei.

**Oviduct.**—From the ostium region, the oviduct has a relatively thin wall
with longitudinal mucosal folds covered by a ciliated columnar epithelium.
The tunica propria is surrounded by scattered smooth muscle cells in the
ostium. Posterior to the ostium the wall is much thicker and the muscularis has a prominent circular layer surrounded by a less well-developed
longitudinal one. The mucosa is thrown into a number of tall longitudinal
folds by the tunica propria. The covering epithelium is peculiar in its
composition. There is a single layer of tall slender ciliated columnar cells,
some with the nucleus in the distal third and other more numerous ones
with the nuclei in the extreme proximal region; so that two rows of conspicuous nuclei appear, except at the free ends of the folds where a pseudostratified appearance is present due to tapering cells with nuclei at different
levels. The cytoplasm has an abundance of various sized granules and
some cells appear with distal accumulations of secretion. The muscularis
is composed of an inner circular and an outer longitudinal layer. A serosa
forms the external coat of the oviduct over its entire length. (Fig. 183.)

**Uterine Region.**—The posterior portion of the oviduct is here associated with retention and maintenance of the developing embryos. The lumen becomes broader and a submucosa of loose fibroelastic tissue forms a peculiar and characteristic network of folds. (Fig. 184.) The mucosa is composed of a stratified cuboidal epithelial membrane with small polyhedral cells resting on a vascular tunica propria. The surface cuboidal cells are larger, have a striated border and a denser acidophilic cytoplasm than the underlying small cells. The tunica propria extends numerous small papillæ with capillaries into the epithelial membranes. The free ends of the submucosal folds contain large blood-vessels and the submucosal tissue has the appearance of mucous connective tissue with strands of collagenous fibers forming a loose network.

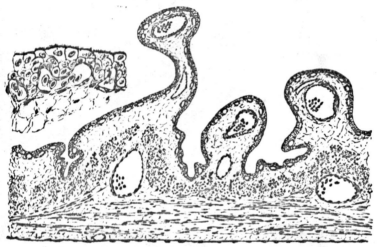

Fig. 184.—A longitudinal section of the uterus of a dogfish with young, showing the vascular ridges involving the submucosa. The insert to the left gives greater detail of the mucosa and its vascular supply.

## FEMALE REPRODUCTIVE SYSTEM OF AMPHIBIA

**Ovaries.**—Nearly all of this group are oviparous and lay their eggs in water. During the breeding season, when one opens a female amphibian such as a frog, a mass of eggs is found occupying the greater portion of the abdominal cavity. These are not free in the body cavity, but are held in a pair of swollen ovaries covered by a reflected fold of peritoneum. Dorsally this peritoneal fold extends from each ovary to attach it to the dorsal wall of the body cavity and is continuous with the peritoneum. This mesentery, the mesovarium, carries blood-vessels, nerves, and lymphatics to each ovary. Beginning in the region of the mesovarium, the oögenic cells of each lobulated portion of the ovary begin proliferating for the reproductive season. Each maturing ovum becomes surrounded

by a layer of cuboidal cells that gradually elaborate more and more yolk which is added to the cytoplasm of the ovum. Surrounding this layer of nurse cells is a delicate sheath, or theca, of connective tissue with a few encircling smooth muscle cells incomplete on the coelomic side of the follicle. Continued proliferation and consequent maturation of the eggs distends the ovary and its peritoneal covering to the point observed above. When mature, the eggs are forced from the follicle by constriction of the smooth muscle and pass into the body cavity. They are carried into the oviducts by ciliary action of the mesothelial cells in the ventral regions of the body cavity. After the mature eggs of the breeding season have been discharged, the ovary collapses to a small body having the appearance of a bit of folded whitish membrane. Within this membrane are the small undeveloped oögenic cells that will give rise to ova of the succeeding breeding seasons. The gelatinous mass that surrounds the discharged eggs of amphibians is added by the oviducts as the eggs pass outward.

**Oviducts.**—Amphibian oviducts consist of a pair of long, contorted tubes, each connected with the wall of the body cavity in the dorso-lateral region by a mesenteric sheet. Anteriorly, each opens by a ciliated funnel-shaped ostium into the body cavity; posteriorly they unite with the dorsal wall of the cloaca near the entrance of the ureters. In immature animals and between breeding seasons the oviducts are small, thin-walled structures, but during the breeding season there is a great increase in size and they become more convoluted. Cilia carry eggs rotating down the oviducts as gelatinous coats are added. Over the greater part of its length each duct is of uniform size, but near the cloaca there is a dilated uterine region. The entire duct has an outer adventitia of connective tissue covered by peritoneum. A thin muscularis of circular smooth muscle cells adjoins the adventitia and it is difficult to distinguish where the glandular mucosa forms the greater portion of the wall. The lumen of the upper coiled portion is lined by ciliated columnar cells with goblet cells interspersed. Over the lower and longer portion of the duct, the mucosa is composed of long tubular glands. These glands secrete the albumen surrounding the eggs as they pass down the oviducts. At the dilated portions, the walls are thinner and the glands are absent, and the lumen is lined with columnar cells. Eggs may collect in the dilated portion until a female is clasped by a male, when the eggs are liberated and fertilized externally in the water. The secretion of the oviducts absorbs considerable water, and a characteristic mass of gelatinous material surrounds the eggs shortly after fertilization.

17

## Frog

**Ovary.**—With development of the ovum, nuclear material of older nurse cells appear in the cytoplasm as chromatic masses, the "yolk nuclei," the nucleus of the ovum becomes larger, filled with granular or flaky chromatin, and a distinct nuclear membrane is present. The yolk nuclei form a ring about the nucleus of the ovum, then an area of finely granular cytoplasm is followed by a peripheral region of large acidophilic yolk granules. The cell membrane of the ovum is surrounded by a clear bright vitelline membrane about which the follicle cells are closely applied. The yolk increases and the egg grows in size with approach of the breeding season and melanin pigment appears. The yolk becomes concentrated in the vegetal pole; pigment is diffused through the cytoplasm at the animal pole where the nucleus is located in the mature ovum. The ova which do not reach maturation can be observed in various stages of degeneration (atresia) and absorption, during which processes the yolk granules are lost, the cytoplasm becomes vacuolated and the pigment is clumped. (Fig. 185.)

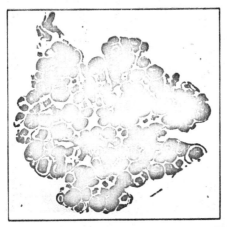

FIG. 185.—Photograph of a section of an ovary of the frog. The ovarian tissue is composed of several lobes, each containing a number of immature ova supported in a delicate connective tissue. × 15.

**Oviduct.**—Each oviduct is a long and much-coiled tube which can be divided into several parts. The first and most anterior portion, ending in the ostium, is a relatively thin straight tubule lined by ciliated columnar cells thrown into longitudinal folds by a thin tunica propria. Smooth muscle cells occur scattered in the connective tissue but not as a distinct coat. A serosa forms the outermost coat over the entire tube. (Fig. 186.)

The second part is intricately coiled and much thicker-walled due to the development of tubular glands in the mucosa. A superficial ciliated columnar epithelium is thrown into small longitudinal folds with closely packed tubular glands opening at their base. The secretory cells of the glands are columnar in form and secrete a mucous substance that forms the gelatinous mass surrounding the eggs after they leave the body and water is absorbed by this coating. Bundles of smooth muscle cells surround the vascular tunica propria supporting the glands and a thin serosa forms

the outermost coat. The glands become much less prominent after the breeding season and resemble the condition in the non-functional oviduct found in the male.

The third or terminal portion broadens into a *uterine region* that has a thin wall with glands only in the anterior part adjoining the preceding

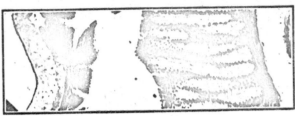

Fig. 186.—Oviduct of the frog. Left portion shows structure of upper third of duct with ciliated columnar lining cells. Right portion shows the structure from middle third posteriorly with tubular glands forming the mucosa. Photomicrograph. 16 mm. obj. and 5× oc.

glandular division. The mucosa is thrown into longitudinal folds covered by ciliated columnar cells. The tunica propria is encircled by a thin muscularis of circular smooth muscle. This region opens into the cloaca.

## FEMALE REPRODUCTIVE SYSTEM OF REPTILES AND BIRDS

The representatives of these two classes present very similar conditions in the structure and composition of the ovary and associated ducts. A pair of ovaries is usually present among reptiles, the right being commonly more anteriorly located than the left; among birds the right ovary may be poorly developed or degenerate entirely leaving the left ovary and oviduct to compose the system. In both classes the oöcytes develop into yolk-laden ova to which an additional coating of albumen and a shell are added by glands of the oviduct.

**Ovaries.**—The ovary of a reptile or bird during the breeding season is composed of a number of eggs of various sizes. The ovaries are not lobulated, as in the case of the frog, and the germinal centers are quite compact and more easily discovered. (Fig. 187.) Developing oöcytes and a series of developmental stages continue into an adjacent string of ova of increasing size. At first each ovum is surrounded by a single layer of nurse cells, but these cells become more numerous and stratified as the egg increases in size and a vitelline membrane becomes prominent. The increase in egg size is due to the increasing amount of yolk supplied to the ovum by the nurse cells some of which are larger than others. The size of the egg, therefore, indicates the relative age, the largest being the most mature, the smallest the least mature. A theca of vascular connective

issue surrounds the follicle cells.  When the elaboration of yolk is
completed the nurse cells are flattened into a thin membrane and a
rupture occurs in the connective tissue theca of the follicle and the

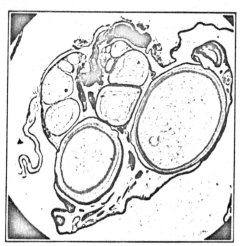

Fig. 187.—Photograph of a section through two oögenic masses in the ovary of a
lizard.  A series of maturing ova is shown on the left and another series on the right.
Even the largest eggs are immature and still retained within the connective tissue
sheath.   × 15.

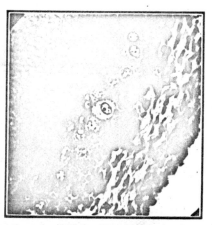

Fig. 188.—Section through a follicle of the lizard, showing yolk to the left, then
the layer of nurse or follicle cells, surrounded by the connective tissue theca.  Photomicrograph.   4 mm. obj. and 5× oc.

membranous covering of the ovary.  The egg is discharged from
its follicle into the body cavity where it is picked up in an oviduct,
and fertilized by sperm present there, before being surrounded by

the secretion of the oviducts. In some reptiles, as in the common water snake, development is internal.

**Oviducts.**—The oviducts are divided into three regions: the most anterior adjoining the ostium having a lining of ciliated columnar cells and goblet secretory cells; a middle region with a superficial epithelial membrane of cilated columnar cells and numerous tubular glands composed of cells filled with acidophilic granules associated with the albuminous secretion; a distal broader region with similar but more prominent glands associated with secretion of material forming the shell. The region of the oviduct joining the cloaca is free of the tubular glands but goblet cells are present.

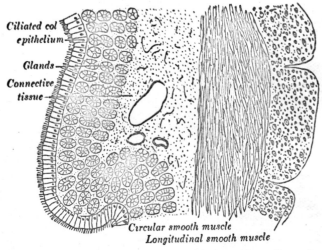

FIG. 189.—Drawing of a section through the oviduct of a turtle.

The tunica propria of the uppermost regions forms intricate foldings which become fewer and broader in the lower regions and also involve a submucosa. The muscularis is composed of an inner circular and an outer longitudinal layer, both being more developed in the lower portions of the duct. (Fig. 189.)

## FEMALE REPRODUCTIVE SYSTEM OF MAMMALS

**Ovary.**—The ovaries are small, round, or oval bodies, one located on either side of the midline near the dorsal wall just posterior to the kidneys. Along the mesial border there is an indentation, or hilus, where the mesovarium connects the covering tissue of the ovary with the peritoneum of the body wall. The mesovarium is surfaced with mesothelium similar to that of the peritoneum and continuous with the cuboidal or low columnar epithelium covering the vary. The epithelium covering the ovary is spoken of as the germinal epithelium, and within it the ovary is divided roughly into two zones. An outer portion immediately beneath the germinal epithelium is the *cortex*; an inner region below the cortex and toward the hilus is the *medulla*. The fibroelastic and reticular connective tissue of the cortex supports a vascular supply. Just beneath the germinal epithelium there is usually a dense region of encircling connective tissue fibers forming the region known as the tunica albuginea. Distributed through the cortical connective tissue are the primary ovarian follicles, each with a maturing ovum surrounded by a layer of follicle cells. In the medulla, ovarian follicles are absent; there are many elastic fibers, scattered smooth muscles, and the larger branches of the ovarian vessels in a fibroelastic tissue stroma. (Fig. 190.)

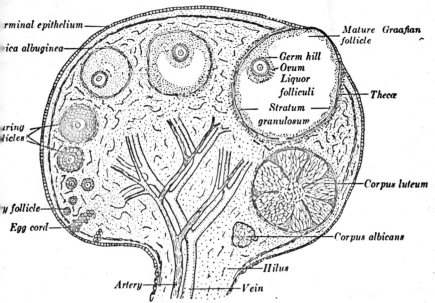

Fɪɢ. 190.—Diagram of a mammalian ovary.

Groups of special cells, derived from mesenchyme or germinal epithelium have been identified in some ovaries as *interstitial cells*, and are believed by some to have an endocrine function similar to the interstitial tissue of the testes. These cells, when present, are large, polyhedral, epithelioid cells with lipoid droplets in their cytoplasm. There is no evidence yet to show that they are endocrine or that they act as intermediaries for nutritive transfer between the blood-vessels and the ovarian follicles.

The conditions of the ova and follicles in the cortical region of the ovary vary with the animal under consideration and with the age of each individual. Beginning with an indifferent gonad in which primordial sex cells are scattered among the indifferent cells, there is a progressive differentiation. The cuboidal epithelium covering the embryonic ovary proliferates cords of cells, called Pflüger's egg cords, which extend in toward the embryonic connective tissue and earlier formed germinal cells. (Fig. 201.) Regions of the cord segment and a large central cell, the oöcyte, is surrounded by several of the smaller follicle cells. The early ovum surrounded by the several flattened follicle cells is known as a primary follicle. (Fig. 190.) Just before birth in man, and shortly after birth in some of

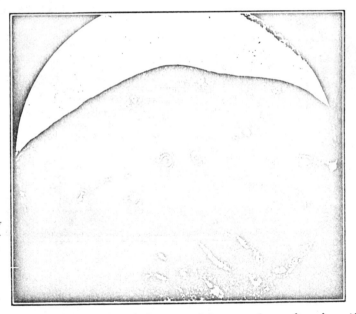

Fig. 191.—Photograph through the cortex of the ovary of a new-born dog. Along the outer margin is a region with many primary follicles. A few developing follicles occur in the deeper region toward the medulla. 16 mm. obj. and 5X oc.

the other mammals, the up-growing mesenchyme develops the tunica albuginea subjacent to the germinal epithelium. The formation of this layer of connective tissue may mark the end of further development of cords of cells from the germinal epithelium in some forms, but in others the germinal epithelium continues to be active and supplies elements for new primary follicles. During this period the primordial sex cells and indifferent cells in the deepest regions of the ovary have degenerated, and this region becomes the medulla. The cortex now contains all the remaining primary follicles, and some of these begin a progressive development preliminary to sexual maturity and the beginning of a reproductive cycle. Thousands of primary follicles are present in the ovaries of a new-born female, but most of these undergo gradual degeneration and resorption, a process known as atresia. The primary follicles that are to mature undergo a complex development before the ovum is ready for fertilization.

*Maturing Primary Follicles.*—The rudimentary ovum, or oöcyte, is only slightly larger than the surrounding follicle cells. Both the nucleus and cytoplasm of this cell increase in size with an accompanying increase in the number of surrounding cells which are now cuboidal in appearance. During this early period the chromosomes of the oöcyte are organized for the first maturation division, after which the chromatin material returns to the reticulated condition characteristic of these cells. The second maturation division occurs after the egg leaves the ovary. A highly refractive membrane, the *zona pellucida*, forms between the ovum and the surrounding polyhedral cells of the follicle which have multiplied to form several layers, the *zona* or *membrana* granulosa. Ensheathing the granulosa there is a thin layer of connective tissue, the *theca folliculi*, which carries a capillary network. The cells of the membrana granulosa continue to divide by mitosis and their multiplication increases the size of the follicle. Spaces begin to appear in the mass of follicle cells composing this region and are filled with liquid, the *liquor folliculi*. The follicle cells continue to increase in number; more spaces and more liquid appear. The fluid filled spaces begin to fuse and finally form one large space into which a band of granulosa cells, the *cumulus oöphorus*, or *germ hill*, supports the ovum and its surrounding radiating cells, the *corona radiata*. (Fig. 192.) The ovum and corona radiata are thus separated from the peripheral granulosa cells by the increasing amount of liquor folliculi. With this development there is an accompanying development of the connective tissue immediately surrounding the granulosa to form a *theca folliculi* divisible into two regions. The inner portion, the *theca interna*, is composed of connective tissue supporting a network of capillaries and also containing peculiar polyhedral cells with lipoid material in their cytoplasm. These cells are associated with the production of the hormones of the ovary. Outside the theca interna is the *theca externa*, composed of denser connective tissue carrying small blood-vessels and smooth muscle cells. These maturing follicles are called *Graafian follicles*. (Fig. 193.)

*Ovulation.*—The maturing follicle soon occupies the entire width of the ovarian cortex, having increased many times the size of the primary follicle. The germ hill with the enclosed ovum may shift

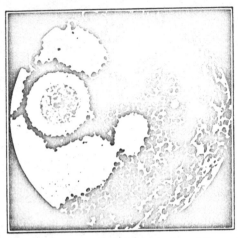

FIG. 192.—Photograph through a follicle in the region of the germ hill (Cumulus oöphorus). Ovary of the dog. 4 mm. obj. and 5× oc.

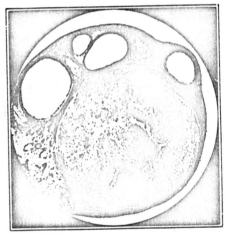

FIG. 193.—Photograph of a section through the ovary of a cat. In the upper region 4 maturing follicles are shown; the light areas were filled with follicular liquid The large circular body below is a corpus luteum verum. At the lower left margin near this is a corpus albicans. × 10.

its position toward the surface and the follicle may cause an appreciable bulge in the ovarian surface. It should be remembered that outside the zona granulosa at this point are the theca interna, theca externa, tunica albuginea, and the germinal epithelium. Due o the great increase in follicular liquid, all these coats are under considerable tension and are relatively thin. There is finally a rupture at this point, and the liquor folliculi pours out, carrying with it the ovum surrounded by the cells of the germ hill. This rupture at time of ovulation may be accompanied by a hemorrhage into the follicle, so that a *corpus hæmorrhagicum* is formed.

After ovulation, the ovum with the surrounding corona radiata passes into the oviduct, in the upper portion of which the corona radiata is lost and second maturation division occurs and fertilization takes place. There are two sites of continued activity and histological change following normal ovulation, one in the follicular mass and the other in the uterus following the descent of the fertilized egg.

*Corpus Luteum.*—Following the rupture of the mature Graafian follicle and discharge of the ovum, the zona granulosa of the follicular wall collapses and folds in so that the previous spherical cavity is reduced and irregular in shape. The cells of the granulosa layer begin to increase in size and number and a yellow lipoid substance forms in their cytoplasm. The yellow color is often prominent and gives the structure the name of *corpus luteum* at this period. These cells are now called *lutein cells*. Strands of reticular and fibroelastic tissue migrate radially inward from the theca interna toward the follicular cavity, as do sinusoidal capillaries which develop between the enlarged granulosa cells. The theca externa remains much as it was before ovulation. If the ovum is fertilized after it enters the oviduct and implants in the uterus, the further changes in the corpus luteum (or follicular body) are quantitatively different than those in the case where no fertilization is effected. In the latter case a corpus luteum spurium is formed, and in the former a corpus luteum verum forms. In either case a hormone is produced which inhibits follicular growth.

*Corpus Luteum Spurium.*—When fertilization does not occur, the corpus luteum reaches the climax of its development and greatest size shortly after ovulation. At this period the yellow color may be pronounced if such color develops at all. Vacuolation marks the beginning of the degeneration of the corpus, and gradually the whole body is resorbed until all that remains is a small mass of fibrous connective tissue called the *corpus albicans*.

*Corpus Luteum Verum.* (Fig. 193.)—This body is histologically identical with the corpus luteum spurium during the first part of its development. However, if the ovum is fertilized and the embryo implants, the corpus grows larger over a longer period of time than the corpus luteum spurium. Instead of reaching the climax and

beginning to degenerate shortly after ovulation it continues to develop and remains present for the greater part of the period of pregnancy. This structure begins to degenerate shortly before birth of the embryo and with birth of the fetus it degenerates rapidly to leave a corpus albicans.

In mammals with relatively short cycles, such as the rat, numerous ova are in the process of maturation and a number mature over short intervals unless fertilization occurs. Numerous corpora are formed in such forms and follicular changes are correspondingly rapid.

**Oviducts.**—In monotremes there is still but one external passageway for both the urogenital and digestive systems, the cloaca. In other mammals there is a urogenital vestibule separated from the anal opening of the digestive tract. Into this vestibule the genital system opens usually by a single passage, the vagina, which receives the copulatory organ of the male for insemination. The upper end of the Müllerian duct functions in conducting the egg to the lower region, or uterus, which is specialized to receive and nourish the developing embryo. In some cases the egg-conducting portions, the oviducts or Fallopian tubes, may join a single uterine portion; in others, the lower portion of each tube has a uterine portion and fusion occurs just before the vagina is reached.

In many mammals, including numerous rodents (mice, rabbits, and beavers), certain bats, and other forms, there is a condition known as uterus duplex, in which there are two separate uteri opening into separate vaginæ that fuse near the vestibule. In other mammals, as in certain rodents, some ruminants, and carnivors, there is a condition known as uterus bipartitus, in which there is a partial fusion of the two uteri near their junction with the single vagina. Among certain other ruminants and carnivors there is a greater posterior fusion of the uterus and an anterior prolongation to join each Fallopian tube, a condition known as uterus bicornis. Among the primates generally, there is a complete fusion of the uterine portions to a single uterus continuing into a single vagina, a condition known as uterus simplex.

Each oviduct is a relatively short, narrow, convoluted duct, extending from the ovary toward the midline, where it connects with the anterior lateral face of the uterus. The ostium abdominalis is surrounded by finger-like processes which are closely associated with the ovary. The structure of the tube varies somewhat, but three regions can be distinguished throughout. Externally there is an adventitia of connective tissue surfaced with mesothelium. Medially there is a muscularis composed of an external sheath of longitudinally disposed smooth muscle cells and an internal sheath of circular cells. Internally there is a mucosa of ciliated columnar and occasional glandular cells resting upon a tunica propria of connective tissue. No submucosa is distinguished. Near the ostium the mucosa is elaborately folded, so that sections show a great number of spaces among the labyrinthine folds. (Fig. 194.) Toward the uterus these foldings decrease and the tube wall is much thicker in proportion to the lumen. The cilia of the columnar epithelial cells beat away from the ostium, so that the egg and follicular fluid are propelled toward the uterus. The epithelial lining shows variations in the appearance of the columnar cells associated with different periods of the ovarian cycle. Ciliated cells appear more numerous

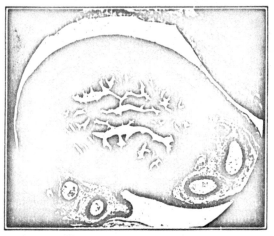

Fig. 194.—Photograph of a section through the oviduct of a kitten near the ovary. The mucosa is much folded. 32 mm. obj. and 5× oc.

at or just before the period of ovulation. Entrance of the ovum and passage through the first portion of the oviduct is effected by ciliary action but muscular action plays an increasing part in movement of duct contents through the lower portion of the oviduct into the uterus.

**Uterus.**—Regardless of its anatomical variations, whether simplex, bicornis, or duplex, the uterine structure is the same fundamentally. At the end of the oviduct the uterus begins as an abruptly expanded tube containing the same three coats of tissue. However, two of the three divisions, the muscularis and mucosa, are much more developed than in the preceding portion of the duct. The thin serosa surrounds the muscularis which becomes the *myometrium;* and the mucosa is called the *endometrium.* (Figs. 195 and 196.)

In the connective tissue framework of the myometrium are many types of connective tissue cells, including an embryonic variety capable of forming muscle cells when pregnancy occurs. In pregnancy the myometrium increases many times its size in the diestral or resting uterus, due to increase in cell numbers as well as to increase in cell size. The connective tissue fibers also increase and there is a looser arrangement and more tissue juice.

The uterus is interpreted usually as having no submucosa; the connective tissue of the mucosa continues into that of the subjacent muscularis region. The mucosa or endometrium undergoes remarkable modifications in its cyclical periods. (Figs. 195 and 196.) In

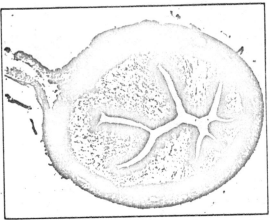

FIG. 195.—Photograph of a section through the resting uterus of the rabbit. The endometrium is thrown into several broad folds and many shallow tubular glands occur in it near the lumen. The dark band surrounding the endometrium is the myometrium. At the left the peritoneum is shown continuing as the serosa. × 20.

humans, a series of changes are repeated each lunar month of the productive period if pregnancy does not occur. During each of these months an ovum is normally discharged from the ovary and, provided no sperm are present in the oviduct to fertilize the ovum, the special preparation of the mucosa is not utilized. A consequent loss of the major portion of the mucosa takes place under the name of menstruation in humans, but in other forms degeneration and resorption takes place in such cases. Following fertilization, more profound changes occur in the body of the uterus if the embryo continues to develop, so a description of the histological structures of the uterus must also indicate the relation to ovulation and pregnancy. At certain periods of the lunar month in humans, and at diestrus periods for other animals, there is a condition which may be described as the resting condition of the uterus. The lining of such a uterus shows longitudinal ridges, due to the folding of the tunica propria beneath the superficial layer of columnar cells some of which are ciliated.

Also in the mucosa are tubular glands extending more or less perpendicularly toward the myometrium. Some of the columnar cells forming these glands are also ciliated. Just beneath the

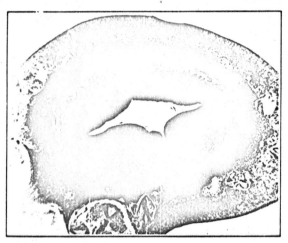

Fig. 196.—Uterus of the cat in heat, showing glandular endometrium and broad myometrium in the progravid stage. Photomicrograph. × 10.

superficial epithelium of the lumen and surrounding the gland cells is a rich reticular network with many mesenchyme-like cells and leukocytes (especially lymphocytes). In the underlying tunica propria there is a rich capillary network derived from the vessels in the myometrium. At its posterior extremity the uterus narrows to a short neck-like portion, the cervix, which joins the vagina. In this region the mucosa has only the superficial covering of columnar epithelium without any glands. The changes that occur in the uterus preliminary to and following menstruation and pregnancy will be considered separately under those headings.

**Vagina.**—This is a tubelike portion continuous with the uterus and receives the copulatory organ, the penis, of the male. The same three coats are present in it as in the anterior portion of the ducts, an adventitia, a muscularis, and a mucosa. The adventitia is similar to that of the uterus and Fallopian tubes. The muscularis is much thinner than that of the uterus, with an external longitudinal and an internal circular region of muscle tissue. At the lower end of the vagina the muscularis forms a sphincter. The mucosa consists of a coat of stratified squamous epithe-

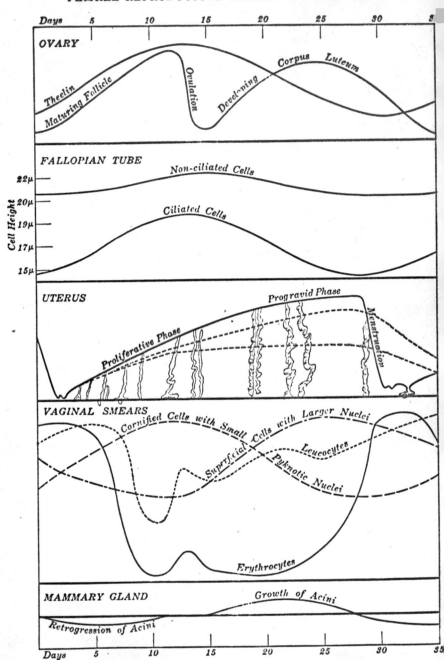

Fig. 197.—Chart indicating possible correspondence in time between cyclical changes in the female reproductive system. (The graphs for the Fallopian tube are from Lucas, after Tietze, and those for the vaginal smears were supplied by Papanicolaou, Cowdry's Histology.)

lium lining the lumen and a subjacent vascular region of connective tissue, the tunica propria which may have projecting papillæ that throw the epithelium into ridges. Three zones are distinguishable in the epithelial lining: the one adjacent to the lumen is composed of several layers of flat degenerating cells little, if at all, cornified; the middle zone has several layers of flat cells with a more granular content, suggesting the stratum granulosum of the epidermis; the deepest zone has a number of cell layers comparable to the stratum germinativum of the epidermis. The basal layer of cells are short columnar and polyhedral in shape and are active in giving rise to new cells. During pregnancy and at the time of ovulation the cells become filled with mucus in all layers above the germinativum. Between adjacent cells of the upper layers of the basal zone there may be intercellular bridges, giving the appearance of prickle cells found in the epidermis. In the tunica propria are many leukocytes, especially lymphocytes and heterophils. Smears from the vagina commonly show a series of changes, and the type of cells cast into the lumen indicates the progress of ovulation. Squamous cells increase in numbers up to the time of ovulation at which time larger mucous cells with distinct nuclei appear and increase in number. Heterophils decrease just before and increase with and following ovulation.

**Vestibule.**—The vestibule is a shallow depression posterior to the vagina. Its surface is covered with stratified squamous epithelium, which rests on a tunica propria of fibroelastic connective tissue. Below the tunica propria are muscles of the skeletal variety. A pair of vascular bodies form the *clitoris* adjacent to the entrance of the vagina. This is a structure similar to the corpora cavernosa of the penis and functions as erectile tissue in periods of sexual excitation. Several small glands are also present in the connective tissue around the opening to the vestibule, and their columnar cells secrete a mucous substance. The *Bartholin glands* which occur on either side of the vestibule may be homologous with the bulbourethral of the male.

**Menstruation.**—In humans, ovulation occurs about every twenty-eight days. The changes undergone by the uterus may be indicated by separating this lunar period into four parts, understanding, of course, that the tissue changes are gradual and grade into each other. Beginning to count the days with the onset of menstruation the four stages are:

| | |
|---|---|
| Menstrual . . . . . . | First to fourth day. |
| Postmenstrual (follicular) . | Fifth to tenth day. |
| Intermenstrual (progravid) . | Eleventh to twentieth day. |
| Premenstrual (progravid) : | Twenty-first to twenty-eighth day. |

The description already given for a resting uterus applies to the intermenstrual period. At the beginning of the premenstrual period the mucosa

gradually increases in thickness until it is almost twice as thick as during the resting condition. (Figs. 198, 199, 200.) The glands become longer, assume a twisted course, and may branch externally. Droplets of glycogen and lipoid material develop in the cytoplasm of the gland cells, and the lumen of each gland becomes distended with secretion. The cells in the connective tissue immediately below the epithelium increase greatly in size. Capillaries in the tunica propria enlarge and are filled with blood to the point that their walls begin to give way and blood issues forth to

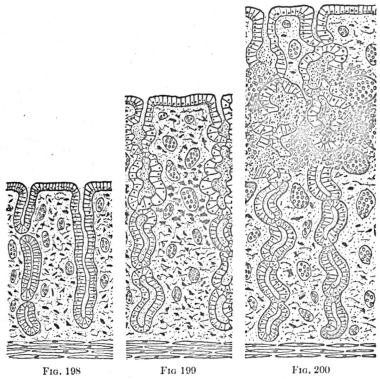

FIG. 198            FIG 199            FIG. 200

FIGS. 198, 199 and 200.—Three diagrams illustrating changes in mucosa of the uterus during premenstrual period.

FIG. 198.—Below is the myometrium. In the mucosa are simple tubular glands lined with simple columnar epithelium. The tunica propria is fibrous, with many connective tissue cells and also leukocytes. The mucosa is very vascular.

FIG. 199.—The mucosa increases in thickness; the glands become elongated and more tortuous. Somewhat below the internal surface, connective tissue cells become much enlarged and are known as decidual cells. The capillaries increase in size. The epithelial cells in the zone of decidual cells enlarge and secrete the mucus collecting in the adjacent lumen.

FIG. 200.—The mucosa is much thicker (possibly twice as thick as in Figure 198). The decidual cells are more prominent. Epithelial cells of the glands in the neighborhood of outpocketings filled with secretion give way; fluid seeps out from capillary spaces in this region—the capillary walls give way and the mucous secretions and blood mingle in pools. The process continues until there is a general sloughing off of the internal lining of the mucosa. Half way through this menstrual period the surface of the mucosa lacks an epithelial lining. Later epithelial cells from ends of glands still left in deeper portions of the mucosa organize a new lining and also outlets for the glands.

collect in pools beneath the epithelium. The glands also begin to rupture laterally, and their secretion mingles with the escaped blood. The surface epithelium eventually can no longer withstand the distention, due to the continued collection of subjacent fluids, and begins to give way at numerous points. With the ruptures in the epithelial covering, the underlying fluids pour into the lumen of the uterus, carrying along small masses of epithelial tissue, mouths of glands, and tunica propria. Eventually the entire spongy internal lining of the uterine mucosa is sloughed off. Muscular contractions in the uterine wall begin during this period and continue until material accumulated in the lumen is expelled.

The postmenstrual period begins with the closure of the small blood-vessels and cessation of loss of blood. Epithelial cells from the broken ends of the uterine glands proliferate and spread over the surface to reform the epithelial lining. The glands are likewise reformed and the connective tissue is restored to its former condition, so that by about the tenth day following the beginning of menstruation the uterine mucosa is entire again. The uterus then enters into the intermenstrual, or resting period, during which time there are few changes until at the beginning of the premenstrual period, when renewed preparations are made for reception of the fertilized egg. Sometime between two menstrual periods, generally accepted now to be about the tenth to the sixteenth day following the onset of menstruation, a follicle ruptures and discharges an ovum. Upon entering the oviduct the ovum undergoes its final maturation division and is fertilized if sperm are present.

**Pregnancy.**—Following fertilization, development begins and continues as the egg passes along the oviduct toward the uterus. During this passage, which takes about three days, a number of cells are formed. The embryo comes to rest in some pocket or fold of the uterine mucosa and continues its development. While the uterus develops to a condition of the premenstrual period, the embryo develops the fetal membranes, and the *chorion* with tuftlike projections begins to form. This extremely small globe erodes its way into the uterine mucosa and, with development, establishes an intimate contact with the uterus through the placenta. To understand the relationship between the developing embryo and the uterine wall, reference should be made to embryological texts for developmental details of the fetal membranes.

**Placenta.**—Among the marsupials, as in the opossum, gestation, or uterine development of the young is brief and the young are born relatively immature. In these cases the chorion is a smooth membrane in close contact with the vascular uterine mucosa. The outer face of the rudimentary yolk sac unites with the inner face of the chorion, and thus food compounds of the maternal blood-vessels in the uterine wall are in juxtaposition with those in the membranes of the embryo, and these food compounds pass into the chorionic vessels to be transported *via* yolk stalk vessels to

the embryo. Oxygen is obtained similarly. Excretions pass from embryonic to maternal vessels. At the end of its uterine development the membranes surrounding the embryo pull loose from the uterine mucosa and the young is born with little destruction of the uterine mucosa.

In higher mammals the chorion develops branching vascular villi that penetrate and erode the uterine mucosa to establish varying degrees of intimate relationships. Such associations of embryonic and maternal tissues result in formation of an organ called the placenta where nutritive, respiratory, and excretory exchanges are carried on. The uterine mucosa has in the meantime grown over the entire surface of the chorion. Although the placenta varies in form in different mammals, it never involves the entire outer surface of the chorion. As the embryo and its membranes grow, the amniotic sac and surrounding chorion covered with an overgrowth of uterine mucosa bulge into the uterine cavity. That part or aspect which from the beginning has been in closest relation with the uterine wall will be the site of the formation of the placenta. The placenta in humans is a disclike plate, consisting of two components, one chorionic and one derived from the uterine mucosa and called the *decidua basalis.* The uterine mucosa which grows over the chorion of the embryonic mass, where it fills the uterine cavity, is known as the *decidua capsularis* and is continuous with the decidua basalis, or placenta. The remaining uterine lining also shows a mucosal thickening and is known as the *decidua vera.* Branching tuftlike outgrowths from the chorion invade the mucosa of the decidua capsularis and basalis. The chorionic villi of the decidua basalis are much more elaborate, and it is here that fetal nutrition, respiration, and excretion are effected.

Certain large or giant cells, the *decidual cells,* derived from the elements of the uterine tunica propria (histiocytes and reticular cells are favored), are oval or spherical in form with finely granular acidophilic cytoplasm and one or more darkly staining nuclei, each with one or more nucleoli. These cells occur after the onset of pregnancy and become the outstanding elements in the placenta but may degenerate and become less numerous towards the end of pregnancy.

*Chorionic Villi.*—The squamous epithelium covering of the chorion and its villi appears to be syncytial in character. From the underlying mesenchyme, connective tissue and blood-vessels develop. These villi become much extended until only a very thin layer of epithelium separates the fetal blood-vessels from the blood in the sinuses of the uterine mucosa into which the villi project. The old superficial uterine wall epithelium disappears, although the superficial connective tissue is still quite firm. The deeper portions of the chorionic villi of the basalis lie in pools of blood in the deeper zone of the uterine mucosa, where the blood has escaped from the broken vessels, as described in the premenstrual condition of the uterus. The villi are covered with a syncytial epithelium which becomes thinner with greater expansion during embryonic growth. Within the epithelial covering of each villus is a connective tissue core, containing two small arteries, veins, and capillaries. These vessels connect with those in the umbilical cord which arise from the center of the placenta opposite the surface associated with the uterine mucosa. The umbilical cord has a jelly-like mucous connective tissue which encloses the two umbilical arteries, the unbilical vein, the allantoic stalk, and the rudimentary yolk stalk. Nutritive material and oxygen pass from the blood in the uterine pools through the epithelial membrane of the chorionic villi into the capillaries, which pass it through the umbilical vessels to the fetus.

The fetus and its membranes grow rapidly until the uterine cavity is filled and the decidua capsularis fuses with the decidua vera. At birth, the amniotic sac is usually torn open, the contained liquid flows down into the vagina, and the young is expelled by the powerful contractions of the hypertrophied myometrium of the uterine wall aided by contraction of the abdominal muscles. After the young emerges there is an after-birth which consists of the amnion and the deciduæ. This process involves considerable hemorrhage in case of intimate relationship between the chorionic villi and the uterine mucosa. After the birth process is completed, the hemorrhage usually ceases and there is a new follicular or proliferative phase which gives rise to the intermenstrual phase of the next cycle.

# CHAPTER XIV

## THE MALE REPRODUCTIVE SYSTEM

In the male vertebrate the organs of reproduction generally consist of a pair of testes, each of which is a compound tubular gland with seminiferous tubules, representing secretory end-pieces, where the spermatozoa are formed. The associated collecting ducts within the testis connect with the anterior part of the functioning mesonephros or derivatives of it and thus empty into the mesonephric duct. Among mammals, accessory glands are associated with the main excretory ducts, the vas deferens and the urethra, and their secretions are added to the sperm.

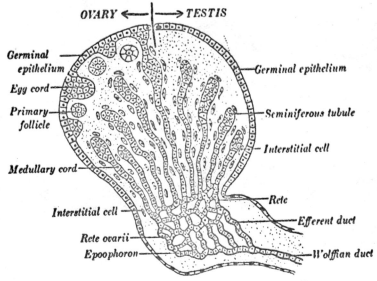

FIG. 201.—Diagram of the development of the testis and ovary. (Adapted from Kohn.)

**Development of the Testes.**—As in the case of the developing ovary already described, there is an indifferent stage of gonad development during which both testis and ovary are similarly composed. Relatively early, however, there is the beginning of differential development leading to formation of either male or female organs of reproduction. (Fig. 201.)

The developing cords of cells, which in the ovary broke into numerous follicles, continue unbroken in the testis to form seminiferous cords in which a lumen later occurs and seminiferous tubules

( 277 )

result. The mesenchyme between the tubules forms thin walls about them and also septa dividing the organ into compartments called lobules. The septa connect with the sheath of connective tissue surrounding the testis.

When the early epithelial mass forms cords of cells, two types of cells become distinguishable. Of these, the greater number are small polyhedral or cuboidal, and among them are fewer larger, more or less spherical primitive sex cells with large nuclei. The small cells correspond to the follicle cells surrounding the oöcytes in a developing ovary and the large cells with the oöcytes.

When the testis is mature, two types of cells, namely, *spermatogonia* and *nurse* or *Sertoli cells*, are the main components of the tubules. Spermatogonia, which will give rise to spermatozoa, are descendants of the large primitive sex cells, and the cells of Sertoli develop from the small cells corresponding to ovarian follicle cells. However, there are repeated cycles of cell degeneration and proliferation in these seminiferous tubules before maturity and, according to some investigators, the early sex cells may be lost in the process and the spermatogonial cells of the functional testis are derived from the original small follicle cells that survive. In either case, spermatogonial cells alternate in location with Sertoli cells in the walls of the testis tubules. The spermatogonial cells multiply to form a number of layers of spermatocytes with the less numerous Sertoli cells remaining along the basement membrane of the tubule. (Fig. 202.) The process of sperm cell formation from the spermatogonial cells is called spermatogenesis. Before maturity of the animal there is a series of abortive efforts to carry through development of sperm to completion, until finally the process is well established and fully differentiated and functional sperm are produced.

Testes, like ovaries, are not always active but show seasonal periods whose duration and occurrence vary with the species. Both testes and the sperm ducts show variations, depending on whether they are studied during or between breeding seasons. During the inactive stage following or preceding a breeding season, the lumens of the tubules are lost, interstitial connective tissue between the adjacent tubules increases in amount, and cords of inactive spermatogonial and Sertoli cells remain. The conditions at these times resemble those of the immature or developing testis before spermatogenesis has begun. To study the active condition it is necessary to secure the testis of an animal during the breeding season.

**Spermatogenesis.**—In general, spermatogenesis shows little variation among vertebrates, the series of divisions of cells and differentiation of the sperm presenting similar stages. The wall of each

seminiferous tubule consists externally of circularly and longitudinally disposed collagenous and elastic fibers and connective tissue cells. Between adjacent tubules there are regions filled with interstitial tissue composed of loose fibroelastic connective tissue and

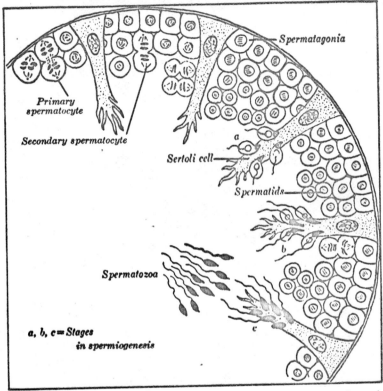

Fig. 202.—Diagram of a section through a seminiferous tubule, showing formation of spermatozoa from spermatogonial cells.

certain special elements, called *interstitial cells*. At the beginning of spermatogenesis there is, within the connective tissue sheath of each tubule, a basement membrane on which rests the specialized germinal epithelium composed of two or three layers of spermatogonial cells interrupted by the Sertoli cells. (Fig. 202.)

Sertoli Cells.—These are long columnar-like cells with broad bases resting on the basement membrane, with the elongated portions of the cells extending like spokes of a wheel part way toward the center of the lumen and are best seen before or after completion of spermatogenesis. The nucleus is oval and palely staining; the cytoplasm is lightly acidophilic and not clearly outlined by a cell membrane. Sertoli cells occur at quite regular intervals around the lumen of the tubule among the more numerous and smaller developing spermatogenic cells.

**Spermatogenic Cells.**—Beginning at the basement membrane, and extending in toward the lumen, spermatogenic cells form a stratified epithelial tissue several layers deep, interrupted at regular intervals by Sertoli cells. When activity begins, which will ultimately lead to the formation of sperm, a series of mitotic divisions take place in the spermatogonia, during which daughter cells of the dividing basal cells are constantly pushed inward toward the lumen. A reduction of the chromosome number from diploid to haploid is effected, and then a differential process takes place as a result of which sperm are produced. The phases of development up to and including reduction of the chromosome number constitute spermatocytogenesis, and the following stage of differentiation of the more or less spherical cells with haploid chromosome number into spermatozoa is called spermiogenesis. In animals with a limited seasonal activity, as in the dogfish, there may be a more or less complete development and differentiation of spermatogonial cells in the tubules, leaving only nurse or Sertoli cells so that new tubules are presumably formed at the beginning of a new cycle from primitive germinal epithelium in the sheath region of the testis.

In other cases, not all the tubules or all portions of any one tubule may be actively producing sperm at any one time. In an active tubule there are rounded cuboidal spermatogonial cells resting on the basement membrane and undergoing mitosis. The number of spermatogonial divisions appears to show some variation in different animals, but the cells resulting from this early proliferation period are known as *primary spermatocytes*. Later they undergo a maturation process involving a reduction division and the formation of *secondary spermatocytes* followed by a regular mitotic division which produces the *spermatids*, small spherical cells with a haploid chromosome number.

The spermatids are arranged in columns and later associate themselves closely with the cytoplasm of the Sertoli cells. As a result of a transformation process, these small spherical cells become fully developed spermatozoa, with head, middle-piece, and tail. The head is composed of the condensed nuclear matter of the haploid number of chromosomes; the middle-piece immediately behind the head contains some of the cytoplasm and the centrioles; and the tail is a long flagellum-like process. Much of the cytoplasm of the spermatid is sloughed off during differentiation of the sperm and discharged into the lumen where it may join the sperm in their passage toward the efferent ducts or be resorbed in part by the

Sertoli cells. During the process of spermiogenesis the head remains buried in the Sertoli cell and the tail, when formed, extends into the lumen of the tubule. When fully formed the sperm become free of the Sertoli cells and pass into the lumen, but are themselves as yet quite inactive. The sperm show some variations with regard to size and shape, but the parts are fundamentally very similar.

If a particular section of a seminiferous tubule shows activity, a number of cells usually appear to be in the same stage of development. If spermatids are present, a number in the same stage appear; similarly only spermatocytes in the same phase, or only spermatogonia may be apparent. If one crop of spermatids is completing metamorphosis into sperm, then mitotic activity may already have begun in the spermatogonia initiating another group of spermatids. In many mammals it appears that spermatogenic activity passes along the seminiferous tubule in waves.

**Interstitial Cells.**—Between the adjacent seminiferous tubules there is a loose fibroelastic connective tissue similar to that forming the wall of the tubules. In this tissue region are the blood and lymph vessels, nerves, and so-called interstitial cells. These cells appear to have about the same size as the granular leukocytes and show variation in shape. If they are connective tissue cells they appear to be a special variety and their activity is thought to be endocrine in nature. The spherical nucleus is relatively large, with few coarse chromatin granules and one or two nucleoli; the cytoplasm shows variation in the degree of granulation of a fatty nature. Compounds with the chemical properties of testosterone have been observed in these cells, evidence of their rôle in the endocrine function of the testes. Transitional forms indicate the origin of these cells from fibroblasts and their return to a fibroblast type under conditions of inflammation.

Endocrine secretion on the part of the testis is evidenced by the effects following its removal and transplantation. For example, if the testes are removed from an immature animal, the secondary sexual characters of males do not develop; if this removal takes place after maturity there is a loss of sex emotions and reproductive activities, and the body accumulates considerable adipose tissue. The transplantation of a testis into the body of a female causes secondary sexual characters of the male to make their appearance in the absence of the ovaries. A number of such experiments point to an endocrine activity on the part of the testis, with the interstitial cells partly if not entirely responsible.

**Sperm Ducts.**—In studying the urinary system, attention was called to the fact that in the male parts of the mesonephric tubules become associated with the testis as efferent ducts for the sperm. At the same time the seminiferous tubules are developing in the testis, associated tubules or cords of cells develop, as the vasa efferentia, which join them to the modified anterior tubules of the mesonephros, which in turn empty into the mesonephric or Wolffian duct. The latter acts as a combined urinary and genital duct in some forms but becomes the vas deferens in forms where a ureter develops.

Variations exist through the ascending groups as regards the completeness of a separation of the two systems. In cyclostomes the sperm may have no duct system, but pass directly to the cœlome and out through abdominal pores. Among the Amphibia the efferentia join a number of the mesonephric tubules through which sperm are conducted to the mesonephric duct. With the reptiles, birds and mammals the mesonephric duct is converted to the vas deferens which carries only genital products. The tubules of the anterior part of the mesonephros are still associated with the efferentia but become larger, heavier-walled tubules coiled to form the epididymis before they join the vas deferens.

In general, the collecting ducts associated with the seminiferous tubules within the testis and the vasa efferentia are lined by cuboidal epithelium which changes to ciliated columnar type as the larger ducts are approached. The epididymis and part or all of the vas deferens may be lined by columnar cells although the vas deferens commonly has a stratified columnar epithelium in some forms. Ciliated cells often alternate with those of glandular type whose secretions enter the lumen and join the sperm. The epithelium rests on a connective tissue sheath encircled by scattered smooth muscle cells in the smallest ducts but a definite muscularis coat occurs in the vas deferens. Surrounding the ducts peripherally is a vascular fibroelastic connective tissue which becomes more prominent as the size of the duct increases.

## MALE REPRODUCTIVE SYSTEM OF FISHES

In elasmobranchs the testes are ovoid or cylindrical bodies. The mesonephros is the functional kidney and in the male the anterior end degenerates so far as its urinary function is concerned, and its ducts establish connections by the efferentia with the testis during development. Some of the embryonic mesonephric tubules of the anterior end form a much-coiled tube, the *epididymis*, through which sperm pass from the testis to the mesonephric, or Wolffian duct. In some cases the kidneys and testes develop separate duct

systems which join into a urogenital sinus from which a papilla, the *urogenital papilla* extends into the cloaca. The posterior ends of the two Wolffian ducts may be enlarged as *seminal vesicles* and act as sperm reservoirs during the breeding season.

### Dogfish

**Testes.**—In the adult functioning testes there are cords of primitive germ cells in a thickened median dorsal connective tissue region of the capsule. Some are large cells, the spermatogonia, with large nuclei and one or two nucleoli like the early oöcytes; other more numerous smaller cells surrounding them have oval nuclei and no nucleoli. Adjoining this region are small tubules of the smaller nurse cells with one or more large

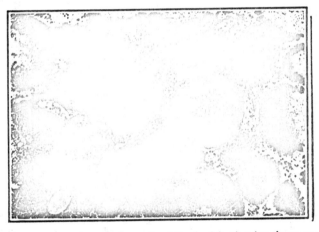

FIG. 203.—A section through the testis of the dogfish, showing the appearance of tubules in progressive stages of spermiogenesis from left to right; at the extreme right the sperm are in clusters associated with Sertoli cells. Three small intralobular ducts join a larger interlobular collecting duct. Photomicrograph. 16 mm. obj. and 5× oc.

cells in the lumen, at first, but shortly the latter migrate in among the surrounding nurse cells to form part of the tubular wall as the spermatogonia. A series of mitoses in the spermatogonia results in a wall of several layers. The lumen is lined by elongate nurse cells while the basal three or four layers of spermatogonial cells are isodiametric with large spherical nuclei in mitosis or with one or two prominent nucleoli in the interphase. More divisions of the spermatogonia form the primary spermatocytes which push out and migrate among the nurse cells; the latter sink among the primary spermatocytes to occupy a position along the basement membrane and the lumen is practically obliterated at this stage. The primary spermatocytes divide into the secondary spermatocytes which undergo a final reduction division and the lumen is filled completely by spermatids. Then much of the cytoplasm of the spermatids is lost and they cluster in radiating columns leaving a lumen with discarded fibrillar acidophilic cytoplasmic material. Scattered along the basement membrane of each tubule at this time large pale nuclei of the nurse cells are prominent. All the small spermatids undergo a differentiation of the nucleus into the elongated deeply basophilic head and a cytoplasmic acidophilic tail of the spermatozoa. Large numbers of the heads form a cone-shaped cluster or tuft with the apex buried in the cytoplasm of the nurse cell, closely adjoining the basement membrane. The nurse cell nuclei appear in the region between adjoining tufts of sperm. The large lumen left by this process is filled by acidophilic débris and the tails of the sperms. The basement membrane of the tubule is surrounded by a delicate reticulum supporting a capillary network and no smooth muscle appears. The testis sheath has smooth muscle in it and it is probably through its contraction that mature tubules are compressed and the sperm, loosened from the walls, leave the nurse cells behind and are forced into the small cuboidal lined intra- and then interlobular ducts. The latter have a delicate fibroelastic sheath and encircling smooth muscle cells and may propel the sperm and discarded cytoplasmic material into the larger vasa efferentia leading to the Wolffian duct. The structure in this testis would indicate a regeneration of seminiferous tubules from the median dorsal thickened sheath region containing the cord of primitive germinal cells.

**Sperm Ducts.**—As already indicated, the smallest ducts within each testis, the *intralobular ducts,* adjoin the seminiferous tubules and are lined by a low cuboidal epithelium resting upon a delicate reticulum. The *interlobular ducts* into which the intralobular ones empty are slightly larger with cuboidal cells and more connective tissue in their walls. The *efferentia* are lined by a cuboidal or low columnar epithelium and have scattered smooth muscle cells in the connective tissue of their wall. The *epididymal tubules,* derived from the anterior mesonephric tubules, are much coiled, have a broad lumen with mucosal folds, and the epithelium is composed of ciliated columnar cells among which goblet cells occur. Posteriorly a single tube, the *mesonephric duct,* acts as a vas deferens and is lined by plain pseudostratified epithelium. This duct has a wall containing an encircling muscularis and conveys the sperm to the cloaca. An enlargement of the duct forms a seminal vesicle with elaborately folded mucosa with columnar cells.

## MALE REPRODUCTIVE SYSTEM OF AMPHIBIA

The testes are more or less elongated, tubular bodies in the urodeles and lower forms, and ovoid in anurans. They appear as yellowish-white bodies lying alongside or ventral to the kidneys and connected to the latter by a mesenteric sheet of tissue. Each testis is a mass of tubules fitting the general description given for the seminiferous tubules. The seminiferous tubules connect with a number of small collecting tubules within the testis which join the vasa efferentia that in turn connect with the necks of a number of mesonephric tubules. In this case, the mesonephric duct functions as both a urinary and a genital duct. (Fig. 204.)

During development of anurans, an anterior part of the testis, possibly derived from pronephric tissue, has large cells resembling oöcytes or enlarged spermatocytes. This structure, Bidder's organ, may persist between the fat body and the testis for some time in the adult, but gradually

degenerates. The remains of the pronephric ducts passing along the mesonephros form Bidder's canal. Its lumen is lined with columnar epithelium
supported by a connective tissue and a few smooth muscle cells. The
outermost region of the canal has connective tissue continuous with that
of the covering of the kidney in which it is partially embedded.

In many Amphibia, the Müllerian duct, which is the functional oviduct
of the female, is present in the male. It may be without a lumen in some,
but in others it has the features of the resting oviduct of the female.

In some urodeles, as in Amblystoma and Triton, the males discharge
packets of sperm, called *spermatophores*, which are formed by the addition

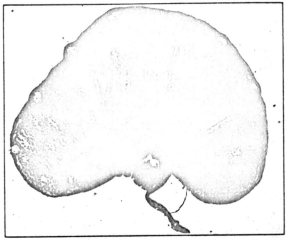

Fig. 204.—Longitudinal section of testis of Necturus, showing seminiferous tubules
converging towards collecting ducts in the connective tissue below; the efferentia
occur in the lowest part of this tissue and in the adjoining mesentery as small white
cavities.   Photomicrograph.   × 15.

of cloacal gland secretions to the sperm to form an enclosing sheath or
spermatheca. After these packets have been discharged during the seasonal
sexual congress of these forms, the female crawls over such a packet until
the swollen lips of the cloaca seize and withdraw it into the cloaca where
the spermatheca is dissolved and the sperm freed for fertilization of the
descending ova.

## MALE REPRODUCTIVE SYSTEM OF REPTILES

With this class the mesonephros becomes an embryonic structure
that is replaced by the functional metanephros and the newly
cloacal derived ureter which collects from it. However, a number of
the anterior mesonephric tubules are transformed into the epididymis which may form a body as large or larger than the testis. A
structure derived from the cloaca for transmission of sperm to the
cloaca of the female also occurs in this group.

### Lizard

**Testis.**—The testis is similar in structure to that of the frog with seminiferous tubules converging from the enclosing sheath, tunica albuginea, towards the collecting tubules which empty into the vasa efferentia. Depending upon the season, the tubules are either inconspicuous cords of indifferent germinal cells or actively multiplying spermatocytes and maturing spermatids.

**Sperm Ducts.**—The intratesticular ducts are lined by low cuboidal or squamous cells with a thin connective tissue sheath. The vasa efferentia which are 12 or more in number, are lined by ciliated cuboidal or low columnar cells and join the much larger tubules composing the epididymis. The epididymal tubules are lined by very tall slender columnar cells with small proximally located nuclei and a cytoplasm filled with acidophilic granules. These granules appear to be liberated unchanged into the lumen to join the sperm which mature here. The supporting tunica propria of these tubules is surrounded by circular smooth muscle and a fibroelastic adventitia. The epididymis collects into the vas deferens which has a lining of lower columnar cells, a layer of circular smooth muscle, and a fibroelastic adventitia joining the connective tissue supporting the ureter and blood-vessels passing to the cloaca.

**Cloacal Penis or Hemipenis.**—On each side of the transverse cloacal aperture a sac forms in the dorsal cloacal wall, retractor muscles are attached to them and they are withdrawn into pockets. The epithelium lining these sacs is continuous and similar to that of the cloaca (stratified squamous) and is supported by a very vascular connective tissue. Congestion and dilation of the vascular wall everts these sacs and spermatic fluid is transmitted to the cloaca of the female along grooves on their surface. In other reptiles, a single structure is derived from the ventral cloacal wall with a groove in the upper surface; this is similar to an early stage in the development of the penis found among mammals.

## MALE REPRODUCTIVE SYSTEM OF BIRDS

A pair of small bodies along the mid-dorsal line near the anterior end of the kidneys exhibit structural characters similar to the reptile. Studied during the inactive periods, they are small and the seminiferous tubules are reduced to relatively few spermatogonial cells and Sertoli cells. With onset of the spermatogenesis the usual cellular proliferation occurs, the tubules become dilated and sperm are formed for passage through the efferentia lined by cuboidal epithelium into the epididymis and then to the cloaca.

The epididymis is much reduced and the tubules have a ciliated low columnar epithelium and a few circular smooth muscle bundles. In the vas deferens the cells become columnar and there is a well-developed muscularis. The cloacal penis is similar but more elaborate than that of reptiles.

## MALE REPRODUCTIVE SYSTEM OF MAMMALS

**Testes.**—Among the mammals the testes are paired, ovoid, compact organs which show some variation in their location, not only in

different species, but often in the same species at different periods. In such animals as elephants and whales the testes remain permanently within the body cavity, but in marsupials, rodents, bats, and some insectivora they pass out of the body into a sac, the *scrotum*, during the breeding season. In primates, carnivora, and ruminants they remain permanently outside.

In the testes that have descended during the breeding season, or in the case of primates where they are permanently outside the body cavity, the scrotal sac adds several tissue sheaths about the testes.

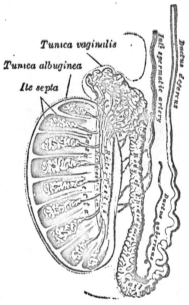

Fɪɢ. 205.—Vertical section of the testis, to show the arrangement of the ducts. (Gray's Anatomy.)

The *scrotum* is formed by an evagination of the body wall. Externally it has a covering of skin with its stratified squamous epithelium, glands, and hairs, supported by layers of connective tissue and muscle. Internally it is lined with a tissue similar to the peritoneum and known as *tunica vaginalis parietalis*. The same type of tissue is reflected over the anterior and lateral faces of the testes and somewhat ventrally and dorsally as the *tunica vaginalis visceralis* so that a free movement of the testes is possible within the scrotum. Within the tunica vaginalis, a connective tissue sheath, the *tunica albuginea*, extends perforated partitions, or septa, into the testis and forms compartments or lobules containing the seminiferous tubules. A mid-posterior region of this tissue located toward the surface of the testis is very vascular and called the *mediastinum*. The lobules so set off in the testis contain from

several to many convoluted seminiferous tubules described in the
general consideration at the beginning of the chapter.   (Fig. 206.)
As the tubules approach the mediastinum they unite to form less-
coiled tubules until a few much smaller straight tubules are formed
which connect within the mediastinum into a network of small ducts
called the *rete testis.*

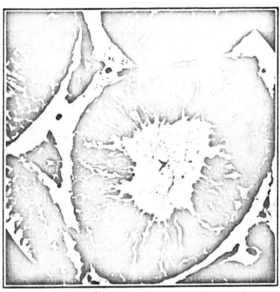

Fig. 206.—Photograph of a cross-section of a seminiferous tubule of the woodchuck,
showing interstitial tissue between it and adjacent tubules.   4 mm. obj. and 5× oc.

**Sperm Ducts.**—From the upper region of the rete testis a number
of small vasa efferentia pass toward the upper posterior region of
the testis to join the larger twisted and coiled epididymal tubules
which, together with the coiled vas deferens, form the epididymis,
a mass divided into a head and tail portion at either end of the
testis, and the body of the epididymis along the central portion.
In the tail portion of the epididymis the vas deferens straightens
and passes upward through the inguinal canal into the body cavity
with the spermatic cord.  The spermatic cord is composed of connective tissue containing the vas deferens, the spermatic artery,
spermatic vein, the nerve trunk, and a plexus of veins, called
*pampiniform plexus.*  After entering the body cavity, the vas
deferens continues anteriorly for a distance, then turns ventrally
around the ureter to join the urethra somewhere along its passage
from the bladder to the exterior.  Each vas deferens has an enlargement, called an *ampulla,* near its terminal region in the case of

primates, shrews, bears, dogs, and most rodents.  In some, the walls
of this region have mucous glands.

*Tubuli Recti.*—Where the seminiferous tubule transforms into a
straight tubule, the spermatogonial cells are lacking, and the straight
tubules are lined with columnar cells resembling the Sertoli cells
of the tubules.

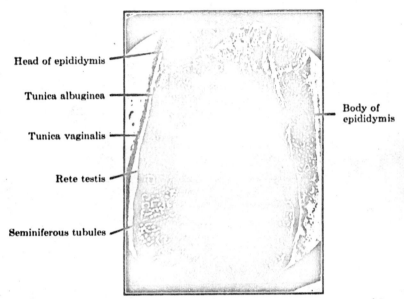

Head of epididymis

Tunica albuginea

Tunica vaginalis

Rete testis

Seminiferous tubules

Body of
epididymis

Fig. 207.—Sagittal section of the rat testis.  Photomicrograph.  32 mm. and 5x
ocular.

*Rete Testis.*—The irregular meshwork of these spaces is lined with
short cuboidal or squamous epithelium.  In between the rete testis
is connective tissue, nerves, and vessels of the mediastinum.

*Vasa Efferentia.*—The cells lining the ducts rest upon a basement
membrane and vary in size.  A clump of tall, ciliated columnar cells
may have adjacent to them progressively shorter cells so that pockets are formed in the wall of the efferent ducts.  The tall cells contain pigment granules and some fat droplets in their broad distal
portion; the low cells have striated and bleb-like modifications of
their distal surface.  In the connective tissue outside the basement
membrane, there is a small amount of smooth muscle.

*Epididymal Tubules.*—The lumen is larger and circular in cross-
section.  Adjacent to the basement membrane are small cells and
internal to them are large ciliated columnar cells of varying heights
and the secretion originating from the cytoplasm of the cells is
discharged into the lumen via the stereocilia.  Pigment and fat

19

droplets occur in the cytoplasm. As the epididymal tubules join the vas deferens the columnar cells are not so tall. In the connective tissue outside the basement membrane there are smooth muscle cells, which constrict the tube and serve to propel sperm and fluid onward toward the vas deferens.

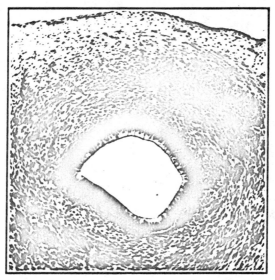

FIG. 208.—A cross-section of a dog's vas deferens. Photomicrograph. 16 mm. obj. and 5× oc.

*Vas Deferens.* (Fig. 209.)—This is a larger tube and its lumen is also greater. The epithelium of its mucous membrane is commonly stratified ciliated columnar. The tunica propria may have low folds which make the lumen irregular in shape. There is no definite submucosa, but outside the tunica propria is a muscle coat which consists of a thin innermost coat in which the smooth muscle cells are arranged lengthwise of the tube, a relatively thick middle circular coat of muscle, and an outer longitudinal coat which is thinner than the circular coat. Outside the muscle coat there is an adventitia of fibrous tissue in which there are groups of smooth muscle cells. As the vas deferens continues into the body cavity a connnective tissue extension of the adventitia supports the spermatic artery, spermatic vein, nerves, and a plexus of veins, called the pampiniform plexus, the whole being called a spermatic cord. The ampulla at the distal end of the vas deferens has large ridges in the tunica propria, and in its walls are glandular outpocketings.

Connected with each vas deferens in the ampullar, or terminal, region is a saccular organ, the *seminal vesicle.* These occur in most mammals, but not in marsupials and carnivora. The neck of each

ampulla and each seminal vesicle unite to form the muscular walled *ejaculatory duct*. There is a large globular mass known as the *prostate gland*, which surrounds the urethra near the bladder, and each ejaculatory duct traverses the prostate to join the urethra. The prostate contains a number of coiled tubular glands and occurs in most mammals, but not in marsupials. A short distance along the urethra toward the exterior is a pair of small sac-like structures, known as the *bulbo-urethral* or Cowper's glands, which are present in almost all mammals, but not in dogs and bears. They are large in rodents and pigs.

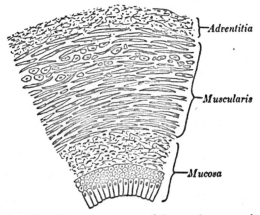

FIG. 209.—Diagram of the vas deferens of a mammal.

**Seminal Vesicles.**—Each seminal vesicle is an elongated, lobulated, twisted- irregular sac, with an adventitia continuous with that of the vas deferens. Within the adventitia is a thin muscularis coat with an outer longitudinal sheath. The tunica propria of loose connective tissue supports an epithelium of simple columnar epithelium or of cells of the same type as the vas deferens, *i. e.*, stratified columnar. Any cross-section reveals many complicated passages and spaces set off from each other. (Fig. 210.) This is because the mucous membrane is elaborately folded and in places the folds have fused to form a complex system of labyrinthine passages within the lumen. The seminal vesicles supply a secretion which is added to the sperm fluid proper at the time of discharge. The lumen is usually filled with an acidophilic colloidal material and granules of yellow pigment may occur in it and in the cytoplasm of the cells.

**The Prostate.**—The prostate is a glandular mass, roughly spherical in shape, which surrounds the male urethra just distal to its origin from the bladder. (Fig. 211.) Within the prostatic mass are a number of small glands of the compound tubular and alveolar type. There are a number of ducts from these glands entering the urethra.

Around the whole prostatic mass is a capsule of fibroelastic connective tissue which has extensions within the mass between adjacent glandular structures. The epithelium lining the glands varies from

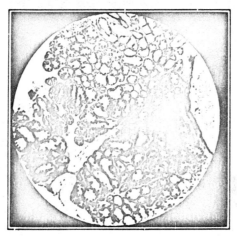

Fig. 210.—Photograph of a section through the seminal vesicle of the rat with the lumen of the ejaculatory duct at the right.   × 15.

cuboidal to columnar. In the connective tissue between the glandular portions are patches of smooth muscle cells indicating that the mass may contract and force its secretions into the urethra. The secretion is a thin, whitish fluid and forms the bulk of the spermatic fluid. Sometimes spherical masses, prostatic stones, of varying size with concentric lamellæ occur in the lumens of the glands.

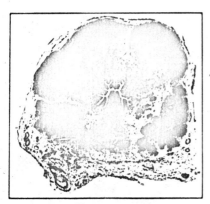

Fig. 211.—Photograph of a cross-section of the dog's prostate, showing 5 glandular masses opening into the urethra by numerous excretory ducts.   × 20.

**Cowper's Glands.**—Cowper's glands are also known as bulbourethral glands and are a pair of small masses located a little further along the urethra from the prostate. They consist of connective tissue, smooth muscle cells, and small branching compound tubulo-alveolar glands. The walls of the glands have small pockets and simple epithelium of different types lines them; in some places the cells are squamous, in others columnar. The main ducts are lined

with transitional or stratified columnar epithelium. Other, smaller glands of mucous appearance may occur along the course of the urethra.

**Penis.**—In the body or shaft of the penis, masses of mesenchyme tissue give rise to *corpora cavernosa* or erectile tissue and also to cartilage or bone which forms in some species. The urethra passes only a short distance from the bladder before becoming associated with the ducts and glands of the genital system. Near the bladder it has a transitional epithelial lining, but this often changes to stratified columnar further along and then to stratified squamous at the opening. Three regions of the urethra have been separated. The prostatic portion extends from the neck of the bladder through the prostate gland, where the ejaculatory duct usually joins it. Among the rodents the ejaculatory ducts may not join the urethra until they reach the tip of the penis. The membranous, or middle part, is short, extending from the prostate region to the beginning of the corpora cavernosa of the penis. The cavernosa portion extends through the length of the penis. Along the course of the urethra are glandular out-pocketings of the dorsal and lateral walls, already described, embedded in the fibroelastic connective tissue, with varying amounts of smooth muscle also represented.

A cross-section through the body of the penis shows that the major portion of it is formed by the corpora cavernosa. In man, two corpora cavernosa occupy the upper portion, but in other mammals they usually fuse to form an unpaired U-shaped mass. In man a third, *corpus cavernosum urethra*, surrounds the urethra and is located ventral to the other two (corpora cavernosa penis). In many mammals the urethral cavernosa tissue is poorly represented. (Fig. 212.)

The corpora cavernosa are composed of a vascular spongelike network with irregular venous sinuses capable of being filled with blood and distended under considerable pressure. Each of these bodies is surrounded by a thick fibrous membrane, the tunica albuginea, with outer fibers mainly longitudinal and inner fibers circular. Between the two corpora this sheath forms a more or less complete septum, but toward the glans both corpora may communicate.

The corpus cavernosum urethra is surrounded by a less dense tunica albuginea, in which circular smooth muscle may appear toward the urethral wall. The venous sinuses are more uniform and more elastic fibers are present. When the os priapi, or penis bone, is present, it forms just above the urethra from mesenchyme of the developing penis.

Surrounding the corpora and forming the general groundwork of the penis is a vascular fibroelastic connective tissue which is covered externally by the skin in whose subcutaneous tissue some skeletal muscle may be found.   The outer knoblike end of the penis, the glans, is composed of a mass of dense vascular connective tissue covered by a reflected fold of skin, the prepuce.

Fig. 212.—Photograph of a cross-section of the penis of a chipmunk near the tip. It is externally surrounded by the skin, within which is connective tissue.  The corpus cavernosum penis is a large bean-shaped mass.  The V-shaped opening is the urethra, below which is the ejaculatory duct; both of these ducts are surrounded by scanty corpus cavernosum urethra tissue.  32 mm. obj. and 5× oc.

At times of sexual excitement, erection of the penis follows reflexes conducted to the muscular wall of the arteries leading into the cavernous tissue so that a relaxation occurs resulting in the supplying of an unusual amount of blood to the venous sinuses. The spaces of the cavernosa become engorged, so that the veins emptying them are compressed to the point of interfering with the outward flow of blood.  Continued flow of blood into the sinuses enlarges the corpora under pressure and limitation of expansion by the heavy fibrous sheaths results in making the penis quite rigid. After completion of spermatic discharge or passage of excitement, the arterial walls regain their former tone, become constricted, and the inflow of blood diminishes.  The emptying of cavernosa spaces is slowly effected; the penis slowly contracts and becomes relaxed.

## CHAPTER XV

## THE ENDOCRINE GLANDS

It is known that the nervous system controls integration of bodily activities so that there is a harmonious functioning of the organ systems making possible successful adjustments to changes in the external world. In addition, an important part of the unifying and coördinating function is effected by the system of chemical coördinators, the endocrine gland secretions.

The secretion products of *exocrine glands*, as already described, collect in ducts. *Endocrine glands*, on the contrary, have no excretory duct systems. Their secretions pass into the blood or lymph vessels and thus enter the circulation stream for distribution to various organs and systems.

An endocrine gland may be defined as one that secretes into the blood stream some hormone or chemical substance which stimulates or depresses the physiological activity of other groups of cells, thus affecting growth, development, and the general condition of the body as a whole. Secretion of one gland may affect the activity or effect of the secretion of some other endocrine gland, *i. e.*, they are physiologically interrelated.

Although many, if not all, cells are to some extent endocrine in nature, certain glandular organizations are purely endocrine. Among the outstanding endocrine organs are the thyroid gland, the parathyroids, the hypophysis cerebri or pituitary, and the adrenals. Several organs already considered have an endocrine function, namely, the islands of Langerhans in the pancreas, the liver, and the gonads.

### PITUITARY GLAND

This name, literally meaning "phlegm," is said to have been devised by Galen (130-200 A.D.), since that ancient anatomist-physician thought that nasal secretions were produced by this gland. It is also called the *hypophysis cerebri, i. e.*, that which grows under the brain, and in mammals is located in a little pocket in the sphenoid bone on the floor of the skull posterior to the optic chiasma. The connective tissue sheath of the brain, the pia mater, immediately surrounds it and the lower end of the infundibulum connects it with the brain.

The pituitary is uniformly present in all vertebrates and its origin is similar, but the association of the derivative parts is vari-

(295)

able among the classes. It has a double embryonic origin. An evagination of buccal epithelium (ectoderm) grows upward, forming a pocket, Rathke's pouch, toward the brain. At about the same time there is a downward evagination from the floor of the diencephalon with which Rathke's pouch comes into contact. Rathke's pouch gives rise to three epithelial glandular regions distinguished as the *pars distalis, pars intermedia* and *pars tuberalis*; the neural evagination forms the *pars neuralis*. The connection of Rathke's pouch with the mouth cavity disappears, and the original lumen of this pouch is eliminated, in part or entirely by epithelial cords and

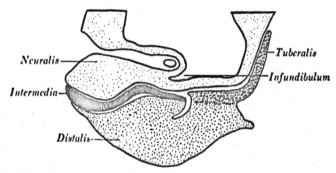

Fig. 213.—Diagram of the pituitary gland of a mammal. (After Atwell, Gray's Anatomy.)

tubules as an overgrowth of the anterior wall to form the pars distalis. Lateral lobe enlargements on either side unite with each other to form the pars tuberalis. The posterior part of the buccal pouch, the pars intermedia, adjoins and becomes closely associated with the pars neuralis and the two are called the posterior lobe; the distalis and tuberalis form the anterior lobe. A slit between the intermedia and the distalis may be all that remains of the original lumen of Rathke's pouch. (Figs. 213 and 214.)

The *pars distalis* of an adult pituitary is a mass of epithelial cells arranged in branching cords separated by broad capillaries. Three types of cells are recognized, namely acidophil cells, basophil cells, and chromophobe cells. In higher vertebrates there are relatively more of the first two types. A fibroelastic capsule continues internally to support the columns of cells and the vascular supply.

The *pars tuberalis* resembles the pars distalis in structure. There may be incomplete follicular arrangements of cells with colloidal secretion within the follicle, and patches of squamous epithelium left over from embryonic buccal epithelium.

The *pars intermedia* consists of epithelial cells, some of which are columnar in type. Follicles may occur. In some cases the cleft

between the pars intermedia and pars distalis has been obliterated, and it is very difficult to note any histological difference between the two regions. Where a residual lumen is present, the cells lining it may be ciliated columnar in form.

The *pars neuralis* appears to possess cells which are more like neuroglia than neurons. Some are spindle-shaped and some stellate with numerous processes. The fibers present are non-medullated. The cavity of the original embryonic infundibular evagination remains in the pituitary of the cat, but disappears in many other animals. (Fig. 214.)

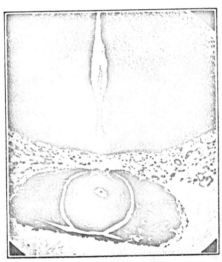

Fig. 214.—Photograph of a section through the diencephalon and pituitary of the kitten. The inner lighter portion of the pituitary is the neuralis and is surrounded by the intermedia. There is a space between the intermedia and the adjacent masses of the pars distalis. 16 ram. obj. and 5× oc.

The *saccus vasculosus* present in fishes is a very vascular development of the continuation of the infundibular stalk and is lined by cuboidal or low columnar cells similar to ependymal cells of the ventricles.

A ventral lobe present in elasmobranchs is difficult to homologize with the parts of higher vertebrate pituitaries. The tuberalis portion is not reported for some reptiles and fishes and the saccus vasculosus so prominent in fishes becomes insignificant in mammals.

Although much positive information has been gathered concerning the functions of the pituitary, further research is necessary before it is completely understood. If the pars distalis is experimentally removed in young animals, they remain small in stature and the skeleton does not grow. Hyposecretion from this lobe causes diminished oxygen metabolism, dry skin, decrease of hair formation, short appendages, and dwarfism. Hypertrophy or hypersecretion in young individuals causes formation of more adipose tissue, larger bones, and gigantism. If the anterior lobe hypertrophies in adults, the bones and soft parts of the face, hands, and feet grow larger, a condition known as acromegaly.

Secretion of the pars intermedia is associated with control of pigment distribution in melanophores.

The pars neuralis apparently produces a secretion which tends to cause a rise in blood-pressure, a modification in the volume of urine formed in a given time, and increased milk flow in active mammary glands. It is somehow related to the change of glycogen to glucose in the liver; it causes contraction of the smooth muscle of the bladder, intestine, and uterus. Because of this last-named property, extract of pars neuralis substance, or "pituitrin," is employed in obstetrics.

Removal of the entire pituitary from living animals results in a lowering of basal metabolism, lowering of body temperature, and in a short time death.

### THYROID GLAND

In fishes this gland is a number of small follicular masses along the ventral aorta. In the frog, two masses are separated, each portion being located laterally in the floor of the mouth between the posterior lateral and thyrohyoid processes of the hyoid apparatus. In higher vertebrates there is a tendency for a combination of the two portions into one gland. In mammals the thyroid is located below the larynx on the ventral surface of the trachea adjacent to the upper tracheal cartilages. The form varies in different mammals. In man there is an oval-shaped mass on each side of the anterior face of the trachea connected by a median "isthmus."

The thyroid of higher vertebrates begins its development as an evagination of cells from the mid-ventral wall of the pharynx in the region of the first pharyngeal pouches or somewhat posteriorly. This mass of early cells, the thyroid "anlage," grows into a long stalk, connected with the mouth cavity at the base of the tongue, behind the papillated region, and forms a distal larger mass which grows into the isthmus of the mature gland. Later the stalk atrophies thus shutting off the "isthmus" from the digestive system. However, the site of origin remains in the adult as the foramen cecum, a small depression at the base of the tongue on its upper surface, just back of the most posterior vallate papillæ in mammals.

Connective tissue grows around the outside, forming an outer loose sheath and an inner firm capsule of fibroelastic connective tissue from which vascular reticular and fibroelastic extensions are carried in between groups of gland cells.

In young embryos the gland cells arrange themselves in the form of more or less spherical follicles resembling the terminal end-pieces of an alveolar gland.

The mature thyroid consists of follicles which are structurally independent of one another. (Figs. 215 and 216.) As they develop,

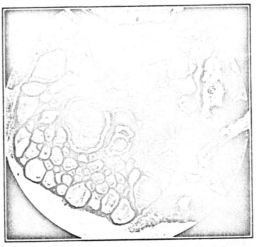

Fig. 215.—Photograph of a section through the thyroid of the water snake, showing follicles of various sizes filled with colloid. The trachea is shown at the top of the figure. 16 mm. obj. and 5× oc.

a clear yellow viscid colloidal fluid with an affinity for acid dyes collects inside each follicle. The follicular wall is composed of cuboidal or low columnar epithelial cells without a basement membrane. (Fig. 22.) The form varies somewhat with age, the breeding season, and the type of food. Both mitochondria and Golgi apparatus have been demonstrated in the follicle cells. The majority of follicle cells have a clear cytoplasm and a large spherical nucleus and are called *chief* cells. Acidophilic cytoplasm may often be observed in the distal part of some cells. Another type of cell, called the *colloid* cell, has a small pycnotic nucleus and acidophilic cytoplasm; it probably represents a degeneration stage of the chief cells. Between adjacent follicles is loose fibroelastic connective tissue and a reticular network. The connective tissue supports a very rich capillary network, so that the gland receives a relatively large quantity of blood. Secretion of the cells passes directly into the capillaries and may accumulate in varying amounts within the lumen of the vesicles.

The colloidal material in the follicles varies with the state of the gland; it is abundant and distends the follicles into regular spherical outlines with low cuboidal cells in the hypoactive state, and it is much reduced with an associated irregular outline and columnar cells in hyperactive follicles.

Formation of new follicles is associated with mitotic activity in the chief cells and budding from existent follicles

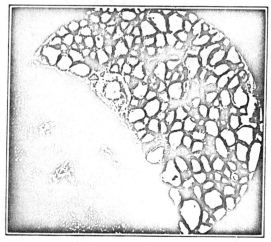

FIG. 216.—Photograph of a section through the thyroid (right) and parathyroid (left) of the dog. 16 mm. obj. and 5× oc.

It has been ascertained that the thyroid collects iodine from the blood and forms an organic compound, called thyroxin, which regulates basal metabolism. Deficiencies in thyroxin result in well-recognized abnormalities. Cretinism is due to failure of the thyroid to develop, and individuals thus affected are known as "cretins," many being idiots, undersized, and dependent. In some cases, daily administration of thyroxin to infant cretins results in normal development. Myxedema is brought about by atrophy of the gland of an adult, as a result of which there is overproduction of connective and adipose tissue, slowing down of the heart-beat, weakened pulse, thickening of the skin, and dulling of the intellectual powers. Hyperthyroid, on the other hand, produces a condition in which there is a speeding up of basal metabolism, tendency to ingest much food, and an increase in rate of heart-beat. Investigations

indicate a functional interconnection between the thyroid and the pituitary which produces a thyroidotrophic factor which plays a part in control of thyroid activity.

## PARATHYROID GLANDS

In cyclostomes these glands occur as small masses of epithelial cells on the ventral portion of each of the seven pairs of gill pouches. In lizards, birds, and mammals they occur as two pairs of small glandular masses. In development, small masses of epithelial cells form as dorsal diverticula from the third and fourth pairs of gill pouches. As the pharyngeal pouches are obliterated by further growth, the four parathyroid anlages separate from their place of origin, migrate backward, and become embedded in the thyroid lobes. (Fig. 216.) Histologically each gland is composed of cords

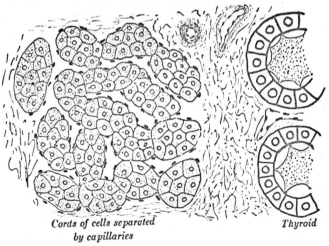

*Cords of cells separated*
*by capillaries*

*Thyroid*

Fig. 217.—Diagram of mammalian parathyroid, showing capillaries between the cords of cells.

of small epithelial cells, with a capillary network in the connective tissue between them. The main cellular components, the *chief cells*, are small and have spherical darkly staining nuclei and pale cytoplasm. A *colloid* or *acidophil cell* similar to those of the thyroid may also be observed here occasionally. The cells are arranged in small masses or columns (Fig. 217) or possibly follicles, in which colloid without iodine collects. In parathyroids of old animals, adipose tissue may develop in the supporting connective tissue. There is no regeneration of parathyroids after their removal.

Removal of portions of the parathyroids causes hyperirritability of the nervous system and sense organs. There is an accompanying decrease in the calcium content of the blood. The normal secretion is essential to normal calcium metabolism, metabolism of sugar, maintenance of the nitrogen equilibrium, and formation of bone and dentine. Proper combination of parathyroid secretion and calcium salts is essential to normal muscle contraction and administration of parathyroid extract relieves tetany due to faulty function of the parathyroids. Entire removal of parathyroids results in death.

## ADRENAL GLANDS

These endocrine glands are composed of two different elements, a chromaffin or medullary portion and an inter-renal or cortical portion, each with a separate embryonic origin. In fishes, small masses of chromaffin cells develop segmentally from primitive cells migrating from the central nervous system (ectoderm) some of which develop into neurons of sympathetic ganglia closely associated with the chromaffin cells. These masses of chromaffin cells occur in the connective tissue along the dorsal part of the mesonephros and also scattered through the body with other sympathetic ganglia. The inter-renal or cortical part is derived from mesoderm in the medial dorsal part of the mesonephros and develops as a long network of cell cords separated by sinusoids, one mass at either side of midline.

### Dogfish

*Inter-renal.*—The cords of the inter-renal portion are composed of columnar or polyhedral cells with a finely granular acidophilic cytoplasm containing many small vacuoles in routine preparations. In frozen sections of tissue fixed in formalin and stained with Sudan IV these cells contain lipoidal material in regions corresponding to the vacuoles of routine preparations. The nuclei have a relatively abundant chromatin content scattered throughout and one or more nucleoli.

*Chromaffin Bodies.*—The chromaffin portion is composed of groups of columnar, polyhedral or fusiform cells whose cytoplasm is packed with coarse basophilic granules in routine preparations but in special preparations these have an affinity for chromium salts. The nuclei are larger than those in the inter-renal cells, are vesicular and do not contain a prominent nucleolus. Closely associated with these cells are the cytons of the sympathetic ganglia.

Although the dogfish has both parts as separate secretory elements there is a closer association or intermingling in the amphibia and reptiles; in birds the chromaffin tissue forms a network among the cords of cortical (inter-renal) cells; in mammals the chromaffin tissue becomes the medulla and is surrounded by the cortical tissue. Similar cell types occur in the two different regions through the groups with the possible exception of special acidophilic cells appear-

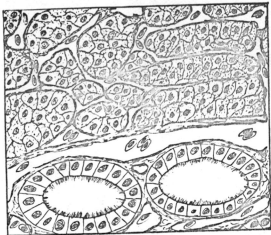

Fig. 218.—A section through the inter-renal body and adjoining **mesonephric tubules** of the dogfish, showing the cords of cortical tissue cells with **vacuolated cytoplasm** and a network of vascular sinusoids. Camera lucida drawing with 4 mm. obj. and 10× oc.

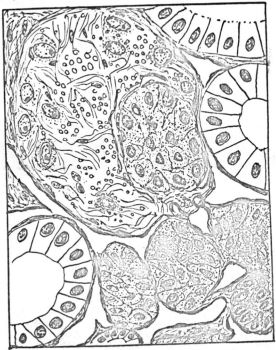

Fig. 219.—A section through a chromaffin body in the mesonephros of **the dogfish.** Cords of the chromaffin cells are separated by vascular sinusoids. In the upper part of the figure a patch of chromaffin cells is closely associated with a sympathetic ganglion. Camera lucida drawing with 4 mm. obj. and 10× oc.

ing in the frog during the summer season (Fig. 220) and the secretions appear to have the same effects to be noted under the description of the mammalian adrenal.

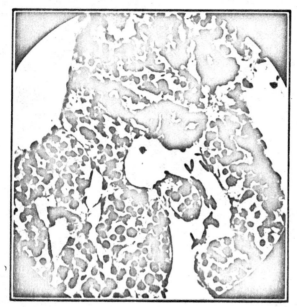

Fig. 220.—A section of the frog's adrenal, showing cords of cells separated by sinusoids; the darkest staining areas are composed of chromaffin cells; scattered dark spherical eosinophilic cells occur among the clearer cortical cells. Photomicrograph. 4 mm. obj. and 5× oc.

### MAMMAL

In quadruped mammals, one of these glands is located at the anterior end of each kidney. In man they are called suprarenals, because they are located at the upper end of the kidneys. In man they are somewhat flattened, small bodies, the right one being triangular in form, the left somewhat crescent-shaped. In other mammals they are bean-shaped masses, embedded in adipose tissue which tends to form near the kidneys. The adrenals are exceedingly well supplied with blood-vessels and it has been estimated that blood to the amount of about five times their weight circulates through them every minute. They are surrounded by a firm capsule of connective tissue, extensions of which pass into the interior of the gland. Cross-sections of fresh adrenal glands made with a sharp knife reveals an outer cortical zone, light yellow in color and of firm texture, surrounding a central medullary region of looser texture, and dark red in color. The two zones have an entirely different embryonic origin. (Fig. 221.)

The cortex develops as a series of buds from the anterior third of the Wolffian body. The cells of the medulla originate from cells related to those of the cœliac plexus of the sympathetic system and form epithelial groups. As development proceeds, the latter mass of cells becomes invested with those of the cortical region. Each gland is surrounded by a connective tissue capsule which supports arteries, veins, capillaries, and lymphatics. Strands of connective tissue extend in between the epithelial cells of the cortex into the medulla, supporting a reticular tissue network and capillaries.

FIG. 221.—Photograph of a longitudinal section through the adrenal of the woodchuck. A connective tissue sheath surrounds the entire organ. The darker cortex surrounds the central lighter medulla, except at the hilus on the right of the figure. Below are sections of blood-vessels. × 10.

*The Cortex.*—Three zones of epithelial cells may be distinguished in the cortex. (Fig. 222.) Immediately beneath the capsule is a narrow zone, the zona glomerulosa, where the flattened and then polyhedral cells are arranged in oval groups in the form of flattened or incomplete vesicles. The nuclei stain deeply and the cytoplasm has an affinity for basic dyes. Internal to this is the zona fasciculata, with long double rows of larger polyhedral or cuboidal cells, often binucleate, radiating in toward the medulla. In the outer portion of these columns the cells have fat droplets and cholesterol, but routine technique dissolves the lipoid substance, so that the cytoplasm may have a vacuolated appearance. Vitamin C occurs in large amounts in the cortical (fasiculata) cells. Internal to the zona fasciculata is the narrow zona reticularis with cells forming a meshwork of cords one cell in width. These cells contain less lipoid

20

but a brown pigment increases toward the boundary of this zone with the medulla and becomes more evident in glands of old animals. A capillary net invests the cell groups in the glomerulosa, and from it capillaries extend between double rows of cells of the fasciculata to become a meshwork again in the reticularis, where they connect with capillaries of the medulla. New cells form by mitosis in the glomerulosa nearest the capsule, pass through their functional phase as they progress through the zona fasciculata, and degenerate within the reticularis, where they are removed by macrophages.

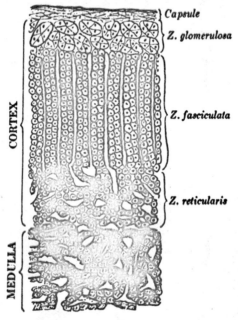

Fig. 222.—Diagram of a section through the adrenal of a mammal.

*The Medulla.*—This region consists of an irregularly arranged meshwork of polyhedral cells separated by sinusoidal capillaries. The medulla cells are also roughly rectangular in section, with the longer sides in contact with adjacent cells and with a sinusoidal capillary adjacent to the short sides. When fixed in chromic acid the cytoplasm of the cells is dark brown in color, and if potassium dichromate is used their cytoplasm shows fine brown granules. Because of this affinity for chromium they are referred to as chromaffin cells. In ferric chloride the medulla stains green and in iodine yellow. The fine brown granules are secretory products which reduce dichromate of potassium to chromium dioxide. The number of granules present indicates the degree of secretory activity.

There is a plexus of fine nerve fibers in the cortex, especially in the zona reticularis. Axons of nerve cells are in close relation with the chromaffin cells of the medulla. Here also are a few ganglion cells, or even small ganglia near the central vein. Since the medulla is derived from the same source as the sympathetic nervous system, this central portion of the adrenal is comparable to paraganglia.

Secretions of the cortex contain a hormone, called "cortin" lack of which in man, due to pathological lesions of the cortex, results in Addison's disease. Animals deprived of adrenals die, but life is prolonged if extract of cortical tissue is administered. Cortical secretion is also correlated with sexual development.

Epinephrin, or adrenalin, or adrenin, is secreted by cells of the medulla. Circulating in the blood steam, it maintains tone in the small arteries, or arterioles, and so assists in regulating blood-pressure. Local injections of adrenalin cause temporary constriction in small vessels, and in this manner it is used for preventing hemorrhage. Injections of it into a heart that has ceased beating for a short period in some cases results in a resumption of rhythmical contractions. The medulla is not essential for life.

## PARAGANGLIA

Occasional sympathetic ganglia are found in various organs of the body associated with a small mass of chromaffin cells resembling those of the adrenal medulla. These glandular masses, known as paraganglia, have a histological structure suggesting an endocrine function, but as yet there is no experimental evidence as to their function.

## PINEAL BODY

The pineal body received its name because of its resemblance to a pine cone. It is also known as the epiphysis cerebri, and is located in the dorsal region of the brain between the cerebrum and cerebellum, where it appears as a small red body. It is attached to the third ventricle by a stalk and is surrounded by the pia mater. Islands of epithelial cells, separated and surrounded by capillaries, are embedded in connective tissue. Some of the cells resemble cytons of multipolar nerve cells. A network of fibers from the sympathetic system occurs in the connective tissue. It has been assumed that this glandular tissue has an endocrine function because it has been observed that a tumorous growth of the pineal gland appears to be associated with an unusually early maturing of the sex glands. That is, it has been assumed that the normal pineal secretes a hormone that delays the too-rapid development of sex organs. However, experiments give conflicting results.

# CHAPTER XVI

## TECHNIQUE

THE ideal method for the study of tissues should present the cells in a normal living condition and involve as little change as possible. Such an approach is possible to a disappointingly limited degree even with much practice and satisfactory equipment, but for the student it is far from practical. The scope of an introductory course permits of little more than an acquaintance with the most commonly used routine procedures involved in making slides such as are the basis for most histological study. The microscopic observation in saline of very small pieces of gently excised tissues is recommended, wherever practical, for comparison with conditions observed in permanent preparations made from the same material. For the use of vital and supravital dyes and special techniques, reference should be made to the bibliography. The routine histological technique involves fixation, embedding, sectioning, and staining of tissues.

### FIXATION

The destructive reactions within living cells are counterbalanced by synthesis of elements for repair and continued life. When cells die, syntheses cease and the enzymes involved in vital processes become active in breaking down the products they formerly helped to build. Such disintegration processes working within the dead or dying cell constitute *autolysis*. In addition, bacteria present, or soon entering dead and dying tissues, rapidly add to the disintegration processes and the accompanying distortion or loss of characteristic cellular structure.

To prevent these changes, and also to make cells and intercellular substance insoluble and stainable, tissues from freshly killed animals are immersed in fluids called fixatives. Such fixing fluids should accomplish certain definite things in addition to preventing autolytic and bacterial decomposition. They should penetrate tissues rapidly and coagulate or otherwise preserve protoplasmic substances, leaving intra- and extracellular structures preserved in the same relative spatial relations as during life. They should prevent subsequent changes, such as shrinkage, hardening, and dissolution, and should not hinder later staining. With these requirements for a fixative in mind, consult the accompanying table and consider the properties of some chemicals in common use as components of various fixing fluids.

( 308 )

These are but a few of the numerous reagents in use, and only a brief note is made of their action. For example, it will be observed that acetic acid and picric acid are both useful, but that the first causes swelling of tissue and the second causes shrinkage. By a proper combination these effects may be counterbalanced. A review of the actions of these effects noted above indicates a reason for the protoplasmic conditions observed in fixed tissues and the use of the component reagents in the following commonly used fixing fluids.

*Bouin's Fluid.*—The formula is as follows: 75 parts saturated aqueous solution of picric acid; 25 parts formalin (40 per cent formaldehyde); 5 parts glacial acetic acid. This is one of the best general fixatives, and in it the effects of the three chemicals are well balanced to give a fair preservation of cellular structure. Chromosomes are especially well fixed. Glycogen, fat, chondriosomes, and the Golgi apparatus are not usually preserved. Tissues may be left for long periods in it without harm, but twelve to twenty-four hours is ordinarily an adequate time. There is little or no hardening or shrinkage, and tissues will later stain well. After fixation the tissue may be washed in 50 or 70 per cent alcohol to get rid of the free fixative remaining.

*Flemming's Fluid.*—The formula is 1 per cent aqueous solution of chromic acid, 15 parts; 2 per cent aqueous solution of osmium tetroxide, 4 parts; glacial acetic acid, 1 cc., or even less, to be added just before using the fixative. This solution is useful for fixing chromosomes, mitochondria, and fat. The amount of acetic acid should be reduced to a few drops for better results with mitochondria. The osmic acid fixes the fats and mitochondria. The acetic acid fixes the chromosomes and aids in preventing shrinkage. The chromic acid fixes proteins and chromosomes. However, fixation may be uneven, part of the tissue being overfixed, part properly fixed, and the inner portion of the tissue being underfixed. Fixation should extend over a twenty-four-hour period when acetic acid is present to the extent of 1 part, but the period should be extended to four days when the acetic acid is reduced and when it is desired to retain mitochondria. After fixation the tissues should be washed for twelve hours in running water to remove all the free fixative present before going ahead with the technique.

*Zenker's Fluid.*—The formula is 2 grams potassium dichromate; 1 gram sodium sulphate; 5 grams mercuric chloride; 100 cc. water; 5 cc. glacial acetic acid. The acetic acid should be added just before using the fluid. Tissue should be fixed for twelve hours. Long fixation causes formation of crystals in the tissue. After fixation the tissues should be washed in running water for several hours.

then transferred into 70 per cent alcohol to which iodine has been added to extract excess mercury salts from the tissue.

A modification of Zenker's fluid is called *Helly's fluid*. It has the same formula as the above, but substitutes 5 cc. of formalin for the acetic acid. It gives an excellent picture of protoplasmic structure, but care must be taken in later steps in technique so that

| MICAL | REACTIONS IN SOLUTION | EFFECT ON ALBUMIN | EFFECT ON NUCLEOPROTEIN | EFFECT ON NUCLEIC ACID | EFFECT ON CYTOPLASMIC PROTEINS |
|---|---|---|---|---|---|
| ALCOHOL $H_5OH$ | Easily oxidized into acetaldehyde, then acetic acid. A reducer. | Immediately ppt. Precipitate insoluble in distilled water or NaCl solution. | Precipitates slowly. Precipitate immediately soluble in distilled water. | Does not fix chromatin. | Causes granular appearance in cytoplasm and shrinkage of cell processes. |
| LDEHYDE $O$ $\parallel$ $-C—H$ | Reducer. Easily oxidizes to formic acid and condenses to form paraformaldehyde. | Does not ppt. albumin or cause it to become hardened or insoluble in water. Prevents hardening by alcohol. | Does not ppt. nucleoprotein unless acid is present. Long action causes additive compounds. Compounds formed by long action are not ppt. by alcohol. | .... | Causes additive compounds to form. Does not ppt. but preserves them. Proteins so treated combine poorly with acids. |
| IC ACID $COOH$ | .... | No precipitate. | Immediate ppt., not soluble in water. If KOH is added precipitate dissolves. Also ppt. mucin. | Excellent for chromosomes but not for interkinetic nuclei or late telophase. | Does not fix so sets up no barrier to penetration. Prevents decay. |
| RIC ACID $OH$ $NO_2$ $NO_2$ | .... | Precipitates albumin picrate, insoluble in water. | Coarse ppt. not soluble. Forms protein picrates. | Fixes protein but leaves nucleic acid in solution. | Precipitates. |
| MIC ACID $CrO_4$ | An oxidizing agent. Reduced to $Cr_2O_3$ by alcohol and formalin. | Immediate ppt. Not soluble. | Combines chemically to give a coarse precipitate immediately. Ppt. insoluble in water. | Moderate or weak precipitate | Coarse destructive precipitate; alone gives poor preservation. |
| ASSIUM ROMATE $Cr_2O_7$ | Oxidizing agent not as strong as chromic acid. Dissociates as $2K + Cr_2O_7$. | Alone does not ppt. proteins. Acidified with acetic acid, rapidly causes a dense ppt. Resembles that of chromic acid. | Alone does not cause precipitate. | Dissolves chromatin. | Poorly preserved unless solution is acidified in which case a network is formed similar to chromic acid. |
| RCURIC LORIDE $gCl_2$ | $Hg + Cl$ $(HgCl)_2O$ or $HgClOH$ | Rapid precipitate. Insoluble in distilled water but dissolves if some saturated NaCl or KI is added. | Coarse ppt. Same as for albumin. Addition of acetic acid slows ppt. and ppt. is not soluble when saturated NaCl or KI is added. | Unlife-like preservation of nuclei. Coarse ppt. | Coarse precipitation. |
| MIUM ROXIDE $sO_4$ | Reduces to $OsO_2$. Strong oxidizer. | Does not ppt. Also prevents ppt. by alcohol or heat. | No ppt. unless acetic acid is added. | Very little ppt. but preservation. | Preserves homogeneity of living cell but is uneven in fixation. |
| OXAN $(CH_2)_2O$ | May be used as solvent for other fixing agents except $K_2Cr_2O_7$. | Preservative. | Preservative. | Preservative. | Preservative. |

distortion through shrinkage does not take place. Chromosomes are not so distinct as with Zenker's fluid, but cytoplasmic structures are well preserved and can be demonstrated by various stains. Helly's fluid must be thoroughly washed out in running water after twelve hours' fixation, and the tissues are usually later immersed in 70 per cent alcohol to which iodine has been added. If dioxan

| Effect on Fats and Lipids | Speed of Penetration | Subsequent Treatment | Shrinkage | Stainability of Material so Fixed | Remarks |
|---|---|---|---|---|---|
| Fat and phospholipids soluble in it. | Rapid penetration. | Requires no special washing out but anything less than 50% alcohol to be avoided. Material may proceed to clearing agent. | Considerable shrinkage carrying cytoplasm inward and leaving periphery empty. | Tissue not readily stainable, but hematoxylin will work. | Mitochondria dis except in cases they contain high tein content. Gly ppt. but precipit soluble in water. |
| Preserves. Fats may disappear through enzyme action in fixing cell. Some fixative effect on phospholipids. | Fairly rapid in penetration though slow in producing its effects. | No special washing out required. Water best avoided so go to 50 or 70% alcohol. | Slight but may be considerable in subsequent treatment with alcohol. | Fair stainability. | Mitochondria caus change from three spheres. Tissue so may be hardened lowing alcohols. |
| No fixing effect. | Rapid. | 50 or 70% alcohol. Prevents hardening in alcohol or subsequent reagents. | Prevents. Causes some swelling and leaves tissue soft. | Not particularly good but not unstainable. | Primarily a preserv not a fixative. P nently distorts coll ous fibers. Mito dria may or may preserved. |
| No effect. Fat droplets fuse together as result of preprecipitation of cytoplasm. | Medium. | Wash in 50 or 70% alcohol. To remove excess of acid add lithium carbonate to alcohol. | Considerable. | Easy. | Mitochondria, if th like, become faint of spheres. |
| None directly. Fat droplets fuse together as result of precipitation of cytoplasm. | Medium. | Should be washed for 12 hrs. in running water to avoid ppt. formation unless, when transferred to alcohol, material kept in dark. | Moderate | Readily stainable by basic dyes. | Mitochondria not served. Bright appears to cause lution of tissue so |
| None. | Moderate but fixation should be for days since action is slow on proteins. | Should be washed in running water. | Slight in this but moderate in subsequent treatment. | Makes mitochondria stainable in acid fuchsin. | Renders proteins i bile in water. acidic it acts like mic acid. Cyto well preserved. chondria preserve |
| None. | Relatively rapid. | Peculiar ppt. forming in tissues so fixed. Has to be washed out by sol. of iodine in 90% alcohol. Not necessary if dioxan is used for long periods (6 to 12 hrs.). | Relatively great. | Tissues stain well. | Mitochondria pre Cytoplasm well p ed. Tissues ha |
| Both fixes and blackens. | Relatively slow action. | Must be washed out carefully in running water. | None but subsequent treatment may produce some, and tissue may crumble. | Difficult. | Fixes unevenly. and blackens Golgi bodies. mitochondria. |
| Does not preserve. | Relatively rapid. | Change of dioxan and then paraffin. | Slight. | Fair. | Used in place of and xylol in embedding elim some hardenin shrinking. |

is used and the tissue kept away from bright light no iodine is needed in steps following fixation in either of these fluids.

*Formalin Solutions.*—A 10 per cent solution serves as a good preservative and fixative in the case of delicate tissues that will stand hardening. It has been used as a preliminary reagent in a number of techniques employed for nervous tissue. Tissues fixed in it should be transferred to 70 per cent alcohol after twelve hours' treatment with the formalin solution. Shrinkage often occurs later during paraffin embedding, using the alcohol and xylol sequence but with dioxan there is little shrinkage or hardening.

*Carnoy's Fluid.*—The formula is: 75 cc. of 100 per cent alcohol and 25 cc. of glacial acetic acid. This fixing fluid fixes chromosomes well, precipitates glycogen, but usually dissolves chondriosomes and the Golgi apparatus. It penetrates quickly, so that an hour serves to fix soft pieces of 1 cm. in thickness. It combines the effects of two chemicals, the alcohol causing precipitation of the proteins and glycogen of the cytoplasm; the acetic acid fixing the nucleo-proteins and preventing some of the shrinkage and hardening of the alcohol. Tissues should be washed in absolute alcohol after fixation before proceeding to embed.

**Containers.**—As containers for the fixative and excised material, it will be found advantageous to use wide-mouthed bottles of 1- or 2-ounce capacity provided with cork stoppers. In order that the fixative may reach all parts of the surface of the material, it is well to place a small pad of gauze in the bottom of each bottle to prevent the tissue from adhering to the glass, and so keeping one surface from free contact with the fixing fluid. Or the tissue may be suspended in a gauze bag from the cork. The bottle should be well filled with the fixative so that there will be many times the volume of the tissue to be fixed.

**Dissection.**—Pieces of tissue should be small. This is important for good fixation. Generally, pieces 0.5 to 1 cm. in thickness can be used. The length and breadth of the piece should likewise be kept to the smallest practical size. The pieces should be handled as little as possible with dissecting instruments and care should be taken not to compress them during dissection. The operator should keep in mind that he is later going to make sections of these pieces, and should remove material from the desired portion of the organ in the proper manner for longitudinal, cross-, or tangential sections. The selected pieces can be transferred from the animal to the bottles of fixing fluid with a spatula, or lifted lightly with forceps, without permitting the instruments to enter the fluid. If dissection is prolonged, it is advisable to keep the organs of the freshly killed animal

moistened with the proper physiological saline solution (0.85 per cent sodium chloride for mammals; 0.7 per cent for amphibians).

**Foreign Matter.**—In fixing parts of the alimentary canal, it is necessary to remove the contents of the lumen. This may be done by washing out with physiological saline before cutting out pieces for the fixing fluid. Or fixing fluid may be forced under gentle pressure into the lumen of the canal with a pipette. If the bladder is dilated with urine, the neck of the bladder can be ligated, and then the entire bladder removed and placed in a beaker of fixing fluid for a few minutes to stiffen the wall in the extended position. The bladder then can be opened, emptied, and so cut that fixative can freely come in contact with the internal surface. The stomach can be handled in the same fashion. Or a small strip of stomach wall can be placed on a strip of stiff paper and thus immersed in the fixative for a few minutes, and then, when stiffened in the extended condition, it can be removed from the paper and entirely immersed in fixative. Pieces of artery or nerve can likewise be placed extended on a paper strip, and this placed in fixative until the pieces are stiff enough to be removed from the paper for further fixation.

**Heat.**—Fixatives are ordinarily used at room temperatures, but the effect is hastened by increasing the temperature. Heat itself is a coagulant of protoplasm, and its effect must be considered in addition to the action of the fixative itself. It will be found that the final picture obtained by different temperatures of the same fixative and the same material will show certain differences, and these modifications should be checked carefully.

**Records.**—One of the most important things to remember is to keep a careful record of the material, the organ or part of the organ removed, the age and sex of the animal, the fixative used, the time of fixation, and any modifying conditions, such as health of the animal and method of killing.

These details may be kept in a note-book and corresponding code number placed with the fixed material, or the entire information may be recorded on the slip that accompanies the fixed material. The writing on these slips should be done with a soft pencil. To avoid confusion, do not place many tissues together in a bottle. It is wiser to place not more than three small pieces in each bottle so that no difficulty later arises in identifying them for further steps in the technique.

## PARAFFIN EMBEDDING

After the proper length of time needed for fixation with each of the fluids described above, the fixed tissue should be thoroughly washed free of all fluid fixative remaining and usually is preserved in 70 per cent (or 80 per cent) alcohol. The next problem is to prepare the material for cutting sections which, after proper staining, can be studied microscopically for their structural organization. Prior to the development of modern technical processes, the early workers cut thin slices, free hand, with a sharp knife or razor. However, a piece of fresh or fixed tissue "gives" when sections are cut in this manner, and the material is more or less crushed. This is avoided if the tissue is infiltrated with paraffin. Paraffin is solid at room temperatures, but a simple yet somewhat time-consuming technique enables one to satisfactorily impregnate the tissue piece with paraffin. This is accomplished as follows:

**Alcohol-Xylol Method.**—Paraffin is not miscible with water, so that all water must be removed from the tissues. To accomplish this, the 70 per cent alcohol in which the piece of tissue has been kept is discarded and 80 per cent alcohol replaces it. After an hour or so the 80 per cent is discarded and replaced with 95 per cent alcohol. An hour or so later this is changed to 100 per cent alcohol. This has no water in it, and when diffused through the tissue, water will have been removed. This process of dehydration must not be too rapid or distortion, caused by too rapid withdrawal of water, may occur. The alcohol may also exert an effect on some of the proto-plasmic substances which have been preserved but not precipitated or coagulated by the fixatives. Tissues should not remain too long in the higher alcohols, *i. e.*, 95 and 100 per cent.

Paraffin does not mix with alcohol; therefore, some other common chemical must be employed that is miscible with alcohol and paraffin which can be used to transfer the object from alcohol to paraffin. Xylol or benzene can be used for this purpose. Xylol is preferable, since it is not so inflammable as benzene, although benzene causes less shrinkage than xylol. Therefore, transfer the tissue from 100 per cent alcohol to a mixture of equal parts of 100 per cent and xylol for a certain period (one hour); then change to pure xylol for one to two hours; then pure xylol and paraffin for a similar period. If the paraffin used has a melting-point of 50° to 52° C., then the mixture of xylol and paraffin must be kept at a temperature not far below this to keep the mixture in solution and so enable it to diffuse all through the tissue. It should be remembered that there must be no free water left in the tissue. So far it is infiltrated with a mixture of one-half xylol and one-half paraffin.

This mixture is discarded and the bottle is filled with pure melted paraffin at a temperature just above its melting-point, *i. e.*, 55° C.

In order to maintain the paraffin in a liquid condition, the supply of melted paraffin and the specimen bottles containing tissues being embedded are kept in a constant temperature oven, called a paraffin oven. A readily improvised unit can be made by using an electric light bulb with a shield which will fit over a tin can sufficiently large to hold the paraffin containers used for embedding. After a certain length of time (one hour) the first supply of paraffin is discarded and replaced with fresh paraffin and placed back in the oven for another hour. It is essential to remove all traces of xylol and to have the pure paraffin diffuse all through the tissue. It is advisable to change the paraffin again and leave one-half hour in the oven.

A paper boat is made or a glass dish (Syracuse dish) is coated with glycerin and the piece or pieces of tissue are quickly poured, together with the paraffin, into the dish or boat. This assures no hardening of paraffin, over the surface of the tissues, due to transfer through air to a filled dish. If the orientation is to be a slow process it will be nec essary to warm the embedding dish before pouring in the paraffin and tissue. With warmed forceps the tissue piece is quickly and properly oriented with a view to the type of sections to be made later. Then a surface film of solid paraffin is produced by blowing across the top of the dish, and the container is gently immersed in cold water for a time, until the paraffin hardens throughout homogeneously and quickly. In a few minutes the hardened paraffin block can be removed and stored indefinitely in this form or prepared for sectioning. If the weather is very warm, or if the technique is carried out in a warm room, one should use a higher melting-point paraffin, while a lower melting-point paraffin is suitable for use in winter or under colder conditions. If very thin sections are required, one must use a harder (higher melting-point) paraffin than if thicker sections are to be made. Ordinarily it is wise to avoid heating the tissue any higher than absolutely necessary in order to avoid the hardening and shrinking effect of heat, so that 58° C. represents a maximum temperature for the paraffin bath.

In the foregoing account of dehydration we passed from 95 per cent alcohol to 100 per cent alcohol and from this to xylol. Since 100 per cent alcohol is expensive, it can be dispensed with by the use of aniline oil. This is cheaper and does not harden or shrink the tissues. The following tables explain the two procedures: It is understood that the tissue has been properly fixed, washed free of fixative, and has been stored in 70 per cent alcohol.

## PROCEDURE

| *Absolute Alcohol Method* | *Aniline Oil Method* |
|---|---|
| 80 per cent alcohol, one hour | ½—80 per cent + ½ aniline, one hour |
| 95 per cent alcohol, one hour | ½—95 per cent + ½ aniline oil, one hour |
| 100 per cent alcohol, one hour | Aniline oil (until translucent), one hour |
| ½—100 per cent + ½ xylol, one hour | ½ aniline + ½ xylol, one hour |
| Xylol, one hour | Xylol, one hour |
| Fresh xylol, one hour | Fresh xylol, one hour |

½ xylol + ½ melted paraffin, one hour and kept in warm place so that the paraffin remains melted

Pure melted paraffin (about 52° to 56° C. m.p.) in the paraffin oven, one hour

Change the paraffin and keep specimen in oven, one hour

Change the paraffin again and keep specimen in oven for about one hour.

Embed as directed above

Toluol is an excellent substitute for xylol and tissues can be left in it for longer periods. Furthermore, it is more volatile and therefore more readily lost during paraffin transfers.

**Dioxan Method.**—A new fluid, diethylene oxide, called dioxan, has been introduced as a substitute for the alcohol and xylol steps in the paraffin embedding procedure. This fluid is colorelss, volatile and inflammable. It mixes with water, alcohol, xylol or paraffin. Care should be taken in handling and inhalation avoided. Dioxan should be kept in tightly stoppered bottles and a quantity of anhydrous calcium chloride may be added to keep it free of water, especially after use. Fixed material may be carried directly to dioxan from the fixative or from subsequent water or alcoholic solutions. The following schedule of minimum times is recommended either following the fixative or subsequent water or alcoholic solutions.

1. Dioxan I . . . . . One to two hours
2. Dioxan II . . . . . One hour (tissues may also be left in pure dioxan for long periods if tightly stoppered)
3. Dioxan III . . . . One-half to one hour
4. Pure paraffin . . . . One hour (an intermediate step of a toluol or xylol-paraffin mixture may be introduced before this step, if pieces are large or infiltrate with difficulty)
5. Pure paraffin II . . . One-half to one hour
6. Pure paraffin III . . . One-half to one hour and embed

Since the dioxan may be used several times it is convenient to place tissues in a gauze bag after removing from the fixative and suspend them from the cork of the container with the dioxan. In this manner the tissue may be changed from corked vial or bottle by simply changing the corks. The bags may be carried through the first two changes of paraffin by hooking over the container mouth and in the last change of paraffin the bag may be cut open before immersing in the melted paraffin. This method permits exposure of all sides of the tissue to fluids better than when the pieces rest upon the bottom of the containers, and likewise eliminates the

waste and carry over of fluids involved in decanting each fluid into the container of fixed materials.

**Celloidin Embedding.**—For material which is tougher, or which demands a technique which does not involve heating, a slower method of embedding in celloidin, instead of paraffin, has been devised. It has the advantage of causing less shrinkage and distortion but does not permit such thin sections to be easily cut. Only single sections are made at a time, and so the handling of large numbers of sections is more time-consuming than is the case with paraffin sections. Solutions of celloidin in an ether-alcohol mixture are utilized in celloidin infiltration.

Celloidin is furnished in small solid pieces. Remove all the pieces from a 1-ounce bottle, dry them thoroughly, and place in a glass-stoppered bottle, adding about 150 cc. of absolute ethyl alcohol and 150 cc. of sulphuric ether. Stopper the bottle and keep the stopper free of the solution at all times. It will take several days before the celloidin has completely dissolved. This will make a stock solution of concentrated celloidin, which we will call the No. 1 solution. When it is in complete solution, make stock solution No. 2 by diluting part of No. 1 with about three times as much of equal parts of absolute alcohol and ether. Also make stock solution No. 3 by diluting solution No. 1 with about ten times as much of equal parts of absolute alcohol and ether. Keep a supply of each of these three solutions on hand, taking care that each is kept in a tightly stoppered bottle, as evaporation of the ether-alcohol soon changes a thin solution to a thicker one.

Tissue in Bouin's or Zenker's fluid can be embedded in celloidin as well as those especially designed for nerve study. It is well to use thin pieces, *i. e.*, about 0.3 cm. thick, because infiltration proceeds slowly and with difficulty. Each successive fluid presently named must penetrate the tissue piece, and as the size is increased the time needed must be extended. It is suggested that the student at first use a piece of soft tissue, such as the liver, about 0.5 by 0.5 by 0.3 cm., and follow the longer time period given in the following table. We will suppose that the tissue has been fixed in Bouin's fluid, washed, and taken from 70 per cent alcohol, where it has been preserved. The process takes place at room temperature and in bottles that can be tightly stoppered. The time can be shortened by keeping tightly covered bottles at a temperature of 50° C.

### Slow Celloidin Infiltration

In this method the various steps are carried out at room temperature. Tissues are taken from the fixative or following water or weak alcohol solution to 70 per cent alcohol. Then as follows:

1. Ninety-five per cent alcohol, two hours.
2. Fresh 95 per cent alcohol, one hour.
3. Absolute alcohol, two hours.
4. Fresh absolute alcohol, twelve to twenty-four hours.
5. One-half absolute alcohol + one-half ether, twelve hours.
6. Celloidin No. 3 (thin), three to four days.
7. Celloidin No. 2 (medium), four to six days.
8. Celloidin No. 1 (thick), five to eight days.

### Rapid Celloidin Infiltration

The slow method may be greatly speeded up by using small screw- or clamp-topped pressure jars, which may be kept in the oven at about 50° C. By this method, the dehydration and infiltration are reduced to the following times:

1. Ninety-five per cent alcohol, one hour.
2. Absolute alcohol, one hour.
3. Fresh absolute alcohol, one hour.
4. One-half absolute alcohol + one-half ether, two hours.
5. Celloidin No. 3, two hours.
6. Celloidin No. 2, four hours, or over-night.
7. Celloidin No. 1, two hours.

*Embedding.*—At the end of either the slow or rapid method, the tissues should be infiltrated with celloidin and one of the following methods may be used for embedding.

1. Fashion a little paper receptacle and fill it with celloidin No. 1. A test for proper consistency, is to hold the stock bottle upside down for two minutes by which time a bulge of celloidin should appear in the center of the free surface but should not drip. Add one or two pieces of dry celloidin until this condition is reached. Add but a few drops at first and wait a moment until they thicken, add a few more drops, and then fill the receptacle. The tissue piece is then placed in the box and arranged properly, with a view to plane of sections to be cut later. The surface of the celloidin rapidly forms a film when exposed to the air. Evaporation of the solvent (ether-alcohol), with consequent hardening, should be permitted to proceed slowly until the celloidin mass is like a heavy gum in consistency. The paper receptacle is now carefully transferred to a covered glass dish containing chloroform, and hardening is completed. The chloroform causes the cellodin to harden sufficiently in one to two hours, when the paper box and excess celloidin can be cut away and the embedded block can be placed in a bottle of one-half 95 per cent alcohol + one-half glycerin until ready for cutting.

2. The other method both embeds and mounts the tissue preparatory to sectioning. Vulcanized fiber blocks formed to fit the clamp of the microtome should be used. Do not use wood blocks. The solvent in the celloidin mixture extracts oils from wood and these discolor the preparation. A strip of stiff paper is fastened about one end of the fiber block so that a receptacle is formed at this end. Celloidin No. 1 is added, drop by drop, to this receptacle, covering the bottom of it with a relatively solid coat which is allowed to thicken before filling the receptacle with celloidin from the specimen bottle. The tissue is transferred also and oriented in the celloidin which covers it on all sides. The celloidin is then permitted to harden somewhat in the air, as in the first case, and then the block with the celloidin-filled receptacle is transferred to a covered dish of chloroform. After hardening in chloroform the block is stored as in the first procedure.

If the first method was used it is necessary to fasten the celloidin block to a fiber block before cutting sections. To do this thick celloidin (No. 1) is poured over one end of the fiber block and over one end (bottom) of the celloidin block. The two are pressed together; the celloidin at the junction is hardened in the air until it is thick, then in the chloroform as before.

## SECTIONING

As soon as material is properly embedded, one may proceed directly to cutting sections for staining. Machines, called microtomes (from the Greek, "to cut small"), have been devised and can be regulated to cut sections of desired thickness easily and uniformly. Two general types of microtomes are in common use: one, working on a rotary principle, is called a rotary microtome, and the other, cutting by sliding movements, is known as the sliding microtome. The rotary type is suited for cutting paraffin embedded material, while celloidin material is sectioned with the sliding mictrotome, although the latter may be used for paraffin material also.

**Rotary Microtomes and Paraffin Sections.**—The following information should be supplemented by classroom demonstration in the use of the machine and also by considerable actual experience in section cutting by each student. Small metal discs or wooden blocks are furnished to which the paraffin block may be attached. These supports can be then fastened into a holding device in the microtome.

Suppose that you have a disc of paraffin containing three pieces of embedded tissue. One of these is cut out of the disc by means of a warm scalpel blade, leaving plenty of paraffin around the tissue. To fasten this paraffin block to metal disc or wood block, an old scalpel blade is heated so that it will easily melt paraffin. The blade is then held against the metal disc or paraffined end of a wood block, and then the paraffin piece is pressed against the other surface of the blade. The blade is withdrawn and the melted paraffin thus produced hardens and seals the paraffin block to the metal or wood holder. It is advisable to place each mounted tissue in cold water for a few minutes to completely harden the paraffin.

The next step is to trim the paraffin block containing the tissue. Some of the extra paraffin about the object is cut away, so that the piece is in the shape of a truncated pyramid, with the base toward the wood block or metal. The paraffin at the free end is trimmed down until little is left between the free face and the tissue. The free face should be rectangular or square in form, and the angles between adjacent edges should be right angles. (Fig. 223.)

It is an easy matter to prepare a considerable number of small wood blocks and these can be furnished to all the students who can proceed to mount embedded material and have it ready for sectioning. Or if one has a good many paraffin blocks to section, it is more efficient to mount all on wood blocks at one time and store them in

boxes properly labeled for sectioning later. Storing trimmed paraffin blocks of embedded tissues in water a week or more before
cutting makes cutting easier and prevents brittleness and cracking
of the tissue.

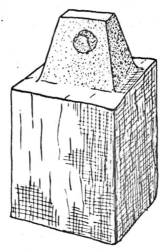

Fig. 223.—Diagram illustrating paraffin block ready for sectioning.

The clamp holding the mounted paraffin-wood block is attached
to a movable part of the microtome that is connected with a finely
threaded screw. The turn of the wheel turns the screw and advances the part holding the paraffin block. It will be noted that
in this process the paraffin block rises and falls. Each machine
has a setting device by which the thickness of the sections can be
arranged. The setting device has a rather wide range of adjustment, but sections 10 microns thick are made in general work in
microscopic anatomy. The special microtome knife, or an adapter
for safety razor blades, is held in a clamp that can be moved by
hand, but must be locked rigidly in place while sectioning. Suppose
the setting device is adjusted for sections 10 microns thick, and
the wheel is turned. Between the time that the paraffin block
passes above the knife edge and then descends to it on the down
stroke, the paraffin block has advanced forward exactly 10 microns,
but does not advance after the tissue passes below the knife edge.
So a section 10 microns thick is cut from the top surface of the
paraffin block each time on the down stroke. However, the position
of the paraffin block must be correct and the trimmed end should
have the form of a rectangle or square. When the knife is placed
in the knife-holder, the back face of the knife should make a slightly
acute angle with the plane of the table. The lower edge of the face

of the paraffin block should be exactly parallel with the edge of the knife. The knife-holder should be advanced so that the edge of the knife is nearly in contact with the descending block of tissue and then locked. The wheel of the machine is then turned and sections begin to be cut. If conditions are correct, each section will remain with its upper edge just along the front cutting edge of the knife. When the next section is cut, its lower edge will fuse with the upper edge of the previous section. Thus a ribbon of sections is formed.

### KEY TO DIFFICULTIES IN SECTIONING

| *Fault in the sections* | *Cause of difficulties or damages in sections* |
|---|---|
| 1. Curling to right or left. | a. Block not correctly oriented with knife.<br>b. Block not trimmed properly so that sides are parallel and at right angles. |
| 2. Breakage and crumbling of sections. | a. Tissue too hard due to faulty infiltration or too much heat. See (c).<br>b. Knife inclined too much.<br>c. If tissue is hard this may be counteracted by soaking in water before cutting. |
| 3. Longitudinal splitting of sections. | a. Nicks in the knife.<br>b. Dirt on the knife edge.<br>c. Cracks, bubbles or hard particles in paraffin; calcium salts, crystals or hard material in tissue. |
| 4. Compression of sections (normally should be about the same size as face of the block). | a. Knife dull or dirty.<br>b. Inclination too great or too little.<br>c. Paraffin too soft.<br>d. Temperature too high (both knife and room conditions too warm).<br>e. Poor infiltration. |
| 5. Static (electrification of sections so that they adhere to knife or other objects). | a. Too great difference in density of material and paraffin in which embedded.<br>b. Tissue too hard. Poor infiltration.<br>c. Dull knife.<br>d. Atmospheric conditions. |
| 6. Irregularities in the thickness of consecutive sections. | a. Knife loose in holder.<br>b. Block loose.<br>c. Carrying arm of microtome at extreme end, or beginning, of thrust.<br>d. Speed of cutting too variable. |
| 7. Sections roll up and fail to form ribbon. | a. Paraffin too hard and cut too thick.<br>b. Inclination of knife too great.<br>c. Temperature too low. |
| 8. Sections adhere to the blade | a. Knife dirty or dull.<br>b. Knife not inclined enough.<br>c. Knife or block too warm. |
| 9. Object separates from the paraffin. | a. Imperfect infiltration of paraffin or failure to remove all of other solvents.<br>b. Object not properly embedded—hardening of surface paraffin about object permitted in process of orientation or transfer. |

21

One *could* cut a ribbon many feet in length. However, it is more convenient to make one about 10 inches in length and then transfer this to a shallow paper box. To do this, the outer end is supported with a section-lifter held in the left hand while cutting. When the desired length is cut, the end next to the knife is carefully lifted off with a scalpel or section-lifter and the length of ribbon placed carefully in the paper box. When the next ribbon is cut, it is laid alongside the first in the box and so on, until the desired number of sections are obtained. If one desires to study all parts of an organ, such as the submaxillary gland, it is necessary to save all the ribbon sections and all the sections can be mounted in regular order, thus making a complete series of slides covering the entire microanatomy of that organ. Ribbons of sections stored away in shallow drawers or paper boxes can be kept indefinitely provided they are stored in a cool, dust-proof place. If kept in a warm room or one which becomes very warm on hot summer days, there is a tendency for the thin paraffin to melt, and the ribbons may become attached to the bottom of the receptacle in which they are stored.

**The Sliding Microtome and Celloidin Sections.**—In the sliding microtome the knife is mounted in a holder that fits over the smooth surface of the slide. The position of the knife may be fixed by the screws that clamp down on the handle. The fiber block with the attached celloidin block containing the embedded tissue is fastened into the clamp at one side of the slide over which the knife is carried. The clamp holding the embedded block is connected with a device which is essentially a fine-threaded screw to which a micrometer is attached. When the micrometer disc is properly turned a certain distance, the screw lifts up the embedded block a certain definite distance above the cutting edge of the knife. The knife must be arranged at an oblique angle with the line of the slide carriage. Both knife and embedded block are kept moistened with 70 per cent alcohol through the sectioning process. The knife is drawn past the celloidin block with the right hand. One can determine by means of the micrometer disc how far to turn the screw, and so determine the thickness of the sections to be cut. The strokes of the knife should be smooth and rapid. The knife should have been correctly sharpened to secure good sections. Sections of from 10 to 30 microns are usually cut, but with practice thinner ones may be obtained. Single sections are obtained by this method, and these must be transferred with a camel's-hair brush as they are cut to a dish containing 70 per cent alcohol.

**Frozen Sections.**—The freezing of tissues was introduced at an early date to give support for sectioning and this method is an extremely useful one for rapid results required in clinical laboratories and also in techniques where it is necessary to avoid the alcohols or clearing agents such as xylol. Material may be frozen as removed in a fresh condition and then fixed, or fixed material may be thoroughly washed in water and then frozen for sectioning. A 10 per cent formalin solution is most commonly used for fixing. To accomplish the freezing, an attachment is available for the sliding microtome which permits the expansion of $CO_2$ in a small disc upon

which the material is placed. The $CO_2$ is released from a small cylinder into the chamber below the tissue and rapidly lowers the temperature of the metal so that the tissue is frozen to the top of the chamber. A similar result may be obtained by surrounding a metal mounting disc with "dry ice" (solid $CO_2$) and placing the tissue upon it. A special container for dry ice mounting is available. A few minutes suffice to freeze the tissue to the disc. It is possible to get tissue frozen too hard and, in this case, sections will curl. The knife must be kept cold to prevent sections from sticking. A saturated sugar solution is recommended to prevent ice crystals forming in fresh tissue. Sections are cut on the sliding microtome by cutting straight across the tissue instead of at an angle as for celloidin. Sections are collected from the knife and placed in water or, if not already fixed, placed in 10 per cent formalin before proceeding to staining. To stain the sections, the same sequence of solutions may be used as in treating paraffin sections which have already been brought down to water, or the collected sections may be stored in 80 per cent alcohol until a later date, then stained and mounted either in glycerin medium or dehydrated and mounted in gum dammar.

**Mounting Paraffin Sections.**—After paraffin sections have been cut and transferred to a paper box, the next step is to attach them to slides. The sections as they come from the microtome are usually slightly compressed or wrinkled, due to the pressure as they cross the knife. This must be remedied when the sections are attached to the slides. In the first place the slides must be thoroughly clean so that no dirt or grease particles are on their surfaces They can be cleaned by boiling in soap and water, thoroughly rinsed in water, then rinsed in 95 per cent alcohol, and dried with a clean cloth free from lint or dust. Next, the sections must be made to adhere to the slide to permit the subsequent steps of the staining technique. A solution of equal parts of carefully strained egg-white and glycerin is used as an adhesive. A small amount of thymol or methyl salicylate added to the adhesive mixture prevents disintegration by bacterial action. A common method of applying the egg-albumen adhesive is as follows: A small drop about the size of the head of a pin is placed in the center of one surface of the slide, and this drop is carefully smeared over the surface with the ball of the little finger that has been thoroughly washed. A few drops of distilled water is then added to the surface. Then a small piece of ribbon containing one or two sections of the tissue is cut from the long ribbon with a scalpel and transferred to the water over the egg albumen on the slide. It is advisable to use water that has been boiled (and cooled) to avoid bubbles gathering between the slide and the sections. The ribbon piece should be arranged parallel with the length of the slide. Two or even three small ribbon pieces may be arranged alongside each other. The same surface that is upward when the ribbon comes from the microtome should be upward on the slide. The under side is more shiny than the upper. After the ribbon pieces have been arranged, the slide can then be transferred to a warming table, the surface of which is kept at a temperature of about 45° C. or a little less. More water can be added to float the sections but not enough to run off the slide. The gentle heat warms the paraffin enough so that the surface tension of the water will pull the sections out flat. Sometimes sections are badly folded, and in that case one can carefully pull them out flat when the slides are on the warming table. However, such sections are never as satisfactory as those which are comparatively flat when received from the microtome. The excess water may be carefully removed after the tissue is expanded. Care should be taken that no air bubbles are left under the sections, since the sections are free from the glass at such points and may later fall off the slides or make uneven places in the stained and mounted sections. The heat used in flattening the section should not be great enough to liquefy the paraffin of the ribbon pieces.

A second scheme for fastening sections to slides is to make a solution of 1 part of egg-albumen fixative to 500 parts of cool boiled water. This thin adhesive is added directly to a clean slide, with a pipette, and the ribbon pieces floated on it; the remainder of the process is similar to the foregoing. A third method is to fill a large shallow vessel with water which has been warmed to about 45° C. Small pieces of ribbon are floated on the water. It will be noted that they flatten out immediately. Then a clean slide lightly smeared with egg-albumen fixative can be lowered under such a ribbon piece to remove it. After draining away the excess water and arranging the section, the slide can be set aside until all the water has evaporated. Good results are obtained from badly wrinkled sections by this method.

In all three cases, the slides should be set aside in a dry place until all the water has evaporated before staining; usually this should be about twenty-four hours.

**Serial Sections.**—After becoming proficient in cutting sections, the student may wish to cut an entire organ into sections and mount these in order. When finally prepared one can study the micro-anatomy of the organ from one end to the other. Usually transverse or longitudinal sections are made. If there is a right and left gland, cross-sections can be made from one and longitudinal from the other. The attempt should be given up if the tissue does not section well. We will suppose that it has been possible to make complete ribbon cross-section of the entire organ, and these have been placed in order in the paper boxes.

If many sections are to be mounted, the student can use larger slides. After the slide is labelled and the albumen added, then, beginning at the front end of the series of sections, one removes a strip *less* than 2 inches (1½ inches) in length, since some expansion occurs with relaxation. Carefully place this strip along the edge of the upper surface of the slide. Then below this, the next strip, and so on. Leave an empty space, about 0.5 cm., along each lateral margin. Place the slide on the warming table, add water, orient, and dry as in single mounts. The number of sections one can get on a slide depends on the size of each section. After completing the mounting of Slide 1, proceed with 2 and remember to label it. Proceed until all the sections are mounted.

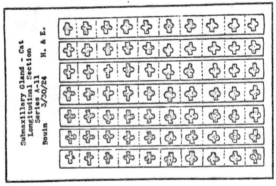

Fig. 224.—Diagram of a preparation of serial sections.

## STAINING

Thin sections of fresh living material examined with the aid of a microscope appear homogeneous, since there is little optical differentiation of cellular structures. Similar examination of fixed tissues which have been cleared reveal more details of structure and organization. These are brought out most distinctly and definitely, however, by the proper treatment of the sections with various dye solutions. The color of the dye or stain is adsorbed, absorbed, or chemically held by the different elements of the cell protoplasm in a characteristic manner. Early studies revealed the fact that the nucleus is acid in reaction and has an affinity for basic dyes, while the cytoplasm is basic and has an affinity for acid dyes. When two dyes, one acid and one basic, are used on tissues, the nuclei and the cytoplasm are differently colored, so that a differential staining effect is obtained. Differentiation of various protoplasmic elements has been the aim of numerous staining techniques, so that it is now possible to employ special processes to demonstrate such cellular structures as centrioles, cell membranes, chondriosomes, Golgi apparatus, secretion granules, fat droplets, nucleoli, chromosomes, chromidia, glycogen, elastic fibers, Nissl bodies, and many others. These special techniques can be found in the references given in the bibliography and may be experimented with after the student has become familiar with the more common general methods used to demonstrate tissue organizations.

**Progressive Staining of Paraffin Sections.**—In progressive staining the object is to treat the sections with the stains until the tissue has the proper color. This is determined by observing the progress of the staining under the microscope at short intervals during the procedure. It is not advisable to stain too deeply, since later removal is never altogether satisfactory, although it is possible. In the following method we will employ Harris' hematoxylin as a nuclear stain and eosin as a cytoplasmic stain.

After preparing the nuclear and cytoplasmic stains, it is necessary to assemble a series of jars just large enough to hold the slides and in sufficient numbers to contain all the reagents needed. Shell vials, a little over 1 inch in diameter and about 4 inches long, are useful for the beginner. The Coplin jar is a more useful vessel, since it can accommodate at least five slides at one time. Fourteen of these jars will be found adequate. The fluid in each should extend about 2 inches from the bottom, so that the upper third of the slide will be free of fluid.

Following is a list of jars and the fluid in each: (1) Xylol; (2) aniline oil; (3) 95 per cent alcohol; (4) 70 per cent alcohol; (5) 50 per cent alcohol; (6) distilled or tap water; (7) hematoxylin stain (one-half stock solution, one-half water); (8) water; (9) 50 per cent alcohol; (10) 70 per cent alcohol; (11) eosin in 70 per cent alcohol; (12) 95 per cent alcohol; (13) aniline oil; (14) xylol.

When using paraffin sections the paraffin must be removed before proceeding, since paraffin does not mix with either alcohol or water, and the dyes are dissolved in the latter. The slide is placed in the xylol jar for about three minutes, during which time the paraffin will dissolve. *After this step the sections should never be permitted to remain out of the fluids until permanently prepared.* After the xylol, the slide is drained of free xylol and placed in the aniline oil jar for two minutes, then drained and placed in the 95 per cent alcohol for two minutes, and similarly in the 70 per cent, 50 per cent, and water for two minutes each.

The slide is placed in the hematoxylin stain for three to five minutes, then rinsed in water and examined under the microscope. The section should have a rich purple or blue appearance. Microscopic examination should show a purplish chromatin network in the nuclei of the preparation. If the general appearance is a light

lavender, the section is understained. It should then be placed in the stain for a minute or so more and reexamined. If the section appears dark purple it is probably overstained. In progressive staining it is desirable to stain until just the right effect has been produced and then to stop further staining by placing the section in water. If overstained, the excess can be extracted by placing the slide in 70 per cent alcohol to which a drop or so of hydrochloric acid has been added. When the correct staining effect has been attained without extraction the slide should be rinsed in water made slightly alkaline by addition of a small amount of sodium bicarbonate or lithium carbonate. After rinsing, the slide is placed in 50 per cent alcohol for a minute or so, then in 70 per cent alcohol for two minutes. It is next placed in the cytoplasmic stain, such as eosin, from which it should be removed and rinsed in 95 per cent alcohol and examined for the cytoplasmic stain effect which should not be too deep in color. Then the slide is placed in aniline oil for two minutes, drained, and placed in xylol for two minutes, and placed in the first xylol jar for two minutes more. The purpose of the two xylol baths is to prevent carrying over any aniline which would stain the final preparation. The student should have at hand a bottle of Canada balsam, or gum dammar, dissolved in xylol to a relatively thick viscous consistency but thin enough to flow easily.

*A*                    *B*

FIG. 225.—Two methods of affixing a cover glass.

Clean and thoroughly dry cover-glasses should also be ready. A pair of fine forceps will also be needed. The slide is then taken from the second xylol jar, the undersurface wiped dry, placed on filter paper on the table and 1 or 2 drops of the gum dammar placed over the section which should *not* be permitted to dry at any point of the procedure. A cover-glass is lifted with the forceps and carefully lowered over the section. It is well to let one edge of the cover-glass rest at the side of the slide and then to let it fall gently by its own weight over the section, thus preventing air bubbles from collecting under the cover. (Fig. 225 *A*.) Another method may be used in which the balsam is added to the cover-glass and the slide lowered until the section touches the drop of balsam which will spread and lift the cover-glass to seal it to the slide, without introducing air bubbles. (Fig. 225 *B*.) After the section has thus been covered, it may be placed on the warming table or in a warm oven for some hours in order that the xylol in the gum mixture may evaporate and thus harden the gum. The hard gum has the same optical refraction as the slide and cover, and so allows light to pass through without refraction and also seals the cover to the slide.

After the gum has hardened the slide can be cleaned by dipping in toluol, draining, and permitting to dry. However, the cover should not be rubbed until the gum has thoroughly hardened. Other mounting media are available, such as balsam, clarite, diaphane, and euparal; the last two permit of mounting from alcohols. Glycerin and glycerogel permit mounting from water.

Dioxan may be introduced as a substitute for the alcohols and clearing agents but xylol is more efficient as the first step for removing paraffin and as the last before mounting in the gum dammar.

**Regressive Staining.**—In this technique the sections are far overstained at first and then excess stain is extracted until just the right effect is produced. An excellent example of a well-tried stain for this purpose is the so-called Heidenhain's hematoxylin. It is highly recommended for differentiation of mitotic figures and is, therefore, indicated for studies in cell division, spermatogenesis, and oögenesis. Two solutions are used, a mordant and the stain.

To proceed with staining, the slides are placed first in xylol and brought down, as before, through aniline oil to water. The slides are then placed in a 4 per cent iron alum solution for at least one-half hour for thorough mordanting. Then the slides are washed thoroughly in water and placed in the hematoxylin stain (0.5 per cent solution) for one to several hours. They will appear deep black if the staining has been effective and no details are at all evident upon microscopic examination. After rinsing in water they are placed in a 2 per cent iron alum solution for extracting excess stain, and after a minute or so examined under the microscope. It is an advantage to have the extraction take place slowly. They should be rinsed, examined, and returned if the stain is still too deep. The de-staining may also be carried out under the microscope in a glass Petri dish containing the 2 per cent alum. The chromatic network in the nucleus should appear sharply outlined. If one has a metaphase stage in mitosis, the chromosomes, should appear clear-cut. When the extraction has gone far enough, it can be stopped by washing the slides in water to remove every trace of the free alum solution. Then the slides are "run up" through 50 per cent alcohol to 70 per cent alcohol. They can be counterstained in a solution of orange G or eosin in 70 per cent alcohol, as in the pre-

ceding techniques. They are then transferred to 95 per cent alcohol, aniline oil, and xylol, as before, and later mounted.

**The Mallory Connective Tissue Stain.**—This stain gives a colorful effect with sections that contain considerable connective tissue, muscle, and epithelium. Two solutions are needed. Solution A is a 0.5 per cent solution of acid fuchsin in distilled water. Solution B is 0.5 gram aniline blue (water soluble) and 2 grams orange G in 100 cc. of 1 per cent aqueous solution of phosphomolybdic acid or phosphotungstic acid, the latter prevents fading of fuchsin. The stain works better with tissues that have been fixed in Zenker's fluid. After the sections have been brought down, as before, from xylol to water, they are placed in Solution A (acid fuchsin) for about four minutes. The time in A and B must be varied until a satisfactory result is obtained with the materials in use. Then this is drained off and the slides are placed at once in Solution B for about eight minutes. They are then rinsed several times in 95 per cent alcohol; it is better to use more than one jar of 95 per cent. Then proceed to aniline oil, xylol, and mount as before. Connective tissue, muscle, and epithelium stain differentially, the prominent colors being blue, red, and yellow.

**Staining Celloidin Sections.**—Assuming that a piece of tissue fixed in Bouin's or Zenker's solution has been embedded in celloidin and that sections of such a piece have been cut with a sliding microtome and collected in a dish in 70 per cent alcohol; these sections can be stained in the Harris hematoxylin and eosin combination as follows: Discard the 70 per cent for 50 per cent alcohol and change this to water, each bath lasting a few minutes. After the sections have been washed in water, the water can be discarded and the dish filled with hematoxylin stain. A section can be lifted out occasionally to determine the degree of staining. When the stain has taken sufficiently, it is replaced with water. From this they pass to 50 per cent alcohol; to 70 per cent alcohol; to eosin or orange G for counterstaining; to 95 percent alcohol; to absolute alcohol (to prevent any dissolution of celloidin, add 1 cc. of chloroform for each 10 cc. of alcohol and stir as sections are added); to cedar oil or oil of origanum. Merely decant off the liquid in the dish each time and then replace it with the next liquid. At the last step transfer a stained and cleared section to a slide with a spatula and, having added 1 or 2 drops of Canada balsam, apply a coverglass.

**Staining Frozen Sections.**—These may be treated in the same manner as celloidin sections except that the aniline oil or absolute alcohol step is followed by two changes of xylol, instead of cedar oil. Or sections may be mounted from water or alcohol in glycerogel or glycerin.

# BIBLIOGRAPHY

## PERIODICALS

The following periodicals are usually available in most libraries and should be referred to by the student wishing to follow the results of past and also current contributions to microscopic anatomy and closely related subjects.

*American Journal of Anatomy*
*Anatomical Record*
*Biological Abstracts*
*Biological Bulletin*
*Endocrinology*
*Folia hematologica*
*Journal of Comparative Neurology*
*Journal of Experimental Zoölogy*
*Journal of Morphology*
*Quarterly Review of Biology*
*Science*
*Stain Technology*
*Zoölogical Record*

## ANATOMICAL TEXTS

The following are a few texts which will be found useful for reference:

ADAMS, A. L. 1938. An Introduction to the Vertebrates, 2d ed., New York, John Wiley & Sons.

AREY, L. B. 1940. Developmental Anatomy, 4th ed., Philadelphia, W. B. Saunders Company.

DANIEL, J. F. 1934. The Elasmobranch Fishes, 3d ed., Berkeley, Calif., Univ. California Press.

ECKER, A. 1889. The Anatomy of the Frog, Oxford, England, Clarendon Press.

GOODRICH, E. S. 1930. Structure and Development of Vertebrates, New York, The Macmillan Company.

HOLMES, S. J. 1927. The Biology of the Frog, 4th ed., New York, The Macmillan Company.

HYMAN, LIBBIE HENRIETTA. 1942. Comparative Vertebrate Anatomy, Chicago, Univ. Chicago Press.

KAUP, B. G. 1918. The Anatomy of the Domestic Fowl, Philadelphia, W. B. Saunders Company.

KINGSLEY, J. S. 1926. Outline of Comparative Anatomy of Vertebrates, Philadelphia, The Blakiston Co.

NEAL, H. V., and RAND, H. W. 1936. Comparative Anatomy, Philadelphia, The Pakiston Company.

(330)

NOBLE, K. G. 1931. Biology of the Amphibia, New York, McGraw-Hill Company.

WALTER, H. E. 1939. Biology of the Vertebrates, 2d ed., New York, The Macmillan Company.

WEISS, PAUL. 1939. Principles of Development, New York, Henry Holt Company.

## HISTOLOGICAL TEXTS

The following textbooks will be found useful for additional reference and illustrations:

BREMER, J. L. 1944. A Textbook of Histology, 6th ed., Philadelphia, P. Blakiston's Son & Co.

COWDRY, E. V. 1928. Special Cytology, New York, Paul B. Hoeber, Inc., 2 vols.

——— 1944. A Textbook of Histology, 3d ed., Philadelphia, Lea & Febiger.

DAHLGREN, U., and KEPNER, W. A. 1928. Principles of Animal Histology, New York, The Macmillan Company.

JORDAN, H. E. 1937. A Textbook of Histology, 7th ed., New York, D. Appleton & Co.

KRAUSE, RUDOLPH. 1921–1923. Mikroskopische Anatomie der Wirbeltiere, Berlin and Leipzig, Walter de Gruyter & Co.

MAXIMOW, A. A., and BLOOM, W. 1942. A Textbook of Histology, 4th ed., Philadelphia, W. B. Saunders Company.

RAMON-CAJAL, S. 1933. Histology, Baltimore, William Wood & Co.

SCHAFER, E. S. 1938. Essentials of Histology, 14th ed., Philadelphia, Lea & Febiger.

SMITH, PHILIP E., and COPENHAVER, WILFRED M. 1944. Bailey's Textbook of Histology, 11th ed., Baltimore, The Williams & Wilkins Company.

WEATHERFORD, HAROLD L. 1944. Bremer's Textbook of Histology, 6th ed., Philadelphia, The Blakiston Company.

## CHAPTER I

### INTRODUCTION

BENSLEY, R. R., and GERSCH, I. 1933. Studies on cell structure by the freezing-drying method, Anat. Rec., 57, 369.

BENSLEY, R. R., and HOERR, N. L. 1934. The chemical basis of the organization of the cell, Anat. Rec., 60, 251.

——— 1934. The preparation and properties of mitochondria, Anat. Rec., 60, 449.

COWDRY, E. V. 1924. General Cytology, Chicago, Ill., Univ. Chicago Press.

DEMPSEY, EDWARD W., and WISLOCKI, GEORGE B. 1946. Histochemical contributions to physiology, Phys. Reviews, 26, 1.

GRAY, J. 1931. Experimental Cytology, Cambridge, England, Cambridge Univ. Press.

HEMPELMANN, LOUIS H. 1940. Staining reactions of the mucoproteins, Anat. Rec., 78, 199.

HIBBARD, HOPE, and LAVIN, GEORGE I. 1945. A study of the Golgi apparatus in the chicken gizzard epithelium by means of the quartz microscope, Biol. Bull., 89, 157.

LEWIS, F. T. 1928. The effect of cell division on the shape and size of hexagonal cells, Anat. Rec., 38, 341.

MURNAGHAN, DONAL P. 1941. Studies on living spinal ganglion cells, Anat. Rec., 81, 183.

SCHRADER, F. 1934. On the reality of spindle fibers, Biol. Bull., **67**, 519.

SEIFRIZ. 1936. Protoplasm, New York, McGraw-Hill Company.

WILLIAMS, MYRA A. 1943. Mitochondria in the intestinal epithelial cells of starved and fed salamanders, Anat. Rec., **85**, 195.

WILSON, E. B. 1928. The Cell, New York, The Macmillan Company.

WORLEY, LEONARD G. 1944. Studies of the vitally stained Golgi apparatus, Jour. Morph., **75**, 261.

# CHAPTER II

## THE EPITHELIAL TISSUES

AREY, L. B., and COVODE, W. M. 1943. The method of repair in epithelial wounds of the cornea, Anat. Rec., **86**, 75.

BOWEN, R. H. 1929. The cytology of glandular secretion, Quart. Rev. Biol., **4**, 299.

BRAUER, A. 1926. The regeneration of transitional epithelium, Anat. Rec., **33**, 137.

CHAMBERS, R., and RENYI, G. S. 1925. The structure of the cells in tissues as revealed by microdissection: I. The physical relationships of cells in epithelia, Am. Jour. Anat., **35**, 385.

COWDRY, E. V., and THOMPSON, HENRY C., JR. 1944. Localization of maximum cell division in epidermis, Anat. Rec., **88**, 403.

FLOREY, H., CARLETON, H. M., and WELLS, A. G. 1932. Study of alterations in epithelia, Brit. Jour. Exp. Pathol., **13**, 269.

GAEBLER, O. H. 1921. Bladder epithelium in contraction and distention, Anat. Rec., **20**, 129.

HAMILTON, HOWARD L. 1940. A study of the physiological properties of melanophores with special reference to their rôle in feather coloration, Anat. Rec., **78**, 525.

THURINGER, J. M. 1924-1928. Mitotic activity in stratified epithelium, Anat. Rec., **28**, 31; **40**, 1.

TRIBBY, C. L. 1943. The intracellular lipin, mucoid, and glycogen of the vaginal epithelium of the guinea pig, Anat. Rec., **86**, 425.

# CHAPTER III

## THE CONNECTIVE TISSUES

ALLEN, LANE. 1945. A quantitative study of tissue fluid, Anat. Rec., **92**, 279.

AREY, L. B. 1932. Certain basic principles of wound healing, Anat. Rec., **51**, 299.

BARDEN, ROBT. B. 1942. The origin and development of the chromatophores of the amphibian eye, Jour. Exp. Zoöl., **90**, 479.

BAST, I. H. 1944. Perichondral ossification and the fate of the perichondrium with special reference to that of the otic capsule, Anat. Rec., **90**, 139.

BATES, EDISON O. 1935. A quantitative study and interpretation of the occurrence of basophile (mast) cells in the subcutaneous tissues of the albino rat, Anat. Rec., **61**, 231.

BENSLEY, S. H. 1934. On the presence, properties and distribution of the intercellular ground substance of loose connective tissue, Anat. Rec., **60**, 93.

BLOOM, WILLIAM, BLOOM, MARGARET A., and McLEAN, FRANKLIN C. 1941. Calcification and ossification: Medullary bone changes in the reproductive cycle of female pigeons, Anat. Rec., **81**, 443.

———— 1942. Calcification and ossification: The formation of medullary bone in male and castrate pigeons under influence of sex hormones, Anat. Rec., **83**, 99.

CARREL, A., and EBELING, A. 1926. Fibroblast and macrophage, Jour. Exp. Med., **44**, 261, 285.

CHANG, CHUN. 1940. Some observations on the pre-adipose cells, Anat. Rec., **77**, No. 3.

DODDS, G. S. 1932. Osteoclasts and cartilage removal in endochondral ossification of certain mammals, Am. Jour. Anat., **50**, 97.

DUSHANE, G. P. 1939. The rôle of embryonic ectoderm and mesoderm in pigment production in Amphibia, Jour. Exp. Zoöl., **82**, 193.

GLÜCKSMANN, ALFRED. 1939. Studies on bone mechanics *in vitro*, Anat. Rec., **73**, 39.

HAMM, FRANCIES DORRISS. 1942. The growth and migration of cultured melanophores from the neural crest when grafted into the embryo, Jour. Exp. Zoöl., **90**, 101.

HEMPELMANN, LOUIS H. 1940. Staining reactions of the mucoproteins, Anat. Rec., **78**, 199.

IASSWOIN, G. 1935. On the formation of the ground substance of loose connective tissue, Quart. Jour. Micr. Sci., **78**, 271.

JORDAN, H. E. 1939. A study of fibrillogenesis in connective tissue by the method of dissociation with potassium hydroxide, with special reference to the umbilical cord of pig embryos, Am. Jour. Anat., **65**, 229.

LACROIX, P. 1945. On the origin of the diaphysis, Anat. Rec., **92**, 433.

LEWIS, W. H. 1922. Is mesenchyme a syncytium? Anat. Rec., **23**, 177.

OSBORN, C. M. 1939. The physiology of color change in flatfishes, Jour. Exp. Zoöl., **81**, 479.

PAYTON, C. G. 1932. The growth in length of long bones of the madder-fed pig, Jour. Anat., **66**, 414; **67**, 371.

SINGER, E. 1933. Structure and relations of the leucophores of Rana pipiens as revealed by the ultra-violet and fluorescent light, Anat. Rec., **58**, 93.

STEARNS, M. L. 1940. Studies on the development of connective tissue in transparent chambers in the rabbit's ear, Am. Jour. Anat., **66**, 133.

———— 1940. Studies on the development of connective tissue in the transparent chambers in the rabbit's ear, Am. Jour. Anat., **67**, 55.

SUMNER, F. B., and WELLS, N. A. 1933. The effects of optic stimuli upon the formation and destruction of melanin pigment in fishes, Jour. Exp. Zoöl., **64**, 377.

WOLBACH, S. B. 1937. Vitamin deficiency experimentation as a research method in biology, Science, **86**, 569.

## CHAPTER IV

### THE BLOOD

BACSICH, P. 1936. On the staining of lipoid granules in leucocytes, Jour. Anat., **70**, 267.

DAWSON, A. B. 1932. The reaction of the erythrocytes of vertebrates, especially fishes, to vital dyes, Biol. Bull., **63**, 48.

DEBRUYN, P. P. H. 1944. Locomotion of blood cells in tissue cultures, Anat. Rec., **89**, 43.

FORKNER, C. E. 1929. Blood and bone marrow cells of the domestic fowl, Jour. Exp. Med., **50**, 121.

JORDAN, H. E., and FLIPPER, J. C. 1913. Hematopoiesis in chelonia, Folia hæmatol., **15**, 1.

JORDAN, H. E., and SPEIDEL, C. C. 1924. The origin, function, and fate of the lymphocytes in fishes, Jour. Morphol., **38**, 529.

———— 1930. Blood formation in Cyclostomes, Am. Jour. Anat., **216**, 355.

———— 1931. Blood formation in the African lungfish, under normal conditions and under conditions of prolonged estivation and recovery, Jour. Morphol., **51**, 319.

JORDAN, H. E. 1932. The histology of the blood and the blood-forming tissues of the Urodele (Proteus anguineus), Am. Jour. Anat., 51, 215.
——— 1933. The evolution of blood-forming tissues, Quart. Rev. Biol., 8, 58.
——— 1934. Extramedullary erythrocytopoiesis in man, Arch. Path., 18, 1.
——— 1934. The transformation of adipose tissue into hemocytopoietic tissue, Anat. Rec., 59, 461.
——— 1939. The lymphocytes in relation to erythrocyte production, Anat. Rec., 73, 227.
KINDRED, J. E. 1932. A study of the tinctorial reaction of hemoglobiniferous cells, Russell body cell, plasma cells and lymphocytes of the albino rat by a new method of selective staining, Anat. Rec., 53, 43.
MAYERSON, H. S. 1930. The blood cytology of dogs, Anat. Rec., 47, 239.
McDONALD, J. G. 1939. Avian bone marrow with particular reference to red cell development, Am. Jour. Anat., 65, 291.
REDFIELD, A. C. 1933. The evolution of the respiratory function of the blood, Quart. Rev. Biol., 8, 58.
RYERSON, DWIGHT L. 1943. Separation of the two acidophilic granulocytes of turtle blood with suggested phylogenetic relationship, Anat. Rec., 85, 25.
SABIN, F. 1928. Bone-marrow, Physiol. Rev., 8, 191.
SCHARRER, ERNST. 1944. The histology of the meningeal myeloid tissue in the ganoids Amia and Lepisosteus, Anat. Rec., 88, 291.
STASNEY, J., and HIGGINS, G. M. 1935. A quantitative cytologic study of the bone marrow of the adult albino rat, Anat. Rec., 63, 77.
YOFFEY, J. M., and DRINKER, C. K. 1939. The cell content of the peripheral lymph and its bearing on the problem of the circulation of the lymphocyte, Anat. Rec., 73, 417.

## CHAPTER V

### THE MUSCLE TISSUES

BOZLER, EMIL. 1938. Physiological evidence for the syncytial character of smooth muscle, Science, 86, 476.
CARR, R. W. 1931. Muscle tendon attachment in the striated muscle of the fetal pig, Am. Jour. Anat., 99, 1.
GOSS, C. M. 1944. The attachment of skeletal muscle fibers, Am. Jour. Anat., 74, 259.
HALL, C. E., JAKUS, M. A., and SCHMITT, F. O. 1946. An investigation of cross striations and myosin filaments in muscle, Biol. Bull., 90, 32.
JORDAN, H. E. 1934. Structural changes during contraction in striped muscle of the frog, Am. Jour. Anat., 55, 117.
KATZNELSON, Z. S. 1934. Histogenesis of muscle in Amphibia: 1. Development of striated muscle from mesenchyme in urodeles, Anat. Rec., 61, 109.
LEWIS, M. R., and LEWIS, W. H. 1917. The contraction of smooth muscle cells in tissue cultures, Am. Jour. Physiol., 44, 67.
LLOYD, W. 1930. The form and function of the auriculo-ventricular bundle in the rabbit, Am. Jour. Anat., 45, 379.
MATHER, V., and HINES, M. 1934. Studies in the innervations of skeletal muscle: The limb muscle in the newt, Triturus torosus, Am. Jour. Anat., 54, 177.
MENEELY, G. R. 1939. The microscopic appearance of contractures of striated muscle, Anat. Rec., 75, 39.
POLLISTER, A. 1932. Mitosis in non-striated muscle eclls, Anat. Rec., 53, 11.
SPEIDEL, C. C. 1939. Histological changes in single fibers of striated muscle during contraction and clotting, Am. Jour. Anat., 65, 471.
ZSCHIESCHE, E. S., and STILWELL, E. F. 1934. Intercalated discs of the heart of the guinea-pig, Anat. Rec., 60, 477.

## CHAPTER VI

### THE NERVE TISSUE

ANDREW, WARREN, and ASHWORTH, CHARLES T. 1944. Morphological similarity of neuroglia fibers to fibers of other connective tissues, Am. Jour. Anat., 75, 329.

BAILEY, P., and HELLER, G. 1924. The interstitial tissue of the nervous system: a review, Jour. Nerv. and Ment. Dis., 59, 337.

BARTELMEZ, G. W. 1920. The morphology of the synapse in vertebrates, Arch. Neurol. and Psychiat., 4, 122.

BARTELMEZ, G. W., and HOERR, N. L. 1933. The vestibular club endings in Ameirus: Further evidence on the morphology of the synapse, Jour. Compt. Neurol., 57, 401.

BENSLEY, SYLVIA. 1944. Cytological studies of the reaction of myelinated nerve fibers to section of the nerve, Anat. Rec., 90, 1.

BODIAN, DAVID. 1936. A new method for staining nerve fibers and nerve endings in mounted paraffin sections, Anat. Rec., 65, 89.

CANNON, W. B. 1939. The argument for chemical mediation of nerve impulses, Science, 90, 521.

CAREY, EBEN J. 1941. Experimental pleomorphism of motor end plates as a mode of functional protoplasmic movement, Anat. Rec., 81, 393.

DE RENYI, G. S. 1931. The structure of cells in tissue as revealed by microdissection: V. The physical properties of nerve cells of the frog, Jour. Comp. Neurol., 53, 497.

DOUGHERTY, THOMAS F. 1944. Studies on the cytogenesis of microglia and their relation to cells of the reticulo-endothelial system, Am. Jour. Anat., 74, 61.

DUSHANE, G. P. 1938. Neural fold derivatives in the Amphibia: pigment cells, spinal ganglia and Rohon-Beard cells, Jour. Exp. Zoöl., 78, 485.

HOERR, N. L. 1936. The preëxistence of neurofibrillæ and their disposition in the nerve fibers, Anat. Rec., 66, 81.

———— 1936. The structure of the myelin sheath of nerve fibers, Anat. Rec., 66, 91.

JONES, D. S. 1939. Studies on the origin of sheath cells and sympathetic ganglia in the chick, Anat. Rec., 73, 343.

LEE, F. C. 1936. A study of the Pacinian corpuscle, Jour. Comp. Neurol., 64, 497.

LEVI, GUISEPPE, and MEYER, HERTHA. 1945. Reactive, regressive and regenerative processes of neurons cultivated *in vitro* and injured with the micromanipulator, Jour. Exp. Zoöl., 99, 141.

MATHER, V., and HINES, M. 1934. Studies in the innervation of skeletal muscle: V. The limb muscle of the newt, Triturus torosus, Am. Jour. Anat., 54, 177.

MURNAGHAN, DONAL P. 1941. Studies on living spinal ganglion cells, Anat. Rec., 81, 183.

MURRAY, MARGARET R., and STOUT, ARTHUR PURDY. 1942. Characteristics of human Schwann cells *in vitro*, Anat. Rec., 84, 274.

PALAY, SANFORD L. 1944. The histology of the meninges of the toad (Bufo), Anat. Rec., 88, 257.

PARKER, G. H. 1935. Neurohumors: Novel agents in the action of the nervous system, Science, 81, 279.

RAWDON-SMITH, A. F. 1939. Theories of Sensation, New York, The Macmillan Company.

SAUER, F. C. 1935. Mitosis in the neural tube, Jour. Comp. Neurol., 62, 377.

———— 1935. The cellular structure of the neural tube, Jour. Comp. Neurol., 63, 13.

SPEIDEL, C. C. 1935. Studies of living nerves, Biol. Bull., **68**, 140.
———— 1936. Studies of living nerves. V. Alcoholic neuritis and recovery, Jour. Comp. Neurol., **64**, 77.
WEISS, PAUL. 1944. *In vitro* transformation of spindle cells of neural origin into macrophages, Anat. Rec., **88**.
———— 1945. Experiments on cell and axon orientation *in vitro:* The rôle of colloidal exudates in tissue organization, Jour. Exp. Zoöl., **100**, 353.

## CHAPTER VII

### THE VASCULAR SYSTEM

CHAMBERS, ROBERT, and ZWEIFACH, B. W. 1944. Topography and function of the mesenteric capillary circulation, Am. Jour. Anat., **75**, 173.
———— 1946. Functional activity of the blood capillary bed with special reference to visceral tissue, Annals of N. Y. Acad. Sciences, **46**, 683.
CLARK, E. R., and CLARK, E. L. 1939. Microscopic observations on the growth of blood capillaries in the living mammal, Am. Jour. Anat., **64**, 251.
———— 1940. Microscopic observations on the extra-endothelial cells of living mammalian blood vessels, Am. Jour. Anat., **66**, 1.
DRINKER, C K. 1946. Extravascular protein and the lymphatic system, Annals of the New York Acad. Sciences, **46**, 807.
DRINKER, C. K., and FIELD, M. E. 1933. Lymphatics, Lymph and Tissue Fluid, Baltimore, The Williams & Wilkins Company.
KROGH, A. 1929. The Anatomy and Physiology of Capillaries, New Haven, Conn., Yale Univ. Press.
NICOLL, PAUL A., and WEBB, RICHARD L. 1946. Blood circulation in the subcutaneous tissue of the living bat's wing, Annals of the New York Acad. Sciences, **46**, 697.
ROGERS, J. B. 1932. Observations on the pericapillary cells in the mesenteries of rabbits, Anat. Rec., **54**, 1.
SANDISON, J. C. 1931. Observations on the circulating blood cells, adventitial (Rouget) and muscle cell, endothelium and macrophages in the transparent chamber of the rabbit's ear, Anat. Rec., **50**, 355.
SHIPLEY, P. G., and CUNNINGHAM, R. S. 1916. The histology of the blood and lymphatic vessels during the passage of foreign fluids through their walls, Anat. Rec., **11**, 181.
ZWEIFACH, B. W. 1934. A micromanipulative study of blood capillaries, Anat. Rec., **59**, 83.
———— 1939. The character and distribution of the blood capillaries, Anat. Rec., **73**, 475.

## CHAPTER VIII

### THE LYMPHATIC SYSTEM

DE BRUYN, P. P. H. 1945. The motion of the migrating cells in tissue cultures of lymph nodes, Anat. Rec., **93**, 295.
DOWNEY, H. 1922. The structure and origin of the lymph sinuses of mammalian lymph nodes and their relations to endothelium and reticulum, Hæmatologica, **3**, 31.
DRINKER, C. K., and JOFFEY, J. M. 1941. Lymphatics, Lymph and Lymphoid Tissue, Cambridge, Mass., Harvard Univ. Press.
EHRLICH, WM. E. 1946. The rôle of the lymphocyte in the circulation of lymph, Annals of the New York Acad. Sciences, **46**, 823.
EMMART, E. W. 1936. A study of the histogenesis of the thymus *in vitro,* Anat. Rec., **66**, 59.
JAMES, E. S. 1939. The morphology of the thymus and its changes with age in the neotenous amphibian (Necturus maculosus), Jour. Morphol., **64**.
JOB, T. T. 1922. Studies on lymph nodes, Am. Jour. Anat., **31**, 125.

JORDAN, H. E. 1934. Hemal nodes in man, Anat. Rec., **59**, 297.
————— 1935. The significance of the lymphoid nodule, Am. Jour. Anat., **57**, 1.
JORDAN, H. E., and ROBESON, J. M. 1942. The production of lymphoid nodules in the bone marrow of the domestic pigeon following splenectomy, Am. Jour. Anat., **71**, 181.
KENT, G. C. 1939. Epidermal concentric corpuscles and their significance in the interpretation of the corpuscles of Hassall: Triturus, Anat. Rec., **75**, 275.
KINGSBURY, B. F. 1932. The developmental significance of the mammalian pharyngeal tonsil: cat, Am. Jour. Anat., **50**, 201.
KRUMBHAAR, E. B. 1926. Functions of the spleen, Physiol. Rev., **6**, 160.
MYERS, M. A. 1928. A study of the tonsillar developments in the lingual region of anurans, Jour. Morphol. and Physiol., **45**, 399.
ROTHERMEL, J. E. 1930. A note on the megakaryocytes of the normal cat's spleen, Anat. Rec., **47**, 251.
WEBB, RICHARD L., and NICOLL, PAUL A. 1944. Behavior of lymphatic vessels in the living bat, Anat. Rec., **88**, 351.

## CHAPTER IX

### THE INTEGUMENT

ALVEY, C. H. 1932. The epidermal "glands" of Ceratodus and Protopterus, Anat. Rec., **54**, 91.
BENTLEY, F. H. 1936. Wound healing *in vitro*, Jour. Anat., **70**, 498.
BROWN, M. W. 1939. The migratory behavior of frog epidermis, with special reference to surface polarity and to factors determining direction of movement, Jour. Exp. Zoöl., **81**, 91.
CAMERON, J. A. 1936. The origin of new epidermal cells in the skin of normal and x-rayed frogs, Jour. Morphol., **59**, 327.
COWDRY, E. V., and THOMPSON, HENRY C., JR. 1944. Localization of maximum cell division in epidermis, Anat. Rec., **88**, 403.
DAWSON, A. B. 1920. The integument of Necturus maculosus, Jour. Morphol., **34**, 487.
————— 1936. Changes in the lateral-line organs during the life of the newt, Triturus viridescens, Jour. Exp. Zoöl., **74**, 221.
————— 1937. Changes in the volume, form, and internal architecture of the nuclei of the granular glands of the integument of the newt, Triturus viridescens, Jour. Morphol., **61**, 385.
DAWSON, H. L. 1930. A study of hair growth in the guinea-pig (Cavia cobaya), Am. Jour. Anat., **45**, 461.
HAMILTON, HOWARD L. 1940. A study of the physiological properties of melanophores with special reference to their rôle in feather coloration, Anat. Rec., **78**, 525.
HERRICK, E. H. 1933. The structure of epidermal melanophores in frog tadpoles, Biol. Bull., **64**, 304.
JUHN, M., and FRAPS, R. M. 1936. Developmental analysis in plumage: I. The individual feather, Physiol. Zoöl., **9**, 293.

## CHAPTER X

### THE RESPIRATORY SYSTEM

BREMER, J. L. 1939. Evidence of an epithelial lining in the labyrinth of the avian lung, Anat. Rec., **73**, No. 4.
————— 1940. The pneumatization of the humerus in the common fowl and the associated activity of theelin, Anat. Rec., **79**, 197.
HAM, ARTHUR W., and BALDWIN, KATHARINE W. 1941. A histological study of the development of the lung with particular reference to the nature of alveoli, Anat. Rec., **81**, 363.

KROGH, AUGUST. 1941. Comparative Physiology of Respiratory Mechanisms, Philadelphia, Univ. of Pennsylvania Press,

LIVINGSTON, E. J. 1935. The nature of the pulmonary alveolar lining, Anat. Rec., **62**, 147.

LOOSLI, C. 1938. The structure of the respiratory portion of the mammalian lung with notes on the lining of the frog lung, Am. Jour. Anat., **62**, 375.

MACKLIN, C. C. 1929. The musculature of the bronchi and lungs, Physiol. Rev., **9**, 1.

MILLER, W. S. 1947. The Lung, Baltimore, 2nd Ed., Charles C Thomas.

OLKON, D. M., and JOANNIDES, M. 1930. Capillaroscopic appearance of the pulmonary alveoli in the living dog, Anat. Rec., **45**, 121.

ROSTORFER, HOWARD H. 1942. The gas content of the swimbladder of the rock bass, Amblopletes Rupestris, in relation to hydrostatic pressure, Biol. Bull., **82**, 138.

STEWART, F. W. 1923. An histogenic study of the respiratory epithelium, Anat. Rec., **25**, 181.

WHITEHEAD, W. H., WINDLE, W. F., and BECKER, R. F. 1942. Changes in lung structures during aspiration of amniotic fluid and during air breathing at birth, Anat. Rec., **83**, 255.

WISLOCKI, G. B. 1935. The lungs of the Manatee (Trichechus latirostris) compared with those of other aquatic mammals, Biol. Bull., **68**, 385.

## CHAPTER XI

### THE DIGESTIVE SYSTEM

BEAMS, H. W., and KING, R. L. 1932. Notes on the cytology of the parietal cells of the stomach of the rat, Anat. Rec., **53**, 31.

BLAKE, I. H. 1930. Studies on the comparative histology of the digestive tube of certain Teleost fishes: I. A predaceous fish, the sea bass (Centropristes striatus), Jour. Morphol., **50**, 39.

———— 1936. III. A bottom-feeding fish, the sea robin (Prionotus carolinus), Jour. Morphol., **60**, 77.

CAWSTON, F. G. 1938. Succession of teeth in sharks, Selachii, Brit. Dent. Jour., **65**, 573.

DAWSON, ALDEN B. 1945. Argentaffin cells of the gastric mucosa of the rabbit, guinea pig, mouse and hamster, Anat. Rec., **91**, 53.

FISH, H. S., MALOW, P. D., and RICHTER, C. P. 1944. The anatomy of the tongue of the domestic Norway rat: I. The skin of the tongue, the various papillæ; their number and distribution, Anat. Rec., **89**, 429.

FRIEDMAN, M. H. F., and ARMOUR, J. C. 1936. Gastric secretion in the groundhog (Marmota monax) during hibernation, Jour. Cell. and Comp. Physiol., **8**, 201.

GLASSTONE, S. 1936. The development of tooth germs in vitro, Jour. Anat., **70**, 260.

GOMORI, G. 1939. Studies on the cells of the pancreatic islets, Anat. Rec., **74**.

GRANT, RHODA. 1945. Rate of replacement of surface epithelial cells of the gastric mucosa, Anat. Rec., **91**, 175.

HAMMOND, W. S. 1939. On the origin of the cells lining the liver sinusoids in the cat and the rat, Am. Jour. Anat., **65**, 199.

HARD, WALTER L. 1944. The origin and differentiation of alpha and beta cells in the pancreatic islets of the rat, Am. Jour. Anat., **75**, 369.

JORDAN, H. E. 1931. The pigment content of the liver cells of urodeles, Anat. Rec., **48**, 351.

NOYES, F. B. 1938. A Textbook of Dental Histology and Embryology, Including Laboratory Directions, Philadelphia, Lea & Febiger.

O'LEARY, J. S. 1930. An experimental study on the islet cells of the pancreas in vivo, Anat. Rec., **45**, 27.

RAMSAY, A. J., THOMAS, J. E., and CRIDE, J. D. 1943. Changes in the acinar cells of the pancreas in response to the presence of peptone in the small intestine, Anat. Rec., **86**, 87.

ROGICK, M. D. 1931. Studies on the comparative histology of the digestive tubes of certain Teleost fishes: II. A minnow (Campostoma anomalum), Jour. Morphol., **52**, 1.

SHARPLES, WYNNE. 1945. The histogenesis of the argentaffin cells in the stomach and duodenum of the rat, Anat. Rec., **91**, 107.

SIMARD, L. C., and VAN CAMPENHOUT, E. 1932. The embryonic development of argentaffin cells in the chick intestine, Anat. Rec., **53**, 141.

## CHAPTER XII

### THE EXCRETORY SYSTEM

CHASE, S. W. 1923. The mesonephros and urogenital ducts of Necturus maculosus (Rafinesque), Jour. Morphol., **37**, 457.

CRABTREE, CHARLOTTE. 1941. The structure of Bowman's capsule as an index of age and sex variations in normal mice, Anat. Rec., **79**, 395.

DEFRISE, A. 1932. Cytophysiological studies of the nephrocytes of unisegmental aglomerular and glomerular nephrons, Anat. Rec., **54**, 185.

EDWARDS, J. G. 1928. Studies on aglomerular and glomerular kidneys, Am. Jour. Anat., **42**, 75.

————— 1923. The renal unit in the kidney of vertebrates, Am. Jour. Anat., **53**, 55.

————— 1935. The epithelium of the renal tubule in bony fish, Anat. Rec., **63**, 263.

GÉRARD, POL. 1936. Comparative histophysiology of the vertebrate nephron, Jour. Anat., **70**, 354.

GRAFFLIN, A. L., and MOSES, J. E. 1934. A microfluoroscopic study of teleostean kidney, Anat. Rec., **59**, 449.

GRAY, P. 1930. The development of the Amphibian kidney: Part I. The development of the mesonephros of Rana temporaria, Quart. Jour. Micr. Sci., **73**, 508.

HOLTON, S. G., and BENSLEY, R. R. 1931. The function of the differentiated parts of the uriniferous tubule in the mammal, Am. Jour. Anat., **47**, 241.

KIRKMAN, HADLEY, and STOWELL, R. E. 1942. Renal filtration surface in the albino rat, Anat. Rec., **82**, 373.

SINGER, E. 1934. Observation of the frog's kidney with the fluorescence microscope, Am. Jour. Anat., **53**, 469.

STEEN, W. B. 1934. Special secretory cells in the transverse ducts of the frog's kidney, Anat. Rec., **61**, 45.

STROER, W. F. H. 1932. The development of the pronephros in the common perch (Perca fluviatilis L.), Quart. Jour. Micr. Sci., **75**, 557.

## CHAPTER XIII

### FEMALE REPRODUCTIVE SYSTEM

ALDEN, ROLAND H. 1942. The oviduct and egg transport in the albino rat. Anat. Rec., **84**, 137.

DAWSON, ALDEN B. 1941. The development and morphology of the corpus luteum of the cat, Anat. Rec., **79**, 155-169.

DAWSON, ALDEN B., and KOSTERS, BETTY ANN. 1944. Preimplantation changes in the uterine mucosa of the cat, Am. Jour. Anat., **74**, 1.

DEMPSEY, E. W. 1939. Maturation and cleavage figures in ovarian ova, Anat. Rec., **75**, 223.

EVERETT, JOHN W. 1945. The microscopically demonstrable lipids of cyclic corpora lutea in the rat, Am. Jour. Anat., **77**, 293.

GREULICH, W. W. 1934. Artificially induced ovulation in the cat, Felix domesticus, Anat. Rec., **58**, 217.

HAMLETT, G. W. D. 1935. Extra-ovarial sex cords on an armadillo ovary, Anat. Rec., **62**, 195.

HILL, R. T., ALLEN, E., and KRAMER, T. C. 1935. Cinemicrographic studies of rabbit ovulation, Anat. Rec., **63**, 239. .

KINGSBURY, B. F. 1939. Atresia and the interstitial cells of the ovary, Am. Jour. Anat., **65**, 309.

LANE, C. E. 1939. The ovary of the adult rat: I. Changes in growth of the follicle and in volume and mitotic activity of the granulosa and theca during the estrous cycle, Anat. Rec., **73**, 429.

MYERS, H. I., YOUNG, W. G., and DEMPSEY, E. W. 1936. Graafian follicle development throughout the reproductive cycle in the guinea pig, with special reference to changes during œstrus (sexual receptivity), Anat. Rec., **65**, 381.

REEDER, E. M. 1939. Cytology of the reproductive tract of the female bat, Myotis lucifugus lucifugus, Jour. Morphol., **64**, 431.

RUGH, R. 1935. Ovulation in the frog, Jour. Exp. Zoöl., **71**, 163.

SWINGLE, W. W. 1926. The germ cells of anurans, Jour. Morphol. and Physiol., **41**, 441.

TURNER, C. L. 1938. Histological and cytological changes in the ovary of *Cymatogaster aggregatus* during gestation, Jour. Morphol., **62**, 351.

VON BONE, CECIL. 1945. Stages in the development of the picked or spiny dogfish, Squalus acanthias Linn, Biol. Bull., **88**, 220.

WARREN, D. C., and SCOTT, H. M. 1934. Ovulation in the domestic hen, Science, **80**, 461.

WISLOCKI, GEORGE B., and DEMPSEY, EDWARD W. 1945. Histochemical reactions of the endometrium in pregnancy, Am. Jour. Anat., **77**, 365.

WOLF, L. E. 1931. The history of the germ cells in the viviparous Teleost, Platypœcilus maculatus, Jour. Morphol., **52**, 115.

## CHAPTER XIV

### MALE REPRODUCTIVE SYSTEM

ADAMS, A. E. 1940. Sexual conditions in Triturus viridescens. III. The reproductive cycle of the adult aquatic form of both sexes, Am. Jour. Anat., **66**.

DEYSACH, L. J. 1939. The comparative morphology of the erectile tissue of the penis with special emphasis on the probable mechanism of erection, Am. Jour. Anat., **64**, 111.

GRAY, J. C. 1937. The anatomy of the male genital ducts in the fowl, Jour. Morphol., **60**, 393.

HANN, H. W. 1930. Variation in spermiogenesis in the Teleost family, Cottidæ, Jour. Morphol., **50**, 393.

HOOKER, C. W. 1938. Regeneration of testis in the fowl, and its bearing on germ cell theory, Anat. Rec., **72**, 371.

JUHN, M., and GUSTAVSON, R. G. 1932. The response of a vestigial Müllerian duct to the female hormone and the persistence of such rudiments in the male fowl, Anat. Rec., **52**, 299.

McCURDY, H. M. 1931. Development of the sex organs in Triturus torosus, Am. Jour. Anat., **47**, 367.

MILLER, R. E. 1939. The reproductive cycle in male bats of the species Myotis lucifugus lucifugus and Myotis grisescens, Jour. Morphol., **64**, 267.

MOORE, C. R. 1926. The biology of the mammalian testis and scrotum, Quart. Rev. Biol., **1**, 4.

———— 1945. Prostate gland induction in the female opossum by hormones and the capacity of the gland for development, Am. Jour. Anat., **76**, 1.

POLLOCK, WILLIAM F. 1942. Histochemical studies of the interstitial cells of the testes, Anat. Rec., **84**, 23–30.

RASMUSSEN, A. T. 1917. Seasonal changes in the interstitial cells of the testis in the woodchuck (Marmota monax), Am. Jour. Anat., **22**, 475.

REESE, A. M. 1924. The structure and development of the intromittent organ of the Crocodilia, Jour. Morphol., 38, 301.

RUGH, R. 1939. The reproductive processes of the male frog, Rana pipiens, Jour. Exp. Zoöl., 80, 81.

SWIFT, C. H. 1916. Origin of the sex-cords and definitive spermatogonia in the male chick, Am. Jour. Anat., 20, 375.

TOOTHILL, M. C., and YOUNG, W. C. 1931. The time consumed by spermatozoa in passing through the ductus epididymis of the guinea-pig as determined by means of India ink injections, Anat. Rec., 50, 95.

## CHAPTER XV

### ENDOCRINE GLANDS

ADAMS, H. E., KUDER, A., and RICHARDS, L. 1932. The endocrine glands and molting in Triturus viridescens, Jour. Exp. Zoöl., 63, 1.

ALLEN, E., DANFORTH, C. H., and DOISY, E. A. 1939. Sex and Internal Secretions, 2d ed., Baltimore, The Williams & Wilkins Company.

ALTLAND, P. D. 1939. Cytology of the hypophysis of the fence lizard, Anat. Rec., 74, 109.

APPLINGTON, HENRY W., JR. 1942. Correlative cyclical changes in the hypophysis and gonads of Necturus maculosus Rafinesque, Am. Jour. Anat., 70, 201.

ATWELL, WAYNE J. 1941. The morphology of the hypophysis cerebri of toads, Am. Jour. Anat., 68, 191.

BENNETT, H. STANLEY. 1941. Cytological manifestation of secretion in the adrenal medulla of the cat, Am. Jour. Anat., 69, 333.

CHARIPPER, H. A., and HATERIUS, H. O. 1932. The histology of the anterior pituitary of the albino rat in relation to the œstrus cycle, Anat. Rec., 54, 15.

DEROBERTIS, E. 1942. Intracellular colloid in the initial stages of thyroid activation, Anat. Rec., 84, 125.

GERSH, I. 1939. The structure and function of the parenchymatous glandular cells in the neurohypophysis of the rat, Am. Jour. Anat., 64, 407.

GILBERT, M. S. 1934. The development of the hypophysis: Factors influencing the formation of the pars neuralis in the cat, Am. Jour. Anat., 54, 287.

HARMAN, M. T., and DERBYSHIRE, R. C. 1932. The development of the suprarenal gland in the guinea-pig (Cavia cobaya), Am. Jour. Anat., 49, 335.

HARTMANN, J. FRANCIS. 1944. Seasonal cytological changes in the anterior hypophysis of the garter snake, Am. Jour. Anat., 74, 121.

HOERR, N. 1931. The cells of the suprarenal cortex in the guinea-pig: Their reaction to injury and their replacement, Am. Jour. Anat., 43, 139.

HOWES, N. H. 1936. A study of the histology of the pituitary gland of the skate, Quart. Jour. Micr. Sci., 78, 637.

JOHNSON, G. E. 1931. Hibernation in mammals, Quart. Rev. Biol., 6, 439.

MATTHEWS, S. A. 1936. The pituitary gland of Fundulus, Anat. Rec., 65, 357.

PAYNE, FERNANDUS. 1942. The cytology of the anterior pituitary of the fowl, Biol. Bull., 82, 79.

———— 1943. The cytology of the anterior pituitary of broody fowls, Anat. Rec., 86, 1.

———— 1944. Anterior pituitary relationships in the fowl, Anat. Rec., 88, 337.

SCRUGGS, W. M. 1939. The epithelial components of the teleost pituitary gland as identified by a standardized method of selective staining, Jour. Morphol., 65, 187.

SINGER, E., and ZWEMER, R. L. 1934. Microscopic observations of structural changes in the adrenal of the living frog under experimental conditions, Anat. Rec., 60, 183.

SMITH, C. 1924. The origin and development of the carotid body, Am. Jour. Anat., 34, 87.

UOTILA, U. U.   1939.   On the fuchsinophile and pale cells in the adrenal cortex tissue of the fowl, Anat. Rec., 75, 439.
WILLIAMS, R. G.   1939.   Observations on the formation of new follicles in living grafts of the thyroid gland in rabbits, Anat. Rec., 73, 307.
————— 1941.   Studies of vacuoles in the colloid of thyroid follicles in living mice, Anat. Rec., 79, 263.
————— 1944.   Some properties of living thyroid cells and follicles, Am. Jour. Anat., 74, 95.
WISLOCKI, GEORGE B., and DEMPSEY, EDWARD W.   1945.   Histolchemical reactions associated with basophilia and acidophilia in the placenta and pituitary gland, Am. Jour. Anat., 76, 277.
WOTTON, R. M., and ZWEMER, R. L.   1943.   A study of the cytogenetics of cortico-adrenal cells in the cat, Anat. Rec., 86, 409.
ZALESKY, M.   1934.   A study of the seasonal changes in the adrenal gland of the thirteen-lined ground squirrel (Citillus tridecemlineatus), with particular reference to its sexual cycle, Anat. Rec., 60, 291.
ZWEMER, R. L.   1936.   A study of adrenal cortex morphology, Am. Jour. Path., 12, 107.
ZWEMER, R. L., and WOTTON, R. M.   1938.   A study of cortico adrenal cells, Anat. Rec., 72, No. 2.

## CHAPTER XVI

### TECHNIQUE

BAIRD, T. T.   1936.   Comparative study of dehydration, Stain Tech., 11, 13.
BAKER, J. R.   1936.   Cytological Technique, 2d ed., London, Methuen & Co.
BENSLEY, R. R., and BENSLEY, S. H.   1938.   Handbook of Histological and Cytological Technique, Chicago, Univ. Chicago Press.
CARLETON, H. M.   1926.   Histological Technique, London, Oxford Univ. Press.
CONN, H. J.   1936.   Biological Stains, Geneva N. Y.
COWDRY, E. V.   1943.   Microscopic Technique in Biology and Medicine, Baltimore, The Williams & Wilkins Company.
DAWSON, A. B.   1926.   A note on the staining of the skeleton of cleared specimens with alizarin red S., Stain Tech., 1, 123.
DEMPSTER, WILFRED TAYLOR.   1942.   The mechanics of paraffin sectioning by microtome, Anat. Rec., 84, 241.
————— 1942.   Distortions due to the sliding microtome, Anat. Rec., 84, 269.
GAGE, S. H.   1936.   The Microscope, 16th ed., Ithaca, N. Y., The Comstock Publishing Company.
————— 1938.   Apparatus and methods for micro-incineration, Stain Tech., 13, 25.
GALIGHER, A. E.   1934.   The Essentials of Practical Microtechnique, Berkeley, Calif., A. E. Galigher, Inc. Lab. of Microtechnique.
GATENBY, J. B., and COWDRY, E. V.   1928.   Lee's Microtomist's Vademecum, 9th ed., London, J. and A. Churchill.
GUYER, M. F.   1930.   Animal Micrology, Chicago, Ill., Univ. of Chicago Press.
MANN, GUSTAV.   1902.   Physiological Histology, Oxford, England, Clarendon Press.
McCLUNG, C. E.   1939.   Handbook of Microscopical Technique, New York, Paul B. Hoeber, Inc.
MOSSMAN, H. W.   1937.   The dioxan technic, Stain Tech., 12, 147.
PANTIN, C. F. A.   1946.   Notes on Microscopical Techniques for Zoölogists, Cambridge Univ. Press.
PETRUNKOVITCH, ALEXANDER.   1943.   Some curious effects of salts of metals and other chemicals on fixation, Anat. Rec., 86, 387.
SILVER, MAURICE.   1942.   Colloidal factors controlling silver staining, Anat. Rec., 82, 507.

# INDEX

(Reference to illustrations given in boldface type)